SEIZURE THE DAY

Living a Happy Life with Illness

Seizure the Day

BRIAN OREND

Freehand Books acknowledges the financial support for its publishing program provided by the Alberta Media Fund, and by the Government of Canada through the Canada Book Fund.

Alberta Government   Canada

Freehand Books
515 – 815 1st Street sw   Calgary, Alberta   T2P 1N3
www.freehand-books.com

Book orders: LitDistCo
8300 Lawson Road   Milton, Ontario   L9T 0A4
Telephone: 1–800–591–6250 Fax: 1–800–591–6251
orders@litdistco.ca   www.litdistco.ca

Library and Archives Canada Cataloguing in Publication
Orend, Brian, 1971–, author
Seizure the day : living a happy life with illness / Brian Orend.
Issued in print and electronic formats.
ISBN 978-1-988298-41-2 (softcover).
ISBN 978-1-988298-42-9 (epub).
ISBN 978-1-988298-43-6 (pdf)
1. Happiness.
2. Chronically ill—Mental health.
3. Chronically ill—Life skill guides.
4. Chronic diseases—Psychological aspects.
I. Title.
BF575.H27O74 2019   152.4'2   C2018-905613-4   C2018-905614-2

Edited by Andrew Wilmot
Book design by Natalie Olsen, Kisscut Design
Cover image © go2 / photocase.com
Cartoons on page 353–354 with permission of www.cartoonstock.com
Author photo by Terry Manzo, terrymanzo.com
Printed on FSC® recycled paper and bound in Canada by Friesens

CONTENTS

Dedicated with love to my family: Mom;
Barry; Tissums; and my beautiful boy, Sam.

INTRODUCTION

Given his violent life and brutal murder—viciously stabbed over twenty times by a group of enraged Roman senators—you might not think Julius Caesar has much to teach us about happiness. But the one-time dictator of ancient Rome gave us two legendary quotes that resonate to this day.

The first is the much-repeated opening line from his book *The Gallic War*, which details Caesar's military campaigns—and ultimate victory—over the various tribes of primitive France (then called Gaul), resulting in France becoming absorbed into the Roman Empire. The line in question, translated, reads: "All Gaul is divided into three parts." Caesar proceeded to show how he came to understand each of the three regions of France—the geography and the different tribes therein—and how he proceeded to crush them one-by-one, bringing them under Roman control and changing European history forever.[1]

The second quote is Caesar's famous declaration "*Veni, Vidi, Vici*"— "I came, I saw, I conquered." He wrote this in a private letter to a friend, after achieving a swift and decisive victory over one of Rome's lesser but still pesky rivals, Pharnaces II of Turkey. The declaration is typical of Caesar's tough-minded and fast-moving writing style, and presumably reflects the man's unsentimental, action-focused, and ambitious character.[2]

Like Gaul, happiness is thought to have three parts (each with several sub-components). This piece of observed wisdom comes from the ancient Greek philosopher Aristotle, who pre-dated Caesar by 300 years. To this day, Aristotle remains one of *the* most systematic and sensible thinkers about human well-being and joyous flourishing. Aristotle argued that the three major components of happiness are: 1) pleasure; 2) "external goods," such as friendship and membership in a good society; and 3) "internal goods," such as having correct beliefs, well-governed emotions, and an upstanding moral character.[3] We can offer the following overview:

FIG 1 THE THREE MAJOR PARTS OF HUMAN HAPPINESS

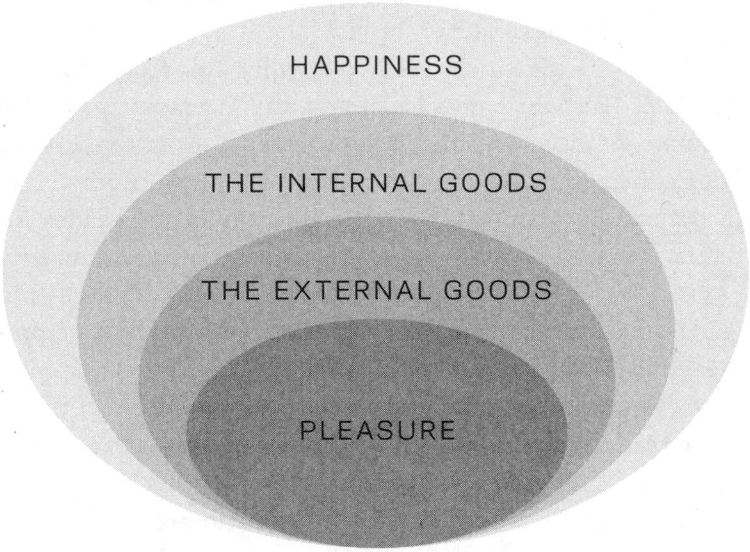

HAPPINESS

THE INTERNAL GOODS

THE EXTERNAL GOODS

PLEASURE

We shall, throughout this book, explore these three parts (and their many fascinating sub-components) in detail: what they mean in our day and age, and what the latest expert research suggests about each of them. We shall also consider what Aristotle missed, or was mistaken about, and how best to view the relationship between these elements of happiness.

Of course, we're not interested in merely *understanding* happiness. Happiness is something universally desired. Aristotle maintained that happiness alone is the one "intrinsic" human good or goal, with all others—the pursuits of money, power, love, and fame—being, by contrast, "instrumental." Happiness stands as the one goal whose pursuit requires no explanation; it is the reason why, Aristotle believed, we do anything at all.[4] Again: we don't just want to read and think about happiness; we actually want to live happy lives and enjoy the experience of being happy people. We don't simply wish to understand happiness; we want, truly, to grasp its component parts, to master and incorporate them thoroughly into our lives. Much as Caesar defeated his rivals and realized his goals, we too wish to come toward happiness, to see it for ourselves, and finally to conquer it and make it our own.

This isn't just one more book about happiness, though. There exist many terrific studies to which we will refer, ranging all the way from Aristotle's *Nicomachean Ethics* (circa 350 BC) to Sonja Lyubomirsky's *The How of Happiness* (2007) and beyond.[5] Yet, while we must, unavoidably, begin by talking about happiness in general, the particular focus and special concern of this book—as the title indicates—is how people with chronic diseases, disorders, injuries, or challenges can improve their experience of happiness. In my view, too many happiness studies lack deeply considered and helpful advice for those wanting to live happier lives while being forced to confront serious obstacles brought on by chronic illness and conditions. Three quick examples:

- One of the most potent threats to a person's happiness is prolonged unemployment. People suffering from chronic conditions are much more likely to be unemployed. Thus, they are more vulnerable to unhappiness and, indeed, to enduring unhappiness of the kind that can slide into clinical depression.[6]

- Evidence suggests that people with chronic conditions become more introverted as a result of their condition(s). (The proverbial wounded animal, hiding alone at the back of the cave.) The "happiness problem" with this is that, other things being equal, the more introverted you become, the less satisfied you report yourself with life.[7]

- As Daniel Nettle says, in *Happiness: The Science Behind Your Smile*, there are two personality traits, or dimensions, which seem most important when it comes to the level of happiness people report. The first is the degree to which people are extroverted over introverted. The second is the degree to which people are well-adjusted over "neurotic"—a term that, though often a pejorative, is here used in a purely technical sense to show how people experience anxiety and difficulty when confronted by certain tasks (whether such tasks be daily and routine, or novel and exceptional). It stands to reason that people with chronic conditions—*because of those very conditions*—are going to have a harder time managing tasks than the average, unafflicted person, and probably also experience more anxiety in general, both because of that and because the condition itself gives them yet one more thing to be anxious about.[8]

Note how relevant these last two observations are. If Nettle is correct—and "introversion/extroversion" alongside "neurotic/well-adjusted" are the two most salient personality dimensions factoring into someone's happiness—then it would seem as though people struggling with a chronic condition (since they are more likely to be *both* more introverted *and* more neurotic) do indeed confront substantial obstacles along the road to happiness.

It's not merely that those with chronic conditions face such complications; it's that the advice required to deal with such obstacles and to augment their happiness will differ from the average, or unafflicted person. It's simply not enough to say, for example, that one "should try to be more social." In addition to issues of willing and wanting such, those afflicted—because of their conditions—are more likely than others to be introverted and to not want to behave in an extroverted way. Their conditions may cause them pain, or hinder their functioning (even something as simple as their ability to stand for long stretches of time), or cause them to exhibit behaviour or traits not accepted or understood by unafflicted people (like having a seizure). These things make it objectively more challenging for such people to "get up and be more social." Thus, offering good happiness advice that is sensitive to such challenges is the main goal of this book.

As I see it, the audience for this book resides between two extremes. On the one hand, there are individuals with severe *mental* health problems—those suffering from debilitating clinical depression, for example. This is not my primary audience, and there are many excellent books offering help and advice for such people, who usually require some kind of expert medical intervention.[9] Likewise, there are those with severe *physical* health problems, such as people who are bed-ridden with inescapable and searing chronic pain, or those who've suffered catastrophic injuries, or face life-threatening diagnoses and, consequently, brutal prescribed treatments. I do not pretend to know what to tell such people, as they too require expert medical intervention—individually apprised of the details of their situation—to try to help them manage their realities.

In between these extremes is another—I think, very large—group of people. Those who *do* have a chronic condition that hinders their ability to function "normally," often (or at times) in a substantial way. However, they are neither bed-ridden nor plagued by inescapable pain. Nor are they suicidal, or otherwise suffering so badly from a mental health problem that they cannot function meaningfully or at all. They *can* function, just *not* to an average, expected human capacity (in some specific regard). They are ill or injured, yet not ruinously so. They are healthy and capable *enough* to do many of the things that average people do, and, like the average person, are keenly interested in happiness and in becoming, if not the happiest possible person they can be, at least measurably happier.* They hope for something

---

* Some "fine print" on definitions: throughout, I'll mainly use the terms "afflicted" or "those with chronic conditions" to describe the group I have in mind, in contrast to "the unafflicted." I have chosen these terms both to be moderate and to have a very broad umbrella of reference. Other terms are perhaps more frequently used, such as "sick vs. healthy," "abnormal vs. normal," "disabled vs. abled," etc. On the one hand, I've no intention whatsoever of offending anyone, and everyone has the right to their own preferred self-description. On the other, these terms are contested, and can be interpreted in various ways by both "insiders" (part of the afflicted community) and others. We see similar debates within other communities about preferred labels: whether certain terms are offensive or okay, or even empowering. *Such a debate over definitions is part of the subject.* Generally, what I have in mind is the contrast between those of average functional human capacity vs. those whose functioning is, in some respect, chronically hampered. And such hampering or dysfunctionality, or "below-average-capacity," isn't merely imagined or socially constructed: it has a factual basis, and I believe that this needs not only to be admitted and "owned" but seen as a necessary condition for appealing for special treatment or accommodation by others and institutions, and indeed for progress toward improved personal happiness.

better, and are confident they can experience such, if only they receive decent advice calibrated to their circumstances. I hesitate to guess just how large this group of people is (much less to list all the relevant chronic conditions that might fall under this heading), but my hunch is that—especially in our ageing society—it's substantial. As such, while the majority of happiness books are "for anyone and everyone," they fail to speak fully to the special interests and needs of this sizable group of people. As with everything else, it is also true that, in regards to happiness, one size does NOT fit all.

———

So, what chronic condition do I have that gives me insight into this group of people and, so to speak, the right and interest to address them this way? If I have written such a book, surely it must be because of some personal reason—some journey I have made from which I have gained experience. Indeed, I have epilepsy, caused by a brain tumour.[10] (Incidentally, most historians agree that Julius Caesar probably had epilepsy, and that it ran throughout his extended family, the so-called "Julio-Claudians.") My own tumour-based epilepsy has given me more seizures than I can count—the majority of which have occurred in broad daylight out in public, and several of which have been so severe that I have been hospitalized, and utterly incapacitated, for days on end.

Here's how I became interested in the subject of happiness.

It was November 2001, just two months after the terrorist attacks of 9/11. I was a thirty-year-old philosophy professor lecturing to a group of twenty-year-old undergraduates at the University of Waterloo in Ontario, Canada. Feeling fine, and without any history of health problems, I suddenly keeled over right in front of my class, losing consciousness and smacking my spine against the blackboard ledge as I fell backwards ... then sidewards ... then down onto the floor. Some thought I'd had a heart attack and had just dropped dead, right before their tender eyes. My memory of the next few days is completely gone: near-total memory loss in and around the event is a common side effect of seizures. Even after being discharged, I still felt like I had been hit by a train—when you have a *"grand mal,"* or major seizure, your muscles can contract so severely, and so quickly, that it can later feel (as inflammation and repair kick in) like you have been completely clobbered. Upon my discharge, after several days' hospitalization that included a glamorous stay in the ICU, I could no longer legally drive a vehicle. It was a mystery as to why I had suffered a seizure in the first place—my vital signs had eventually returned to normal—and so testing was ordered.

It's routine that, upon suffering a grand mal seizure, a Magnetic Resonance Image (MRI) of the brain is ordered to look specifically for evidence of stroke and/or tumour. Following my release from the ICU, I ventured to a larger hospital in another city to receive this, noting with minor irony that it would be the very hospital in which I was born. So, I got my MRI and, as usual, was told that, should anything untoward or suspicious appear in the image, my doctors would all be notified. Well, no one ever called; and so, my doctors proceeded on the assumption that my brain was clear and healthy, and that there was no brain-cause for the seizure. All eyes and medical attention then turned to my heart, and assumption was made that it must be cardiac in nature, such as an irregular heartbeat.

What followed was a quick and deep descent into prolonged unhappiness. In reality, the seizures had no cardiac cause, yet for years—*years*—I was treated as if I'd had a heart problem. I took countless prescribed drugs, and even underwent several surgical procedures. I burned through specialist after specialist, both cardiologists and neurologists. (One memorable visit was to a cardiologist who, supposedly, was Ontario's Very Best heart doctor. After hearing my story, he loudly proclaimed: "You need someone at the top of his game!" Imagine this being declared by someone wearing a white coat and stethoscope, and otherwise looking and sounding just like Will Ferrell in *Anchorman*.) I kept on having seizures, and was in and out of the hospital.

My romantic partner left me in mid-2003, taking our infant son with her. I cannot blame her—she was a young, first-time mom, and the prospect of being suddenly burdened with two "children" instead of just one was perhaps overwhelming. For all she knew, the non-stop seizures were going to render me catatonic, a basketcase. Thus, I was alone to deal with the seizures, adding to everything the pain of relationship break-down and the stress and humiliation of being allowed only irregular, supervised visits with my young son (lest I have a seizure, get knocked out, and he be stranded and helpless). During this time, I still couldn't drive—and I live in a part of the world where this is quite inconvenient. The only saving grace of this terrible time was that I was able to hold on to my job, and even enjoy considerable success as a professor, especially in terms of teaching and publishing. My colleagues supported me, accommodated my scheduling needs, and even dragged me off the floor and/or called 9–1–1 after my latest classroom grand mal. (I even once had a cop come to my rescue in class, as he was the closest emergency official; and then, the next week, the students told me they thought it was "so cool" that I was the only professor they'd ever had, or heard of, who actually had his lecture interrupted by a uniformed police officer.)

As stated, this went on for years: about three or four, to be exact. The cumulative toll of all these experiences left me profoundly unhappy, and with little prospect for substantial improvement. I knew I had to do something, or be mired in this quicksand of suffering indefinitely. So, I resolved to do two things: 1) get to the bottom of the cause behind my epilepsy, once and for all; and 2) learn all I could about happiness in general, and what I could do to augment it in my life. I wish I could tell you that this ultra-nerdy second point is completely fabricated.

Alas, it is not. As a professor, knowledge is and has been one of the most positive, inspiring, and motivating forces in my life. It was only natural that, if I felt I didn't know something—something that was hurting me—I needed to turn that around and learn everything I could about it, and put what I learned into action. I've been told that this is a "systematic approach" to happiness—I suppose this is a polite way of putting it.

In comparison with some of the gruesome stuff I'd had to research regarding human rights violations and wartime atrocities—my two primary areas of expertise—getting to read about happiness in my spare time was an absolute joy. One of the first things that leapt out at me from the happiness literature was the need to widen and deepen social bonds. I knew I had let the epilepsy isolate me quite radically (apart from work-related socialization, I had next-to-no contact with others at the time) and I had to, and needed to, do much better in this regard. So, I started dating again, and socializing more broadly, and my happiness improved.

More on that later. For now, let's return to the issue of discovering the cause behind the seizures. By this time, around 2005, I was on Neurologist Number Nine. Like the others, all he could do was prescribe drugs that were supposed to curtail the consequences of the seizures. But, unlike the others, he admitted that something just didn't add up. If the seizures truly were cardiac in nature, then that cause—after all the experiments, procedures, and testing—really should have been discovered by now. I even remember the exact unsure and agitated look on his face when he said to me, "You know, I went to medical school with a guy who's since become probably the best epilepsy researcher around. I'm going to call him personally and ask him to see you. And I think you should just stop seeing heart specialists now." And then he washed his hands of me, as had all the others.

That's how I got to see the specialist who would change my life. Let's call him Omar. Omar was an immigrant to Canada from Saudi Arabia, and brought with him an enormous work ethic and strict sense of professionalism. Around forty years old, he already had a respected practice of treating epileptics in the region. I still remember the first time I visited the hospital floor where he had his clinic: the rooms and beds were filled with some of the most distressed and fractured people I'd ever seen. Moaning loudly, without hope. Writhing in pain and discomfort. Shaking with near-constant, low-level convulsions and seizures. And one very elderly lady, nearly catatonic, staring fixedly into space—not one glimmer of human awareness about her, mouth open, her little pink tongue darting in and out non-stop. If Omar could treat such people, I assumed he could at least help me.

At our first meeting, he patiently listened to my whole story, and the long list of medical theories and practitioners I'd burned my way through. He examined me physically. Then, in wrapping up, he said, "We're going to begin at the very start and assume nothing. We're going to test you for everything once more, and I'm going to get my hands on that very first brain MRI they did on you back in 2001. We'll do another fresh one, and compare the two tests." I booked my follow-up appointment and looked forward to it.

When I arrived for my second meeting a few months later, the receptionist told me that Omar was waiting for me—was this a first in all medical history, a doctor waiting on a patient?—and that he needed to see me in a different office, outfitted with special computer screens. Fine by me, I replied. "Oh," she continued, "and would you mind if several medical students and young interns attend the first part of the meeting?" That caught my attention. "Sure," I said. When I entered the office, there was a group of four young doctors-in-training, all standing behind Omar and staring at the huge wrap-around screen. They nervously glanced between their feet and me; I felt like a guinea pig on display. Omar looked stressed and focused. I know now why he had asked the young doctors to attend: it was a great "teachable moment" for them. They could see some cool medical images and relevant evidence, and then watch a doctor deliver some bad news to a patient and observe how the patient reacts when he finds out he's been truly fucked over.

Omar began: "You know how we just did that latest MRI on your brain last week, Brian?" Of course—my memory's not *that* bad. "Well," he said seriously, "it found something." Immediately, and without seeing, I knew it was a brain tumour—what else could it be? The news came as absolutely no surprise: there are only so many things, after all, which can cause repeated seizures. He invited me to come around to the front of the screen, and there I saw an amazingly clear portrait of my big, fat, beautiful brain, all clear and grey and gnarly and complex—except for that big patch of a neon-bright white down around my brain stem (like an errant piece of blackboard chalk). I actually felt relief: after all these years, I finally knew for sure.

But what happened next actually did surprise me, and quickly ended whatever relief I'd felt. Omar looked me straight in the eyes, with purpose, and pursed his lips. "Let me show you something further, and put it side-by-side with last week's image." The screen then divided in two, with the image I just saw now on the left, and a new image popping up over on the right. It was an older image, black and white, but still obviously the same brain—my brain—and . . . featuring *the exact same chunk of bright white chalk*, standing out like a supernova amidst the plain greyness of the rest of my brain.

"This was the very first MRI they took of your brain, after your first seizure back in 2001. Two weeks after your first grand mal. I got the old film sent over just last week. There's good news about this, and bad. The good news, as you can see, is that the tumour seems quite stable, and shows very little if any sign of growth. This means that it's probably benign, and thus not life threatening, though we'll need to do more tests to determine that for sure. Plus, this is probably what's causing your seizures, though there, too, we'll need to do tests—immediately—to prove this."

"And the bad news?"

"The bad news is that, as you can see, the original image of your brain tumour is crystal clear. A child could have seen this. Yet no one reported this to anyone. This would seem to violate all kinds of proper medical practice. Brian, you actually may want to think about talking to a lawyer. You can have this image, and I'm going to get every MRI image that's been done on your brain over the years. You can tell your lawyer that I'll talk to him, and may be willing to serve as a witness. This failure to report the tumour might be medical negligence. I have thousands of patients who rely on the correct reporting of such images, and I can tell you that doctors totally depend on that for their treatment recommendations. I would very much want to see anyone found guilty of such to be charged and relieved of their duties. In my opinion, the only way they could have missed this tumour was if they never actually looked at the image at all."

I thanked the good doctor very much for discovering the truth, and for his offer of help, and stormed out of the hospital, fuming and cursing.

———

Since then, I'm glad to report that my life has much improved. I've learned a ton from the happiness literature, having genuine fun along the way, and have implemented many of its recommendations into my life. I'm not perfectly happy—there's no such thing—and there have been bumps in the road (even big ones), and today I have as many ups and downs in my daily mood as the next person. But I can say with 100 percent certainty that I'm much happier than I was back in that dark period of 2001–2005. I've gained much insight, both into human happiness in general and toward the special challenges faced by those with chronic conditions. My seizures, unlike in the early/mid-2000s, are no longer out of control. The proper diagnosis was the first step in being able to manage the condition more effectively. I got rid of all the heart medications, and through trial-and-error we discovered some epilepsy drugs that aided with seizure control. Plus, I made major lifestyle changes to help in this regard, involving rigorous daily exercise, good nutrition, and sound "sleep hygiene."[11] My brain tumour remains stable, I'm pleased to report, and I've been able to drive legally for some time now. I have a decent relationship with my now-teenage son, and see him at least twice a week. We've even visited the Grand Canyon, New York City, and Disney World together. I've been in some loving relationships with great women over the years. My job is as rewarding as ever, and I've been promoted as high as I can be in the professorial ranks. Some of my books (especially those on war) are used as required textbooks at colleges and universities around the world. I take nice trips a few times a year, usually in connection with some lucky and generous invitation to come lecture about something, whether in Italy, Sweden, France, or Greece, or closer to home in Arizona, California, Colorado, or New York.

But what of the MRI images? Well, I did indeed consult lawyers specializing in medical negligence. They confirmed that mine was almost certainly such a case. They even laughed at how glaring it was, agreeing with Omar that the only way the doctors and technicians could have missed the tumour in the original photo was if they failed to look at the MRI at all. So, did I sue everyone in sight—the doctor, the technicians, the very hospital where I was born? I wanted to, but didn't. Why not? It was explained to me that, though my case was almost a slam dunk, the reality was that to prove such would take years of my life and cost tens of thousands of dollars. This, I was told, is because the professional association that represents doctors—as a matter of policy—pays the very best lawyers in the country a ton of money every year to contest, vigorously, every single alleged instance of medical negligence, no matter how obvious the guilt. I was looking at an enormous up-hill battle.

Closure came during a revealing meeting with a celebrated lawyer, who said, "It's clearly medical negligence, Brian. But your other lawyers are right: it'll take you years to prove even so clear-cut a case. Plus, let me ask you something: How is your life now?"

"Really quite good, actually." I cited some of the improvements listed above.

"Bam!" he shouted, while "shooting" his finger at me like a revolver. "Bam! Right there. On the witness stand in court, right there, you just lost your case."

I looked at him with disbelief.

"Brian, you have to understand. I'm a personal injury lawyer. The people I represent have been horribly injured in things like car accidents. I'm used to representing people so damaged that they have to use their tongues to drag their wheelchairs into court because that's the only body part they've got left working! For people like that, I can get millions. Their lives have been destroyed by the actions of others. But you? You've just said that your life is actually better now; as a result, you can forget any hope of getting any money."

I was livid: "But all those improvements came about as a result *of my own efforts*—my own hard work at improving my life and overcoming the consequences of the negligence and the misdiagnosis. They happened *in spite of* the negligence and all the costs it imposed on me and those around me!"

"I know," he said calmly. "And good for you. But, lemme tell you, that's your reward. This new life you've created for yourself. That's your reward. No court is going to give you any money; there will, at best, only be the moral victory of a declaration of negligence. Is such a result worth years of your life, a ton of legal struggle, and tens of thousands of dollars? My advice to you is to let it go, and to enjoy this new life you've made."

So I did.

The rest of this book, therefore, is a summation of my scholarly research and my own private life experience—over ten years of both—into human happiness, and how general advice about happiness needs to accommodate and consider the special needs of those with chronic conditions. I hope it can speak meaningfully to you, and offer both knowledge and advice that you can use to augment your own well-being and enjoyment of life. After all, as Tal Ben-Shahar says in his handy book *Happier*,[12] we might not know everything about happiness, and we might not be able to get every element of happiness into our lives to a complete and perfect degree. But what we certainly *can* do—all of us, even those confronting challenges—is to make use of the best advice available, tailor it to our circumstances, and make ourselves measurably and sustainably happier. A better life, for each of us, awaits.

Happiness in General, and Pleasure in Particular

CHAPTER 1

Can Happiness Actually be Pursued?

Almost everything said in the Introduction is based on the premise that happiness is the sort of thing that *can* be pursued: that through knowledge, effort, and will we can actually make ourselves measurably happier. So much Western thinking and writing about happiness makes this basic assumption: that it's possible to strive toward happiness as a goal. It's a fundamental objective of the United States Declaration of Independence: to create a society wherein it is possible for everyone to enjoy "life, liberty, and the pursuit of happiness." Presumably, the framers of this document—and its main author, Thomas Jefferson—believed the last of these three items, happiness, to be as real, achievable, and as important as life and liberty.[13] Much more recently, countries as diverse as Bhutan and the United Arab Emirates (UAE) have taken concrete steps toward promoting happiness among their people: in 2006, Bhutan announced it would drop the traditional Gross Domestic Product (GDP, or income per capita) measurement of well-being in favour of Gross National Happiness (GNH); and in 2016, the UAE announced the creation of a "Ministry of State for Happiness" to create more joy amongst its citizens. Lastly, and more unofficially, there are currently websites and apps such as "Happify," which offer their subscribers daily tasks, games, and activities to boost happiness: the app claims that 86 percent of its users increase their happiness within the first two months of regular use.[14]

Recent research and literature, however, casts critical doubt on this basic assumption—that happiness is a goal we can achieve, or at least augment. We must consider this important challenge. After all, if it's literally not possible to pursue and grow happiness, then everything that follows is moot.

There are (at least) three ways in which it's been asserted that happiness is actually *not* the sort of thing that can be pursued or measurably augmented:

- Some believe that while it *is* possible for humans to become happier, such augmentation *cannot* come from the deliberate and sustained pursuit of happiness as a goal. The idea being that the more you deliberately try to pursue happiness, the more it will elude you. You have to let happiness come to you, so to speak. Let's call this "the Laid-Back Philosophical Objection."

- Many experts have, through experimentation, discovered and given much evidence in favour of "hedonic adaptation." This is the observed fact that when people report being made happier by something—a wage raise at work, the flush of new romance—quite often that increase in happiness cannot be sustained. People adapt quickly to new and novel experiences, and will require more of the same—another raise, for example—to receive any further "bump" in their subjective pleasure. A sustained and substantial long-term increase in happiness is thus not possible. Let's call this "the Hedonic Adaptation Objection."

- Relatedly, but more deeply (since this doesn't only deal with *particular* goods or experiences), recent evidence suggests that we all have an inherited, deeply structured, and genetically determined "happiness set-point." There's indication that, at most, "boosts" in happiness are only temporary, superficial fluctuations and, very reliably, people return to a previous "set-point" of happiness that remains remarkably stable over the course of their lives. The experience of happiness, after all, is rooted in brain chemistry, and one's disposition to have and absorb certain chemicals over others is most deeply affected by genetic endowment. (As Sigmund Freud declared, "Biology is Destiny.")[15] Let's call this "the Genetic Determinism Objection."

Let's now consider the many ramifications and challenges of these objections.

The Laid-Back Philosophical Objection

I have a hard time sympathizing with this objection, and view the other two as more serious. This one fails to speak to my own experience, wherein the deliberate pursuit of greater happiness was the whole point. Yet, many people do believe this objection, or believe it expresses something important about the nature of happiness: that if you try too hard, you will, by necessity, fail. Nathaniel Hawthorne, author of *The Scarlet Letter*, sketched the following metaphor: "Happiness is a butterfly which, when pursued, is always beyond our grasp, but, if you will sit down quietly, may alight upon you."[16] The notion is that there's an aspect of luck and fate to happiness; indeed, the word "happiness" derives from the Old English word "happ," which meant "luck." And in German, there's the (presumably related) connection between "*glück*" and "*glücklich*" (i.e., "happy" and "lucky," respectively). But is this more than *a sense of* luck? In other words, there's a difference between the *psychological perception* of happiness and the *nature* of happiness itself. After all, being pleasantly surprised by something and being lastingly satisfied and/or truly content seem to be two different things.

There's even a new phrase in this regard, called "happiness anxiety." Supposedly, this depicts people who are so obsessed with augmenting their happiness—chasing after that butterfly—that they experience anxiety in doing so. Consequently, and perversely paradoxically, the very pursuit of happiness results, via happiness anxiety, in less happiness. John Stuart Mill expressed this view best when he opined, "Ask yourself whether you are happy, and you cease to be so. . . . Those only are happy . . . who have their minds fixed on some object other than their own happiness. . . . Aiming thus at something else, they find happiness by the way."[17]

As stated, happiness anxiety is taking this viewpoint to an extreme. I myself have never met or even heard of anyone with a plausible case of "happiness anxiety." I suppose they must exist somewhere: there are always going to be outliers who pursue something to a pathological—or inefficacious— degree. And I am charmed by the Zen-like *"que será, será"* wisdom of Hawthorne's metaphor, about not trying too hard in happiness as with other things. It's a pretty idea, that happiness is a delicate butterfly that may decide to grace you with its presence. But it's also *a passive and complacent idea*. And I believe that the far greater (and more plausible) danger here is being so laid-back about one's happiness that one takes this complacent philosophy too seriously, passively accepting a sub-optimal level of happiness when something constructive could be done about it. One's own happiness, I submit, is worth the effort.

I also fear, more concretely, that when it comes to chronically ill people, complacency and "being laid-back" are—demonstrably—NOT going to lead to any improvements. Imagine if I had just resigned myself to fate, with an inaccurately diagnosed heart condition and out-of-control seizures, for the rest of my life. "Acceptance," in my case, would've meant resigning myself to being a life-long victim. If one has a chronic condition, one's functioning has been damaged and impaired. Leaving it at that and hoping, somehow, to become happier is wishful thinking. Perhaps "normal" or gifted, lucky people can afford such calm complacency—*the chronically ill cannot.* They must, I believe, take the initiative, make an effort to become happier. Rigorous scientific research has shown that even people with severe clinical depression have been able to become lastingly happier when: a) armed with correct knowledge; b) receiving the right support; and c) being absolutely committed to achieving their goals, and to overcoming those obstacles that predictably fall in their way.[18]

Here we turn to Aristotle in two ways. First is the "doctrine of the mean," in which he argued that, in most aspects of life, the pursuit of the middle ground tends to be best: the most rational, the most fitting, and the most likely to generate happiness. Perhaps the sharpest example of this is courage, which he portrays as the mean between the extremes of cowardice (fear and flight) and recklessness (aggressive rashness); courage, however, is doing what needs to be done *even in spite of* one's fears and the danger presented. Aristotle goes on to show how many of life's most desirable things ought to be pursued in this middle-ground kind of way, and that perhaps happiness is yet another thing to be added to this list.[19] We can thusly diagram it, with happiness being the "just right" condition between "too little" and "too much."

FIG 2 DEGREES OF PURSUING HAPPINESS

Deficient Pursuit	Correct Pursuit	Excess Pursuit
Fatalism, Complacency "Not trying enough" Waiting/wishing for the butterfly	Informed, steady, and committed pursuit of the most happiness that can realistically be achieved	Happiness Anxiety "Trying too hard"
Not enough concern for the self and its well-being	Moderate and appropriate concern for the well-being of both self and others; neither fatalism nor anxiety about happiness: the proper concern for it. Since happiness is so desirable, the proper concern will be quite robust.	Too much concern for the self (narcissism; inability to appreciate other goals and/ or the happiness of others)

The second way in which we can learn from Aristotle concerns the nature of happiness as a goal, and what researchers have found about the strong and interesting connection between happiness and committed goal pursuit. As for the nature of happiness as a goal, we leave that for next chapter, as there are many intriguing and deep questions to be raised regarding why we should pursue happiness. But consider that many "positive psychologists" (i.e., those who study the pursuit of happiness scientifically) have found robust connections between the pursuit of goals in general and the augmentation of one's happiness.[20] Conversely, there's evidence that those who are non-goal-directed and apathetic, and/or those who have problems either picking goals or pursuing them in a focused way, can suffer not just from a relative lack of happiness but also full-blown depression.[21]

The pursuit of goals is thought to augment happiness in the following seven ways:

1 It is activating, inspiring, and provides focus in life.[22]

2 It adds structure to one's daily life—an organizing and energizing frame around which to plot the day's activities. This has been shown to be very important, in particular, for the sustaining of happiness after one retires from the workplace, and for those with chronic conditions (more below).[23]

3 Goal pursuit, at least with larger goals such as happiness, also provides a sense of purpose and meaning about life in general. Serious unhappiness can result from believing that one's life lacks purpose or meaning. When such is experienced temporarily, we often speak of people experiencing an "existential crisis" (i.e., "Who am I? What should I really be doing with my life?")[24] When such a thing is experienced for a prolonged period, we speak then of "nihilism" (literally believing in nothing), which is strongly associated with deep depression and even thoughts of suicide.[25]

4 Goal pursuit not only involves one with life but also with other people. And, as stated in the Introduction, few things are more strongly associated with a sustained increase in self-reported happiness than lots of time and contact with other human beings (ideally, family and friends). The reality is, the vast majority of goals that we pursue in life require the participation and help of others, or at the very least their interaction. Whether it's a new job, a new lover, or a new home, such goals involve clear, and often deep and complex, interactions with many others.[26]

5 Goal-directed people are more likely to achieve what they want. This should come as no surprise, as they are actually striving for the thing in question, putting effort or "sweat equity" into achieving their plans, and not, so to speak, merely planning on being lucky.[27]

6 Tal Ben-Shahar cites interesting evidence that the selection of one's goals, and the commitment to them, actually augments pleasure in the present. Consider the "mind-settling aspect": the selection of one's goals settles the mind as to how one is going to spend one's time. Second, in knowing where one is headed, one is assured and feels direction. Once you've selected your destination, and know how to get there, you can actually pay more attention to—and savour—all the details of what you are currently passing through, on your way to journey's end.[28]

7 Finally, there's evidence that being goal-directed enhances one's self-esteem. This is true, in part, because—as mentioned above—goal-directed people are more likely to get what they want. Thus, when they *do* get it, they feel efficacious about their ability to handle life, to understand the world, and to achieve things they desire. Having a sense of mastery over one's environment is very important to one's lasting contentment with life.[29]

This final point has major consequences for the chronically ill. Owing to their condition(s), the chronically afflicted tend to have less control over their bodies, and thus their personal and professional lives. This can be a severe blow to their happiness, at least in the short-term (upon first experiencing their disorder and/or hearing the original diagnosis). Achieving any degree of control over one's illness is, in my view, *absolutely vital* to augmenting the happiness of those suffering a chronic condition.

In my own case, I let the seizures go on for too long before I challenged the doctors and finally, aggressively, sought out the truth—and got the help and knowledge I needed to construct a regimen to get the seizures under control. (I thus concur with the military maxim: "The only way out, is through.") Even once I had an accurate diagnosis, it still took *years* for me to establish a successful daily "groove." I'll discuss the further details of this later in this book.

The Hedonic Adaptation Objection

The challenge here, you recall, is that it is not possible to, deliberately and over time, augment one's happiness in a substantial way: as one does, secures, or acquires things that increase happiness in the short-term, one adjusts and adapts to the new source(s) of happiness, leading to no net long-term happiness gains. Studies have shown, for instance, that winners of major lotteries—in the millions of dollars—usually revert to their pre-winning levels of self-reported happiness and life satisfaction. Additionally, the reversion almost always occurs sometime between (a mere) six months and a year-and-a-half after winning. The initial high of winning is huge but then, after the momentary euphoria and collection of the money, the winners adjust to their new wealth, and their new routines tend, rather quickly, to settle their happiness back down to previous levels. Objectively, their circumstances have changed, and very much for the better; however, subjectively they receive a large boost that dissipates quickly and leaves them totally settled into "their new normal."[30]

Economist Richard Easterlin has performed one of the most vivid experiments showing the hedonic treadmill in action. He surveyed a cross-section of the population of Los Angeles, giving participants a list of major consumer goods that most people want. He then asked two questions: 1) Which of these things represents the good life to you, and 2) which of these things do you already own? The goods in question included things such as: a house, car, computer, TV, swimming pool, second home (or cottage), and so on. Then he asked these same participants the exact same questions sixteen years later. The results were striking: when younger, participants listed on average 4.4 of these items as constituting their ideal, and said that they actually owned 1.7 of them. Sixteen years later, the number of items on the list actually owned had increased to 3.1. But did this translate into greater happiness? No, because participants reported that their ideal number of goods had risen to 5.6. The gap between the ideal and the real for this group had stayed *almost exactly the same*: 2.7 goods (younger) and 2.5 goods (older). Objectively, they had nearly doubled the amount of desired goods they owned but were—for all intents and purposes—just as far away from attaining their ideal as ever.[31]

It's a familiar phenomenon from daily life: you eat some delicious dark chocolate and get, say, ten units of pleasure from doing so. But then if you eat another chunk (of the same kind of chocolate) immediately after, you're going to get fewer than ten units of pleasure, and even fewer if you go for a third, and so on. You've adjusted to the taste and experience of eating and appreciating that chocolate, and so more is going to deliver . . . less. Likewise, when you get a promotion and/or raise and your income increases, you might feel some pride and accomplishment, and take additional pleasure from that fact. But, over time, you adjust your expectations and purchasing behaviours—your very standard of living—to take this raise into account.[32] Experts like Carol Graham and Richard Layard have argued that we can witness the same phenomenon writ large across entire societies, pointing out that, in the developed world anyways—for which there is firmer data across a longer period of time—standards of living (in terms of Gross National Product per capita) have skyrocketed in the past hundred years. Yet, people's self-reported levels of happiness, across these generations, have not come close to keeping up. Adaptation and the hedonic treadmill explain this sad fact: as society has gotten richer, things previous generations would've absolutely marvelled at, and taken ecstatic delight in—our life expectancy, computers and the internet, daily air travel to anywhere in the world, fresh fruit in wintertime, portable high-tech communication devices—have become routine and expected parts of our daily lives.[33]

While there *is* pervasive and persuasive evidence in favour of adaptation, and some kind of hedonic treadmill, does it follow that we cannot augment our long-term happiness through effort of will? Is it all so bleak and dour? The answer is no, and there are compelling reasons as to why. Consider first that we have been conditioned by evolution to adapt. This is good in many respects. It makes us flexible across a wide range of environments and experiences. And failure to adapt can result in being overwhelmed by novel experiences and sensations, including those associated with pleasure. Imagine someone rendered totally stupefied by some intense pleasure (e.g., an orgasm). As great as orgasms are, it's probably quite a good thing that even they, too, dissipate rather quickly—and we are able to get on with the rest of our lives, and to achieve things more impressive and important than staring dreamily at the ceiling, or falling asleep while drooling. It must be noted here that *adaptation goes both ways*: it's not just that we adapt to positive experience; it's also that, when experiencing negative things and suffering pain, we can adapt to that as well, and not remain mired in our depths. This is especially important when considering the happiness of the chronically afflicted: adaptation is not the enemy but a fact of life and—very often—our friend when it comes to dealing with disease and disorder. There's extensive evidence that people who've been permanently injured—even severely—and those with less severe but still challenging chronic conditions, can substantially adjust to the new realities of their lives and recover levels of happiness and satisfaction at least comparable to those enjoyed pre-injury/condition.[34] As mentioned, I myself—admittedly, after too long an adjustment period—managed not just to regain my pre-seizure levels of happiness but also, in most ways, to surpass them. I can honestly say, for example, that as a middle-aged man in my mid-forties, I am overall a much happier person than I was, say, in my early twenties.

A second factor showing the limits of "the treadmill analysis" is that the sorts of things to which hedonic adaptation most readily—and worrisomely—apply are measurable, material things, like income and consumer goods (as in the above Easterlin example). Experiences, by contrast, are *much less susceptible* to hedonic adaptation, as are complex, multifaceted, long-term involvements in an activity or institution to which one remains deeply committed over time.

In terms of experiences, there's evidence that eating breakfast (or whatever your first meal of the day is) almost always produces a similar, and positive, level of pleasure. Obviously, there're evolutionary reasons for why this is the case. Ditto—for most people—with respect to sex. Physical movement, or exercise of any kind, gives most people at least an initial flush of pleasure. And there's evidence that, when people have undergone cosmetic surgery (in particular breast augmentation) and are pleased with the results, they actually get a near-constant amount of pleasure every time they look in the mirror, appreciating their enhanced appearance. Other researchers have stipulated that looking at erotic pictures, at least for men, seems quite resistant to hedonic adaptation and doles out a rather reliable stream of pleasant sensations. A more abstract experience—yet a very important one—apparently immune from hedonic adaptation is that of personal freedom or autonomy (from the Greek *"auto-nomos,"* or "self-rule"). If you think about it, you never really tire of having control over your own body and life. You might not always be aware of such freedom and autonomy, but, when you step back and consider it, *you always appreciate it.* This appreciation never really lessens over time. After all, not too many of us, at the end of our lives, express regret for not relinquishing more control over ourselves to others.[35]

In terms of complex, long-term, committed activity, there's evidence that, while there's *some* adaptation, a happy marriage is nevertheless a very reliable source for generating sustained positive emotions over time. For similar reasons, so too is long-term friendship. In fact, as I'm sure many would agree, true friendship can actually deepen, becoming more meaningful and pleasant over time. Same for working at a career, or long-term hobby, to which one is passionately committed. I can say that I'm still as happy being a university professor today—eighteen-plus years later—as when I started. In some ways, I'm happier: I know the job better; I have constructed, over time, various systems and procedures that have made my job easier; I know better how to handle problems; I can lecture better (though perhaps with less energy); and so on. I'm tempted to speak similarly about being a father, too, and I'm sure there are many other parents out there who would swear to the same thing as they've grown into their complicated roles.[36]

If a source of pleasure is subject to hedonic adaptation—as most are—then a potent strategy to mitigate that is to: a) spread out *the times and ways* in which one experiences that pleasure, and b) spread out one's *sources* of pleasure in general.[37] In terms of the first, I mentioned above the quaint example of eating chunks of chocolate one after another resulting in less pleasure with each passing piece. One way to avoid this is to space out one's consumption. If one has a chunk of chocolate, say, once a week, it's likely that the exact same level of pleasure (maybe even more) can be attained each time. In terms of the second, "variety is the spice of life," and it's a fun task indeed to list out, and experiment with, possible sources of new pleasure. One of the most interesting aspects of contemporary happiness research suggests that an important way to both augment and preserve pleasure—and to resist the likelihood of things like depression—is to cultivate not merely *an openness to different sources of pleasure* (so that one doesn't get "stuck in a rut") but, moreover, *a sense of personal identity that is itself plural*, drawing on different strengths, sources of pleasure, value commitments, and habitual behaviours.[38]

This is very important for the chronically ill to note, and put into practice. Because when one falls injured or ill, it can come—very easily—to *absolutely dominate* your identity and experience. This is especially true if it is a difficult, or challenging, affliction. I still remember one of my students approaching me in a parking lot and asking me extensively about my brain tumour and how I handled it. He told me, sadly, that his father had been diagnosed with a brain tumour the year before, and had just let this news hit him like a sledgehammer. The poor man became completely obsessed with his new health condition (constantly fearing seizures), leading to serious dislocation in his career and with his personal relationships. So, hand-in-hand with coming to as great a degree of control as one can over one's chronic condition, one needs to transcend one's illness as well, in the sense of *aggressively cultivating multiple identities beyond your "illness identity."* I myself am epileptic, and I have a brain tumour, and—when these things flare up and misbehave—then they can indeed dominate my temporary experience. There's no denying that reality. But when they don't, I don't even think about them, regarding how I define myself. Now, this is easier said than done, and I can't stress enough how it must go hand-in-hand with the control strategy, because—at least with me—it's in bringing the condition under a degree of control in which one feels comfortable that enables and opens up the space for the time, interest, and energy to cultivate other sources of pleasure and identity.

To summarize, while there *is* evidence that many of our pleasures and sources of happiness are subject to some degree of hedonic adaptation, it does *not* follow that we should become passive "happiness pessimists" and simply accept the gloomy notion that there's little we can do to deliberately augment our happiness over time. First, there's a range of things that are resistant to hedonic adaptation: experiences, especially; and positive, complex, and involved long-term commitments (like a good career or a happy marriage). Second, one can resist hedonic adaptation by spreading out the timing of similar sources of pleasure, and/or by spreading out and seeking new things that give one pleasure, which can then be made part of one's identity. Complex selves are more resilient and better positioned to handle pain-giving challenges. Finally, one doesn't even have to view hedonic adaptation as bad at all, as it cuts both ways. Our adaptivity allows us to adjust to many negative experiences, and recover from substantial threats and losses.

The Genetic Determinism Objection

This challenge hits home for me. My doctors still have no idea what caused or created my brain tumour. The proof that it's the source of my seizures is undeniable: we've deliberately induced several seizures (through sustained rapid light-flashing and hyperventilation—fun!) while I've been hooked up to both EEGs and MRIs at the same time. These images show, clearly, that when a seizure begins, there's a little explosion—a haywire electrical discharge in and around the tumour, which then radiates out. My core specialists speculate that I may well have been born with this tumour, and the seizures only began at thirty because, as I aged, my brain gradually lost its youthful resilience to somehow "work around the tumour." The upshot of my personal concern here: the cause of my seizures may well have been genetic in origin, and so I certainly feel the force of the claim that our levels of happiness may have been pre-determined at birth. But in spite of my fears, I ask: Is this true?

This notion, that our levels of happiness may be genetically determined, appears to come from three sources:

1 From hedonic adaptation, as just discussed. When we get temporary boosts in happiness, we quickly adjust to them and revert to a kind of resilient baseline level of satisfaction. But what accounts for the baseline itself? It's natural to infer that . . . it must be natural—that is, genetically determined and biologically given.

2 Increasingly, research into happiness is becoming quite advanced and sophisticated. Some of the best—at the micro level—deals with MRI imaging of the brain, as well as monitoring not merely electrical discharges in the brain but also the levels (and flows) of certain chemicals therein. These studies have uncovered at least two important, interesting, and widely endorsed findings: first, people who are happier than average show greater-than-normal brain wave and electrical activity in the left pre-frontal cortex; when people are exposed to negative events, emotions, and stimuli, this instead lights up the right pre-frontal cortex. In other words, there seem to be distinct brain regions clearly associated with happiness and its opposite.[39] Second, and similarly, researchers have identified strong correlations between the prevalence of certain chemicals in the brain and corresponding levels of either happiness or unhappiness. To the plus side, high levels of serotonin and dopamine, as well as endorphin and oxytocin, have been associated with feelings of well-being, relaxation, and happiness; to the down side, high levels of cortisol have been associated with stress and unhappiness. Additionally, very low levels of serotonin have been linked to many kinds of deep unhappiness, ranging from depression to criminal behaviour to suicide attempts. All these potent chemical and physical connections to happiness cause some researchers to speculate

that our feelings of happiness and unhappiness merely piggyback, so to speak, on the flows of these chemicals (or brain waves) within our brain. Such flows, and our receptivity to them, are strongly influenced by our genetic endowment.[40]

3 At the macro level, impressive, influential studies have been done on the happiness levels of twins over time. Authors David Lykken and Auke Tellegen have made bold inferences, citing how identical twins report strikingly similar levels of happiness throughout their lives—even when they have each gone on to lead very different lives. But while identical twins (who are 100 percent genetically identical) report such strong similarities, similar studies on fraternal twins (who only share 50 percent genetic identity) report no more similarity in shared levels of happiness than any two regular siblings, or indeed any two people. If genetic identity produces nearly identical levels of happiness over time, and any kind of genetic difference results in no clear correlation in happiness levels at all, then this seems to point to there being a powerful genetic component to our happiness. Lykken and Tellegen think so, having declared: "Trying to be happier is as futile as trying to be taller."[41]

On the basis of these and related findings, positive psychologists such as Sonja Lyubomirsky have argued that the components of happiness can be broken down as follows:

FIG 3 A PROPOSED PIE CHART OF HAPPINESS

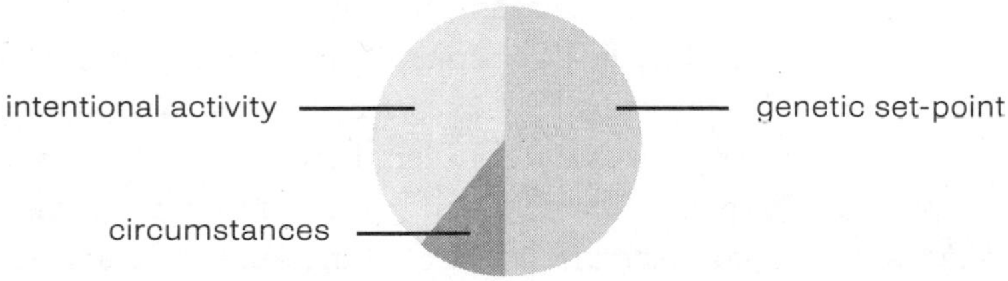

intentional activity ——————— genetic set-point

circumstances ———

The genetically established set-point (i.e., the biologically established "default setting" of your level of happiness) accounts for approximately 50 percent of one's happiness over time, whereas the deliberate results of one's free choices and behaviours (called "intentional activity") account for about 40 percent. The remaining 10 percent is accounted for by such "circumstances" as one's income, marital status, the nature of one's job, one's physical environment (where one lives), and the like.[42]

Lyubomirsky's excellent book, *The How of Happiness*, breaks down much of this, and the existence of the genetic set-point. A version of the above pie chart, for example, is depicted twice in the book's first thirty-nine pages. In her Introduction, she writes about how she was originally going to title her book *The Forty-Percent Solution*: "Why 40 percent? Because 40 percent is that part of our happiness that it's in our power to change through how we act and how we think, that portion representing the potential for increased lasting happiness that resides in all of us. It's not a small number, and it's not a huge number, but it's a reasonable and realistic number."[43]

Though I have much admiration for Lyubomirsky's work, I'm skeptical of these numbers, and this pie chart breakdown. While I admit that our happiness must be composed, in very general terms, of these three components—some kind of genetically given factor, some kind of freely chosen personal factor, and some kind of impact from circumstances (as defined)—the numerical breakdown seems arbitrary and questionable. The "circumstances" number, in particular, seems low (exaggerating hedonic adaptation, which we've addressed above), and the 50 percent given to genetics seems both too large and too neat and convenient. (Why not 58 percent? Why not 44 percent?) Moreover, such a pie chart fails to convey the degree to which there is deep inter-penetration between these three factors: they are presented as given, occupying their own hermetically sealed quadrants. But, for example, one's "circumstances" are at least partly determined by one's free choices. This is most obvious with marital status. And one's income is often strongly correlated with one's occupation and choice of career; and where one has decided to live is, at least partly, within one's conscious control.

More to the point, there's a complex interaction between one's genetic endowment and one's behaviour and free choices, resulting in the kind of person one is and the level of happiness one enjoys. As Lyubomirsky herself stresses, having certain genetic components (or dispositions) does *not* guarantee that one will end up with the full-blown trait in question. She gives, as an example, how people suffering from Phenylketonuria (PKU)—a terrible inherited disorder that can lead to mental retardation, seizures, and premature death—can, with very vigorous intervention from parents, caregivers, and eventually one's self, achieve a diet free from phenylalanine (found in milk and eggs) and, along with supplements, escape many of PKU's worst affects, allowing the person to enjoy an all-but-normal life.[44] Lyubomirsky also—in direct rebuttal to Lykken and Tellegen—points out that average heights have measurably increased over time, especially in countries like Britain and the Netherlands, as a result of: better hygiene, better preventative public health care (such as vaccinations), and greater quantities of protein in diets. Thus, even a trait thought to be "about 90%" genetically determined—height—turns out to be rather plastic, and manifestly impacted by individual and institutional choice and intervention over time.[45] (Importantly, in a later study, Lykken himself "recanted"—his word—his prior statements about the magnitude of the genetic component to happiness, and stressed our freely chosen ability to augment our happiness levels at least by decreasing such common sources of unhappiness as anger, depression, fear, resentment, and shyness.)[46]

There're many other examples of such complex interactions between genes and behaviour. Scientists now think that there might be a genetic component to alcoholism—but, obviously, it's not your teeny-tiny DNA that decides to take a grip of a bottle and drink. That's your own free choice (at least initially). There are many that come from a long line of alcoholic ancestors who, repelled by sordid examples and wasted lives, choose not to drink at all, thereby escaping both the affects and any unwanted labelling.[47] There's also brand-new research suggesting that how one exercises, and the degree to which one exercises, impacts whether and/or to what extent certain genes get "turned on," resulting in a higher synthesis of protein in the relevant muscle tissue. There's even a whole new field of science, called "epigenetics," which has grown up around observations such as these, investigating complex processes for how genes come to operate in the body over time, and how some of these processes move *from* human choice and environment *into* the genetic structure as opposed to the other way around.[48]

There are also clear and proven genetic components to both our intelligence and our musculature. But, once more, these genetic endowments have been shown as being less strictly determining and more providing for an outside range or limit to what we can freely achieve. So we can view it with respect to happiness. There almost certainly *is* a genetic component to happiness; whether it accounts for something as high as 50 percent seems dubious (or, at least, arbitrary), but it's there, and we need to know that *it may establish an outside range or upper limit* on the degree of pleasure and satisfaction that we may achieve and feel. As Lyubomirsky says, though, this is actually not a claustrophobic, confining shame; rather, it can be liberating knowledge. If it looks as though other people are much happier than we are, and we are truly doing our best to enjoy happiness ourselves, it may be through no fault of our own that we have the happiness status that we do.[49]

I like the analogy of musculature in this regard. *Men's Health* magazine reports that, according to certain experts, there are genetic limits on the potential size of one's muscles. For men, they propose the following imprecise "rule of thumb" test: bend your left arm at the elbow and flex all your arm muscles, clenching your fist and "popping your guns" (biceps). Look at the space between the start of your bicep and the inside of the crook of your elbow. If you can comfortably fit your index and middle finger from your other (right) hand into that nook, then you have "short muscles." (This is true of me.) If you have "short muscles," it's been proven that, no matter how hard, often, and rigorously you exercise—even if you were to supplement with a truck-load of steroids—you simply cannot ever become a huge "muscle-bound" person like Arnold Schwarzenegger or Sylvester Stallone or Dwayne "The Rock" Johnson. It's genetically impossible: the structural potential for such large growth is just not there. Now, you could interpret this one of two ways: 1) you could cry that you'll never be like Sly, and bemoan your un-Rocky destiny; or 2) you could view it as a liberation, in that it frees you from all the time and effort spent trying to achieve a goal that is literally impossible.[50]

This is important to know because my guess is that most people who are interested in happiness, and who buy and read books about happiness, probably feel they aren't as happy as they could be—and are interested to see if they can understand things better, or do things differently, to improve their happiness status. Such was certainly true of me. On one hand, it's vital to not give up and resign oneself to one's current happiness status—blaming it on sub-par biology. There are steps one can take to further actualize one's happiness potential, just as with studying (intelligence potential) and exercising (muscular potential). But there likely are genetic limits to what any of us can achieve in this regard. And so, there's another *genetic* reason to not try and chase happiness so much that you suffer from happiness anxiety. You give it the attention and effort it deserves, and no more.

Let's now consider more deeply the micro-level findings—brain region activity and brain chemicals—by considering the helpful work of Daniel Nettle. As mentioned, a number of people have interpreted recent brain research into happiness as showing that happiness is a mere "epiphenomenon" or "supervenient property": it merely piggybacks on what's real, which is the flow and location of both organic chemicals and electricity within the brain, and from there, the central nervous system (CNS). But this kind of observation and attitude seems misplaced, and gives a misleading impression. It unfairly and incorrectly privileges material realities over emotional experiences, dismissing the latter as mere things being "carried along" by the chemicals and electricity—as if to assert that all of our feelings are like this. The more correct understanding is not that the one thing (the flow of chemicals and electricity) is what's "really real" while the other (the experience of emotions) is some kind of second-rate parasite hitching a ride. The truth is that *these are two sides of the same coin*. There's one phenomenon—the experience of happiness—that can be understood:

- **physically**, as the flow of electricity and chemicals within certain brain regions (themselves structured through genetic endowment); *and*

- **mentally**, as the inward "feel" and perception of what that emotion, or flow of electricity and chemicals, is like within one's consciousness.

Some, historically, have said that these two things correspond to "the objective" and "the subjective" respectively: there's a factual side of things, and then there's the personal experience. I get it, but I myself don't like this outdated terminology, as it still implies that the physical is the more real ("objective"), whereas the mental is only appearance. Yet, one's subjective perception of an event (its "phenomenology") is still just as real—just as "there"—as the physical flow of chemicals and electricity. They both exist, and are but two different ways of understanding the exact same event. This is emphatically true when the event being discussed is the experience of a complex emotion, such as happiness. Moreover, the notion that the physical things are "more objective, or real, or primary" comes with the misleading implication that they are what is causally the most important: the mental or emotional experience "supervenes" upon them, or rides in their wake. We know the story is not so simple, though, and in fact the causality can go the other way: research subjects can be made to feel a certain way (disgust or anger, for example), and the flow of electricity and chemicals *follows the experience* of the intense emotion, not the other way around. I'd refer here, once more, to the new science of epigenetics.[51]

The Enlightenment-era philosopher Immanuel Kant once wrote of understanding human beings on the whole as complex creatures who can at once be seen as: 1) purely material animals, dominated by the physical laws of the universe; and 2) as freely choosing moral beings, who struggle to make the right choices as they go about their lives. Kant stressed how these are not only two sides of the same one coin but are also inescapable facets of how we view the human condition. We have *both* physical and material natures, and don't have much choice over that; and we have moral, emotional, and intellectual natures composed of how we perceive things, what we value and believe, and how we freely choose to act in the world. Our lives are unimaginable without both these facets, and we cannot reduce one to the other without sacrificing a whole, deep, vital domain of human experience.[52]

Of course, Nettle notes, it was always going to turn out that happiness had *something* to do with the brain and CNS, and the flow of electricity and chemicals therein. Happiness was never going to be rooted in our big toes, after all. The crucial thing to infer from all this excellent scientific research into brain chemistry is not that happiness is genetically or bio-chemically determined; it's that these new pieces of knowledge may provide us with valuable insight and effective tools into how we can make people happier—or, at least, less unhappy. For instance, based on the left/right brain asymmetry findings, there are now ongoing experiments to see if electrical stimulation of the left side of the brain's frontal lobe can result in sustained increases in happiness, especially among those with clinical depression. And it's well known that, over the past several decades, there has been a determined effort by the psychiatric community to see if chemical intervention—for instance, through ssris and other serotonin-boosting pharmaceuticals—can sustainably increase happiness. So, the scientific findings don't have to spell doom and gloom in terms of free will and happiness—they can be seen as increasing the tools we have in our toolbox to augment our happiness levels.[53]

Now, should we give up on other activities and concentrate solely on these "purely physical" interventions? There's insufficient reason for arriving at that conclusion. Consider, for instance, that repeated and rigorous psychological experiments have shown that the following simple exercise, at day's end, repeated every day for about six weeks, has as big and measurable a boost in self-reported happiness as taking a comparable course of anti-depressant medication: consider and enumerate *three happy things* that happened this day, things for which one is grateful. Such things can range from the very small and trivial (the taste of one's morning coffee/tea, a witty text from a friend, etc.) to large and salient (a new job or promotion, starting a new romance). This strategy and its findings—that this activity is almost as effective as using mood-altering chemicals—is one of the most widely reported and endorsed among happiness researchers on all sides.[54] And note how this "Three Things" strategy is easily available even to people with quite severe chronic conditions. I've made this a ritual in my daily life for years now: I love it and never tire of it. It's an especially nice way to end one's day, right before drifting off into dreamland.

To summarize: all recent scientific progress toward understanding the physical manifestations of happiness does not diminish the reality of the subjective or mental experience of it, nor does it provide evidence that happiness is genetically or bio-chemically determined. If anything, such scientific progress has been shown to be not the enemy but the friend of those concerned with augmenting people's happiness, providing us with more tools (in terms of chemicals, pharmaceuticals, and electrical stimulation) in our happiness-promoting toolbox, alongside many other behavioural things we can do that have proven effective for most people. I trust that such a conclusion is quite germane to those with chronic conditions. For, though scientific knowledge hasn't been able to cure us of our disorders, we all know—and can recognize and respect—just how much advances in medical and scientific knowledge have enabled us to diagnose our conditions, and then subject them to a degree of management that can render our lives liveable and more enjoyable.

CHAPTER 2

Why Should Happiness be a Goal?

Last chapter, we saw how being goal-directed in general produces happiness. Specifically, the pursuit of goals: is activating, inspiring, and provides focus in life; adds structure to one's daily life; provides a sense of purpose and meaning about life in general; not only involves you with life but also with other people; makes you more likely to achieve what you want; augments pleasure in the present; and enhances one's self-esteem.

Sonja Lyubomirsky has made a vital inference for the chronically ill from these important considerations. She argues that, to the extent to which goal pursuit delivers on all these things, it can be said that the framing and dedicated pursuit of goals has a positive and profound connection with the assistance of coping. *Pursuing goals aids with coping*, including the kinds of challenges confronted by those with a chronic condition.[55]

When one considers the manifold obstacles created by chronic conditions, and examines the above list of benefits of dedicated goal pursuit, one can almost go point-by-point and witness how goal pursuit counteracts some of the most common, and salient, consequences of a chronic illness or disorder. Such conditions: are dispiriting; can destroy one's plans, both for the day and longer term; can deprive one of any sense of meaning in life beyond raw survival and bare functionality; can drive one away from other people and into the self; can interfere with one's ability to achieve what they want; can take away from pleasure in the present, usually causing pain; and can diminish one's self-esteem, as one feels ill, broken, inefficacious, alone, in pain, and detached from "the whirl and the rush of humanity."[56]

Thus, I can't stress enough how important it is, upon being confronted with a chronic condition, to challenge its typical effects by selecting and pursuing goals that can counteract its most corrosive tendencies.

Last chapter demonstrated the many benefits of goal pursuit. However, left unsaid were two large, connected issues: 1) which goals one should pursue, to maximize the above benefits; and 2) why happiness should be among such goals.

The overall contention here is that happiness ought to be *the* goal one pursues in life, much like Aristotle had stipulated. However, there *are* possible, plausible rival goals to consider, especially when one cannot achieve the kind of happy attitude, or enjoy the kind of pleasure intrinsic to what we mean by happiness. Respectful consideration needs also be given to such rivals: notably what we might call "the life of meaning."

Before tackling those big-picture philosophical issues, though, let's complete the examination of goal pursuit in general. What are "lower-range" or "mid-range" goals, the pursuit of which will make for a happier life and move one closer to the ultimate objective of becoming lastingly happier and fulfilled?

FIG 4 PROCESS CHAIN/HIERARCHY OF GOALS

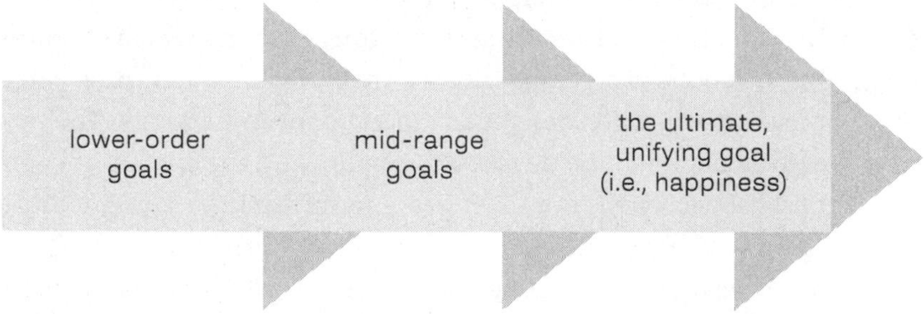

| lower-order goals | mid-range goals | the ultimate, unifying goal (i.e., happiness) |

Simply, lower-order or "Level One" goals are things like daily or monthly tasks that contribute to mid-range goals. Mid-range or "Level Two" goals are things one pursues as large ingredients of happiness. (Both of these sub-level goals are ends themselves, as well as means to further ends.) And the ultimate, unifying goal stands as the final rationale and direction for life: happiness itself. As Aristotle declared: "[H]appiness is something final, and self-sufficient, and the end of all our actions . . . happiness [is, indeed] the highest good."[57] Even more emphatically, he stated: "[H]appiness is at once the most noble and best of all things and also the pleasantest."[58] The ordering could just as easily be depicted as a hierarchy, as no doubt Aristotle would've preferred:

FIG 5 HIERARCHY OF HAPPINESS

i.e.,
HAPPINESS

mid-level (L2) goals:
means to the final (L3) level

lower-level (L1) goals:
means to L2 goals

Now, in many ways, the mid-range or L2 goals are those component parts of happiness sketched out previously in the Introduction, and are the sorts of things around which chapters in this book are organized. Recall that happiness has three parts: pleasure, the external goods, and the internal goods. The rest of this book will be devoted to explaining the nature of each, and the various lower-level goals required in order to achieve the mid-range goal(s) in question. (For instance, mastering the art of *savouring* would be a lower-level, or L1, goal, which contributes to the mid-range, or L2, goal of *pleasure*.) But in this chapter, we are concerned with the abstract characteristics that these lower- and mid-range goals tend to have, or rather should be composed of, to best contribute to one's overall happiness.

The Best Lower- and Mid-Range Goal Selection

Core intuition has it that, while goal pursuit in general has clear benefits, the choice and pursuit of certain kinds of goals are more likely than others to lead toward happiness. Deciding to pursue an interest in violent crime, for example, might indeed "provide focus" or "involve you with other people," but is unlikely in the long term to lead to fulfilling happiness. (Thus, it simply won't do to define happiness in general as "the attainment of one's goals," *whatever* those goals may be.)[59]

So, what have contemporary happiness researchers discovered about proper goal selection? Lyubomirsky has perhaps the best overall schematic. She says that the most efficacious pursuit of happiness will involve the selection and pursuit of lower- and mid-range goals in one's life. These goals should be:

- intrinsic, not extrinsic
- authentic, not inauthentic
- approach-oriented, not avoidance-oriented
- harmonious, not conflicting
- activity-based, not circumstance-based
- flexible and appropriate, as opposed to rigid and inappropriate[60]

Let's consider these briefly in turn, with special eye toward applications for the chronically ill.

Intrinsic vs. Extrinsic

Intrinsic goals are those that you yourself find special, interesting, and meaningful, regardless of what other people think or the kinds of material rewards that may or may not be attached. The pursuit and attainment of such goals has been shown to be much more satisfying and happiness generating than the pursuit of goals undertaken precisely for the sake of material reward, or those resulting from social expectation or perceived pressure. The very definition of an extrinsic goal is that it is undertaken *simply as a means to an end,* usually to avoid some punishment or to gain some form of reward. Thus, an intrinsic goal is one whose pursuit and attainment is its own reward, as it expresses one's deep interests and commitments. (It is a worthwhile activity to try to make a list of some of your intrinsic goals. For example, how would you spend your time if you didn't have to worry about money?)[61]

Authentic vs. Inauthentic

The difference between authentic and inauthentic goals is similar: it's the difference between a goal whose pursuit is the expression of one's deepest values and interests (authentic) and those usually pursued because—as Tal Ben-Shahar says—one "has to" (inauthentic).[62] The difference between an intrinsic and authentic goal on the one hand, and an extrinsic and inauthentic goal on the other, is relative to the person in question. For example, the pursuit of money is often described as a classic extrinsic and inauthentic goal. Many of us go to work to earn money to pay bills because we have to. Meanwhile, those who make wealth creation the main focus of their lives often seem to do so for the sake of conspicuous consumption, and the social status that such lavish wealth enables. One of the most oft-repeated facts in the positive psychology literature posits that those who define themselves as money-driven are also those who—again, by their own admission—report some of the lowest levels of happiness and life satisfaction, and some of the highest levels of stress and anxiety.[63] But researchers like Lyubomirsky point out that that's because the majority of such people are pursuing wealth for extrinsic, inauthentic reasons. It *could* be possible that there are some who pursue wealth for reasons that truly reflect who they are; however, such people tend to view wealth differently. They see it more as a show of their competence and mastery, or as something that gives them and their family personal freedom, as opposed to something that enables them to purchase trendy trinkets and win the approval of fast, false friends. In short, the same goal can have different functions for different kinds of people. The key is that the goal in question be, as Ben-Shahar says, "self-concordant"— in agreement with one's true interests, identity, and values.[64]

One of the unexpected positive consequences of becoming chronically ill may well be that it renders you a more authentic person—or at least provides you with the *opportunity*. After all, a sick person generally has less energy to put on airs and pretences, and less patience for those who cannot deal with their illness or disorder. Afflicted people often speak about finding out who their real friends are when confronted with such situations, and more deeply speak about coming to know themselves better, and being more mature and honest about who they are and the kinds of lives they wish to lead. There's a limit to this, of course: we can't expect people to be grateful for their illnesses. However, I can say from my own case how—even in spite of the costs imposed on me—dealing with the seizures, and then finally getting the right diagnosis and struggling to restore stability, forced me to grow, develop, and reflect in ways that I had not previously, and probably wouldn't have until considerably older.[65]

Approach vs. Avoidance

Approach-oriented goals are those that are framed positively in one's mind as something desirable, which draws you toward them, promising positive results upon attainment. Avoidance-oriented goals, on the other hand, are those that one has, and puts energy into, in order to avoid feared negative consequences. Here, too, the exact same goal can be framed in either approach- or avoidance-based terms: Lyubomirsky gives the example of the goal of losing weight and becoming more fit. This can be viewed either as approach-based (one wants to become healthier and have more energy and capability) or avoidance-based (one doesn't want to be fat). She cites evidence that people, in general, do better, experience less stress, and stick to goals in a more sustained and determined way when they are approach-oriented goals.[66]

I think it's more complex than a simple equation always in favour of approach-based goals. As we'll see when we talk in the "internal goods" section about correct beliefs, a very common human tendency (perhaps implanted in us by the pressures of evolution) is to put greater psychological weight, in the short term, upon negative or threatening information. And while this was valuable and understandable for our earliest ancestors, who were thereby able to be cautious and efficacious about dealing with threats to their survival, for us, it can actually be a contributing factor behind such thinking habits as paranoia, anxiety, and dwelling on the negative in a disempowering way. It's a rule of thumb that for every *one* piece of negative information (e.g., personal criticism from a peer) most people require *three to five* positive experiences to overcome the depressed mood generated by the negative information. This is to say that, in the short term anyway, there's evidence that negative motivation and avoidance goals might actually be considerably stronger than positive, approach-based ones.[67] I myself can testify to this:

the burning desire to end a very negative experience (suffering uncontrollable seizures) was, for me, crucial in motivating the change I needed. But now that such has (long) been achieved, I cannot rely anymore on negative motivation: it's about turning toward the approach-oriented goals. And, after being in a negative place for a long time, it can actually be a disorienting challenge at first to become more positively motivated.[68]

Harmony vs. Conflict

It's vital that one's goals not be in conflict with each other, and thus to that extent be harmonious. There's evidence that, in cases where people pursue conflicting goals (e.g., to both spend more time alone yet also more time in social situations), not only do they fail to attain them, they actually become so frustrated that they give up *on both of them*, as opposed to thinking through and prioritizing them. One of the great advantages of Aristotle's three-fold picture of happiness is that it provides a grounded, internally consistent, and coherent picture of happiness without internal contradictions.[69]

Activity vs. Circumstance

The difference between activity goals and circumstance goals harkens back to the phenomenon of hedonic adaptation. We previously saw that a reliable way to resist hedonic adaptation—that is, adapting to, and thus getting less pleasure out of new things—is for those "things" not to be things at all but experiences, and preferably complex and multifaceted ones. If, for example, your goal is to acquire a new phone or laptop, upon doing so you'll quickly adapt to that added pleasure and move on. But if your goal is, say, to learn ballroom dancing, the pay-off of such a complex activity will be more sustained and lead to a much larger longer-term pay-off.[70]

Flexibility vs. Rigidity

The final requirement for low-level goals is that one be flexible and appropriate in the framing and pursuit of such—as opposed to rigid and inappropriate. Psychological research has shown, time and again, how rigid, repetitive patterns of behaviour (e.g., incessant hand washing, checking for keys, or whether the stove has been turned off) are associated with various low-level "manias"; and how rigid patterns of thinking can lead to serious unhappiness, especially if said patterns have to do with expectations or beliefs about how things "must" be done.[71]

This last criterion has special relevance for the chronically ill. Lyubomirsky gives as example someone who once liked to exercise and workout but has since suffered a serious injury affecting their range of movement. Misery will result, she advises, if that person is rigid in their approach to exercise—it's the old way ("My way!") or the highway, so to speak. But if that person is flexible with the means of pursuing their goal, then pleasure and happiness can still be attained. This former jogger "could [now] take up yoga or the stationary bike." The overall objective of exercising and staying active remains intact, but the lower-level sub-goals and means need to have flexibility built into them.[72]

Further comment on this is needed, as the chronically ill no doubt walk a fine line in this regard. On the one hand, illness or injury has thrown them for a significant loop—thus, striving to regain mastery and control is the order of the day. As argued last chapter, coming to as great a degree of control as possible over one's disorder is vital in re-establishing a sense of freedom and autonomy, and of efficaciousness and "normality." Yet, the new daily schedule or routine, once achieved, should only be taken so far, or else rigidity and inflexibility—both physically and mentally—can set in. This can lead to emotional ruts and setting oneself up for disappointment when others, and the world, fail to remain in place. Over the years, I've sometimes found it difficult to achieve this balance, and have erred too much on the side of control. Being out of control for so long, I think, inclined me in this direction. I know this tendency was and continues to be a mistake, and is something I need to work on for the future. We can never go wrong in reminding ourselves of Aristotle's wise counsel: "Moderation in all things."[73]

Lyubomirsky describes a particularly successful research experiment, out of Montreal, related to these issues. A group of newly retired people (self-chosen) were unhappy because they were having trouble finding new structure and goals to commit to, in light of the end of their professional careers and the free time they now had on their hands. They were able to turn those emotions around by adhering to the following program:

Step One: They got together and brainstormed, freely, some things they *might* be interested in pursuing individually. They actually did this over several sessions, so as to ensure that the list was serious and reflected sustained and considered interests, not just momentary whims and wishes.

Step Two: They ranked these free-wheeling interests into actual goals, and focused on *making one goal the top-priority*.

Step Three: They then considered, in detail, what it would take to achieve their individual goals, in both a positive and a negative sense. The negative sense involved them imagining what the obstacles and costs would be to pursuing such goals. (Participants later mentioned this as one of the most important and useful facets of the experiment.) The positive sense involved enumerating the particular benefits of "going for it."

Step Four: This involved specifying the highest-priority goal in as fine detail as possible, taking it down from the clouds and making a concrete plan for achievement. *They each shared this written plan with the rest of the group.* (Numerous studies have shown that making a public commitment to something—like losing weight—considerably increases the odds of success, as it adds social pressure and expectation; people don't want to be seen flaking out, or quitting, on their goals and commitments.)[74]

Step Five: This involved taking feedback from the group and crafting a final implementation plan: the actual who, what, where, when, why, and how of goal pursuit—and especially the formulation of *strategies to deal with expected obstacles.*

Step Six: Carrying out the plan, with ongoing feedback to (and from) the group, and all members committed to supporting each other in pursuit of their individual goals. (This ongoing support was later mentioned as perhaps the most valuable aspect of the process.)

The target group of new retirees reported, at the end of this three-month process, being able to accomplish on average about 75 percent of the goals they had set out to achieve, and more importantly, reported higher levels of happiness over six months later, which is considered a very strong result for a "happiness intervention" of this sort. This general rubric for identifying and achieving lower-levels goals can be used by anyone for any purpose, but seems especially relevant for the chronically afflicted, *especially those who find themselves newly such*, as the sense of being adrift can be quite similar to being at the end of one's career and/or the beginning of a whole new and different phase of one's life. Lyubomirsky also says that planning out and giving oneself treats and rewards for the achievement of important milestones have been shown to augment both success and enjoyment of the process.[75]

Pursuit vs. Attainment

One final, important thing to note: There's much evidence that, when it comes to these lower-level goals, the *pursuit* is at least as gratifying—and probably even more so—than the actual achievement. There're many anecdotes of people achieving big goals, only to feel a sense of loss and purposelessness afterwards. Soldiers often report this after returning home from their intensely structured, highly goal-driven tours of duty.[76] And after returning from the Moon—the Moon!—American astronaut Buzz Aldrin famously sunk into a deep depression, and at one point became a heavy drinker and was even reduced to selling used cars for a living.[77] Ben-Shahar, now a psych prof at Harvard, begins his book *Happier* by describing how, as a teenager, his pursuit of the national squash championship introduced him to the subject, and phenomenon, of happiness. Consumed by his pursuit of the title, he found that it ordered his every move and imbued his young life with focus and purpose. But upon attaining his much-desired goal, he subsequently felt let down, and was gripped by a kind of malaise.[78]

Luckily, though, this well-documented phenomenon is true only of lower-level goals, and perhaps some mid-range goals as well. It cannot be true when considering the overall, ultimate goal of happiness itself. But we must always be mindful of how this phenomenon—the pursuit generally being more enjoyable than the attainment—constantly demands that we turn to the next thing, lest we feel let down and lose our sense of direction. Once more we see the pervasive importance of having goals, framing goals, and pursuing them with passion and diligence. Since happiness is THE GOAL, and since it is so complex and manifold, with at least three large and many-layered components, it truly affords us *a lifetime's worth of work, effort, and orientation.*

The Benefits of Being Happy

There're many benefits to pursuing a variety of goals, as described above. But why pursue happiness as one of these goals, or even *the* goal? This question might seem akin to observing how bees seem to enjoy and chase after honey. I won't spend too much time on it, especially since opinion polls around the world—and across cultures—show that the majority of people in almost any given country say that happiness is already their main aim in life: for themselves, and for their loved ones.[79]

There are at least two big reasons to pursue happiness. One we've encountered before, in the Introduction: Aristotle's claim that happiness has intrinsic value, and represents the fulfillment and completion of human potential. Only happiness, he stated, is targeted for its own sake: all other goals are targeted because people believe (either correctly or mistakenly) that doing so will increase their happiness. Happiness is the one ultimate and intrinsic goal: that which orders and gives rationale and impulse to every other goal we might pursue.[80]

That's a strong argument, and here's another: today's positive psychologists don't much fancy sweeping philosophical claims about the one intrinsic good in life. They prefer to look at measurable results. And recently, they've shown that being happy actually brings with it a range of positive consequences. If true, we have two mighty legs to stand on in terms of answering the query: Why pursue happiness? Because happiness has both *intrinsic* and *instrumental* value. Parsing it further, I would say there are four strong legs to this table. We should pursue happiness because:

- it promises to deliver to us a range of good consequences
- it has intrinsic value, as the un-moved mover of human striving
- it represents a complete, desirable, and well-lived human life
- it provides an ordering and rationale for every other goal we might wish to pursue

FIG 6 MAJOR REASONS TO PURSUE HAPPINESS

intrinsic value:
"the un-moved mover
of human striving"

good consequences
(including, but beyond,
warm feelings)

MAJOR
REASONS
TO PURSUE
HAPPINESS

represents the
fulfillment of one's
potential

orders and explains
the pursuit of any and
all sub-goals

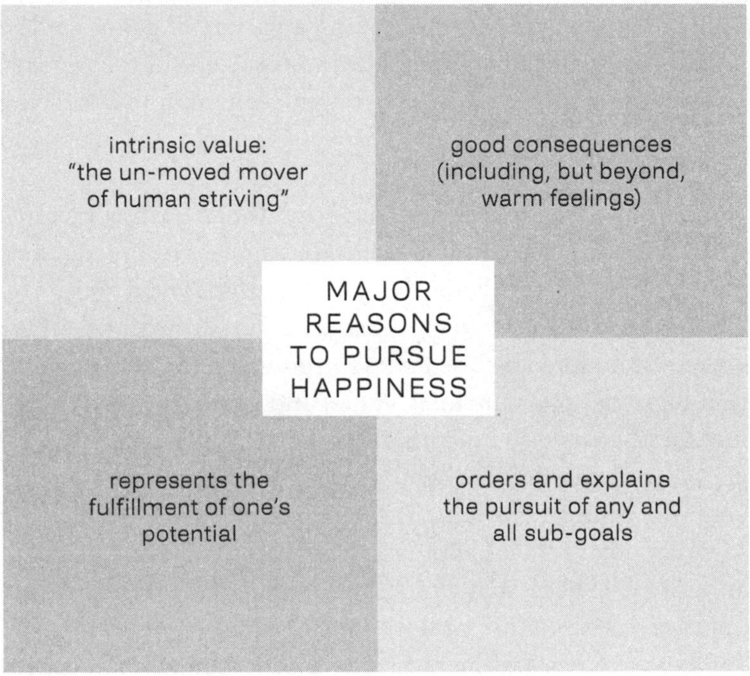

Let's now focus in on the nice consequences of being happy (or, at least, substantially happier—either than what one was before, or above and beyond average happiness levels). Happy people—according to the research of Lyubomirsky, Ed Deiner, and Laura King—have been shown, *in general*, to enjoy the following advantages over their less-happy, or unhappy peers:

- they tend to be more social and energetic

- they seem better liked by others

- they generally have a larger circle of friends, and more close or "high-quality" friends

- they are more likely to get married, stay married, and report themselves happy with their marriage

- they incline toward being more charitable, co-operative, and giving of themselves

- they tend to have thinking that is broader and flexible, and are better at problem solving

- they generally do better at school and work, and report themselves as enjoying both more

- they tend to earn more money at their jobs

- they are often better negotiators, and get asked to take leadership roles more often

And of special significance for this book, happy people:

- tend to have stronger immune systems

- are overall of more robust health (both physically and mentally)

- enjoy longer life expectancy[81]

Happiness, it seems, has everything going for it. Some further comments and interesting factoids, in connection with some of the above findings:

In terms of the greater, and deeper, social connections, this should come as no surprise. People are often more drawn to happy than unhappy people, as they find them more pleasant and fun to be around. We've noted, and will tackle in further detail in Chapter 8, the connection between social orientation and extroversion on the one hand, and on the other a more pleasant, engaged, and expansive mood. (Significantly, even introverts, when questioned, say they feel happier and better about themselves after having engaged in a comparatively more extroverted task or event. They may have found it draining and/or challenging, but they still seem to have found it more pleasant—and wish that they could bring themselves to do more of it.)[82]

The findings about happier people being more giving and charitable are some of the most grounded in this regard, and serve as a nice counterpoint to those who argue, or suspect, that making happiness one's major goal in life is a deeply selfish and antisocial orientation. It's not: happier people actually share more of their time, more of their money, and more of themselves with others than those who are unhappy. (Think of the fictitious but well-drawn case of Dickens' Ebenezer Scrooge.)[83]

Evolutionary psychologists have crafted interesting theories related to this. They speculate that negative emotions exist in the first place to warn us about potential threats and dangers to our survival and fitness. Thus, when experiencing negative emotions, there is a kind of overall narrowing and collapsing—emotionally, cognitively—focusing in on those things that may signal a threat. But if negative emotions signal danger and threat, then positive emotions signal safety and the potential for growth. Barbara Frederickson has formulated an influential "broaden-and-build" theory, according to which the evolutionary function of positive emotions isn't merely to give us pleasure in connection with rudimentary things needed for our baseline survival and fitness (e.g., food, drink, sex, and sleep) but, further, to give us a sense of safety, openness, and confident curiosity, leading us to broaden our experiences and—crucially—further develop our capacities, talents, and knowledge. In other words, happiness triggers a *"broaden-and-build"* response, whereas unhappiness triggers a kind of *"collapse and dismantle"* response.[84]

This theory both explains and is supported by recent research confirming that happier people tend to experience superior cognitive functioning in general (at least in the short term) when compared with their unhappy peers. Research subjects made to feel happy and relaxed (through film clips previously proven to elicit such responses) were tasked to perform a variety of cognitive tests, the results of which were compared to peers who were made to feel such negative emotions as anxiety, fear, anger, and sadness. The results were even stronger than what the researchers predicted: the happier people displayed broader and sharper attention, enhanced ability to spot global (as opposed to merely local) visual patterns, greater short-term working memory, enhanced verbal fluency, and greater openness to new information. Another happy discovery of the same research? The researchers also measured the physiological responses of participants throughout (heart rate, vasodilation, blood pressure, etc.). When those who went through negative emotion conditioning were then given positive emotion conditioning, the temporary physiological negatives previously induced were actually turned around and made better. Psychologist Christopher Peterson argues that the experience of the positive emotions "undid the anxiety" and damage of the negative emotions. As the saying goes: the best cure for unhappiness . . . is happiness![85]

The enhanced social and cognitive skills, and the more general "tuned in, turned on" quality of happier people no doubt accounts for strengths in terms of school and work performance, as well as comparative advantages in negotiation and leadership (wherein unhappy people either don't feel comfortable in an enhanced social role, or they default to antisocial behaviours like withdrawal or aggression). In terms of higher wages, a long-term study compared happy college freshman to non-happy or unhappy ones (as determined by the appearance of a so-called "Duchenne smile" in their yearbook photos—a sincere, un-fakeable, full-faced, joyous smile). It found that the happy ones, sixteen years later, had higher salaries (researchers had factored out any initial wealth advantages).[86]

A related study, in terms of method, found that sincerely happy freshmen females were more likely to be married before they were twenty-seven, and at fifty-two were much more likely to have marriages they defined as satisfying. The findings with respect to friendship and marriage summarize the general interconnections between a host of good happiness consequences. People want to be married to happy, rather than unhappy, people. There's evidence that happy people can be more giving of themselves, and share more—obviously desirable traits in a partner. And the openness to new experiences and new information lends itself to tackling the many adjustments and compromises that married life requires.[87]

In terms of health and longevity, much of the findings presumably speak for themselves. Happier people are probably, by definition, scored better in terms of various measurements of mental health. Profound unhappiness (such as clinical depression) is, after all, one of the paradigm cases of a mental health problem.[88] And in terms of physical health, high levels of cortisol (related to stress and unhappiness) have been linked to all kinds of physical health problems, in particular heart disease, sleep disorders, and digestive problems. Happier people have lower levels of cortisol and higher levels of the various "happy chemicals" (like serotonin), and thus are more relaxed, sleep better, have better digestion, and—most immediately—have better cardiovascular functioning.[89] There's even evidence suggesting that happier people might have an easier time making healthy eating choices, as unhappy people may sometimes be prone to seek temporary mood boosts from high-fat, high-sugar choices (and/or large quantities), which can come to haunt them later.[90] Finally, and again perhaps as a matter of definition, happy people find it much easier to resist the repeated lure of addictive substances, to which some unhappy people can be tempted to return time and again—seeking temporary boosts (or at least escapes) in ways that can end up creating serious long-term physical- and mental-health challenges. (We'll talk more about substance abuse next chapter.)[91]

The material about longevity is both interesting and provocative. Nuns, it may surprise you to know, are actually among the most studied groups of people, especially by psychologists and sociologists. There are many reasons for this, not the least of which is their "good-sport" willingness to participate in so many studies in the first place. One of the main reasons why nuns are sought after as a subject group for these sorts of studies is that a number of factors thought to potentially bias and skew research results—things like income, lifestyle habits, and so on—are held steady among nuns. They live together, have no income of their own, lead very routine lives with strict diets, and so on. Thus, they form something of a pre-filtered body of willing research subjects: perfect!

There exist a range of longitudinal studies on nuns, testing for a correlation between happiness and longevity. Happiness gets measured in various ways (e.g., self-report surveys, other-report surveys, photographs of them smiling—looking for that Duchenne smile—and so on). Further, each nun (at least at major American convents) usually has to write a very detailed statement upon first being enlisted in a religious order. The statement asks specific questions, and some are linked to happiness (such as: Are they looking forward to joining the order?). Psychologists can then rank the content of these statements in terms of the level of happiness expressed. Using these methods, researchers have suggested that the correlation between consistently high levels of happiness (thus construed) and longevity may be as high as ten years—*a full extra decade of life*! If true, this is a stunning finding. Other longitudinal studies have concluded that the decision not to smoke, for example, adds approximately seven years to the average lifespan. Thus, being happy is even better for your physical health than being a non-smoker![92]

Alternatives to Happiness as Life's Major Goal

I vividly recall an illuminating conversation I once had, several years ago now, with a very distinguished professor from Israel. He and I were sharing breakfast one morning during an academic conference. We had bumped into each other, over the years, at various conferences and institutions, and always seemed to enjoy each other's company (in spite of at least a twenty-year gap in our ages). Let's call him Levi. Our common research interest was the ethics of war and peace (really, anything to do with armed conflict), and so he asked what I was currently working on. I mentioned two things: cyberwarfare, which he knew all about, and happiness. This immediately got his attention. He smiled and congratulated me for spreading my wings, and then looked away and was thoughtful for a second while he chewed on his bagel.

Then Levi abruptly declared, "Myself, I can't ever be happy again." He stated this purely as a matter of fact, with no melodrama or show of emotion.

This, of course, caught my attention. What a confessional thing to say over breakfast. And from such a distinguished man, with a successful career.

"What do you mean, Levi?"

"Ever since my wife died a few years ago, I can't ever be happy again. I've tried all these tricks and techniques and suggestions that all these people make, but nothing can heal the grief in my heart. I can't even begin to describe it, Brian. I mean I can still do things, of course. I'm functional. I can get momentary, small-scale pseudo-pleasures, such as the taste of this breakfast. But it can't be sustained, and I can't ever enjoy a fully happy mood for even one single day. Without her, there's a huge hole in my life, and in my heart, and it can't ever be filled or healed. I once was happy, back when we were together, but shall be so never again. Never. All I can hope for is a *meaningful* life, focused on my work and the political cause it serves, which is the security of the state of Israel and the protection of Jewish people more broadly."

Another relevant story was related by Daniel Nettle, and concerns the philosopher Ludwig Wittgenstein, who was Austrian by nationality but wrote in English. Wittgenstein (1889–1951) was born into an extremely rich family and inherited a fortune; however, he shunned his wealth, eventually giving away his money to his siblings—most of who, sadly, went on to commit suicide in spite of their enormous affluence. He himself contemplated such a thing several times. On top of this, Wittgenstein struggled throughout his life in a variety of careers (including twice, to his credit, as a war hospital volunteer), and had a reputation of being a difficult and demanding person with a history of losing his temper (including hitting school children). Upon discovering philosophy, he devoted the rest of his life to it, and went on to write acclaimed and influential works. He was long associated with Cambridge University in England, and was affiliated with such famous geniuses as Bertrand Russell. Wittgenstein's philosophical reputation may since have dimmed somewhat, but for decades there was no one in philosophy who didn't read Wittgenstein and take lessons from his works. And as Wittgenstein lay dying, after a long struggle with various cancers, the only one around him was the wife of his doctor, who had called for his friends and former students. At the moment of his death, Wittgenstein called to her, and made the following surprising declaration: "Tell them all I've had a wonderful life." The upshot of the story is this: How could a man so miserable have thought that he lived a wonderful life?[93]

This paradox or "mystery" dissolves when one moves from the perspective of happiness to the perspective of something else as the major aim or goal in life, such as the meaning mentioned by Levi. From the perspective of happiness, Wittgenstein did not seem successful, especially since he appeared not to get much pleasure out of many of life's activities. But from the perspective of intellectual achievement and creativity, he could justifiably look back on his life with considerable pride and have felt it worthwhile—even wonderful. Similarly with Levi: bereft of pleasant feelings, he could (and can still) make sense of his life and feel it meaningful and worthwhile, even if he cannot describe himself as being happy.

Artistic genius Vincent Van Gogh (1853–90) comes to mind when thinking of meaningful lives that may not have contained much of what we consider happiness: crushing depression and eventual suicide combined with unforgettable, colourful, distinctive, powerful, and world-famous achievements in painting.[94] Or Russian author Fyodor Dostoyevsky (1821–81), whose father was murdered by his own serfs (slaves), and who then had to endure extreme poverty for most of his life. Jailed repeatedly for his supposedly "anti-Tsar" views, Dostoyevsky actually spent four years in a hard labour camp in Siberia, after which he came to suffer from repeated epileptic seizures (Van Gogh, it is said, suffered similarly). Dostoyevsky was further gripped by a gambling addiction. Yet in spite of all these things, he went on to pen remarkable pieces of literature, including *Crime and Punishment*. (Late in life, he did come to find some happiness with a particularly lucky marriage to a very supportive wife, along with a deep religious conversion, and conviction, which offered him peace).[95]

Or consider more recently Nelson Mandela's bitter experiences suffering racism and brutal inequality under apartheid, and eventually being thrown in jail for twenty-seven years, resulting, among other things, in the collapse of his marriage and not being able to see his children grow up. Yet throughout, he remained committed to the cause of resisting and overthrowing the apartheid government in South Africa, and served as the major symbol for that struggle for decades before ultimately becoming President of South Africa. While it's safe to assume that, at the end of his life, he was pleased to witness the achievement of a democratic South Africa, for much of his life there was only struggle, and presumably not much in terms of pleasure and happiness. But throughout it all there was meaning: in his case, the struggle against racial injustice, and the drive to defeat apartheid and establish democracy in his home country.[96]

Perhaps no one has made the philosophical case for "meaning over happiness" more eloquently than Viktor Frankl. In his mega-bestseller *Man's Search for Meaning*, Frankl—a trained neurologist and psychiatrist—detailed his personal experiences in Nazi labour and death camps during WWII, including Auschwitz. Suffice to say, there's very little happiness to be found during such horrific experiences—unjust imprisonment, exhausting forced labour, starvation, brutal violence, constant fear and intimidation, and utter dehumanization—and Frankl speaks openly and clear-mindedly about that. Happiness is absent here; however, he believed that, even in the midst of such terrible circumstances, one can still select and pursue purposeful goals. There can be direction, there can be authenticity, there might even be hope regarding the future attainment of goals and the achievement of a better life. But there's little talk here of happiness, and certainly not in any robust, Aristotelian sense. There's meaning, which is perhaps the best we can hope for during our short lives on this sub-optimal world. (In the book, Frankl developed a method for achieving this, which he labelled "logotherapy"—therapy and survival *through* meaning.)[97]

The Backlash

Resulting from examples like these, and reflections on their profound lessons, there's arisen something of a backlash in recent times against the resurgent popular interest in happiness and the spectacular growth of such fields as positive psychology. The backlash seems convinced that happiness is a fundamentally selfish and/or shallow pursuit, and that ultimately a life of meaning—exemplified in the above illustrated—is superior, more serious and important, and more fitting for grown adults. The life of happiness can be derided as a particular product of modern Western (especially American) civilization, and not the nicer aspects of it, either: the inward-looking individualism, the consumerism and status-seeking, and an unwillingness to enter difficult, socially minded, long-term projects and commitments. The pursuit of happiness can be seen as nothing more meaningful than "life as a selfie."[98]

Of special interest to readers may be Barbara Ehrenreich's *Bright-sided*. In this 2010 book, Ehrenreich—an accomplished journalist, bestselling author, and Ph.D. in biology—writes about getting diagnosed with breast cancer. She was devastated, angered, and bewildered by her diagnosis and the treatment choices forced upon her as a result, including a mastectomy and chemotherapy. But perhaps the most surprising and annoying thing she encountered—"bright-siding" her (as opposed to "blind-siding" her)—was a culture of upbeat optimism in the face of such a serious diagnosis, which was urged upon her at every step by the breast cancer survivor community. It seemed like everyone was telling her not merely to "keep a stiff upper lip," as it were, but actually to smile radiantly at every step. Ehrenreich was offered soothing words, brainless cheerleader slogans, and soft, fluffy pink ribbons to wear (or stick on her car bumper). She was particularly appalled at advice she received instructing her to consider her cancer a profound gift that would deepen her as a person. So she wondered where this "positive thinking" culture originated, and proceeds in her book to trace it historically, at least in America, to quack nineteenth-century "medical" treatment fads: the conceptual equivalent of snake oil, and the slick charlatans who sold it. She then goes on to argue how such blind optimism can lead to dangerous results—for example, the deep recession from 2007–09, which she blames on ordinary Americans blindly taking on huge mortgages they could not afford.[99]

The Reply

To Ehrenreich in particular, we can certainly sympathize with her struggle, and understand her impatience with those urging on her a coping attitude for which she wasn't ready. I agree with her that there's something suspicious and perhaps pathetic about chanting feel-good cheerleading slogans to oneself on a daily basis. And while I *did* say earlier in this chapter that it's too much to ask people to consider their illness as a gift, I do believe that the experience of going through what I have gone through with epilepsy has strengthened me as a person. But it's more *the response to the illness that has been the gift*, not the illness itself.

To the general critics of "happiness as a mania of selfishness," there's no denying that some people really do seem to pursue their own happiness in this kind of superficial, self-absorbed way. It's easy (and correct) to criticize such people for the smallness of their horizons, and their petty preoccupation with their own eccentric interests. But there's nothing to the very idea of happiness, or to the pursuit of happiness as such, that mandates such mania. Recall that earlier last chapter we spoke in Aristotelian terms of the correct pursuit of happiness as constituting a mean between extremes of excess and deficiency: not so much so that one becomes consumed by an invincible mania regarding one's private pleasure, but also not so little that one becomes fatalistic and resigned about accepting a sub-optimal quality of happiness. And, as stated previously and shown in many studies, the evidence is convincing that, for the most part, people who define themselves as consistently happier actually are *more* giving, *more* social, and *less* self-absorbed than those who see themselves as unhappy. There are reasons why that is the case: positive emotions render one feeling secure, and looking to broaden and build their experience, growth, and connection to others. There's nothing to the genuine feeling of happiness, and being happy, that renders it silly, superficial, or selfish.

Relatedly, there's no reason to believe that there exists a sharp, binary choice between a Life of Happiness and a Life of Meaning. No melodramatic, Kierkegaardian (*Either/Or*) lifestyle choice between them, as if one stood on a cliff considering whether to jump one way or the other.[100] Granted, for some people there *may* be a choice—in the sense that they are literally incapable of experiencing all the elements of happiness, in particular pleasure. We think here of Levi and the inescapable grief of his personal loss. Or Wittgenstein, who seemed constitutionally incapable of pleasure or the kind of smiling good cheer we associate with happiness. But this doesn't set happiness and meaning on an objective collision course. I prefer to think of it thusly: the most choice-worthy life—the human ideal—is a life of happiness as defined by Aristotle, and which we are keen to refine, revise, and explain in this book. This is to say a life that: is pleasurable, experiences external and internal goods, and has a preponderance of positive emotion over negative.

But sometimes—because it's not a perfect world, and bad things happen out of our control—it's not possible for everyone to fully experience, or have, each of the major elements of happiness. In these cases, it makes sense to say that they are pursuing meaning instead of happiness, especially if what is lacking is pleasure and consistent positive emotions, which seem a necessary condition for anything we might describe overall as a happy condition or life situation. I myself would still say that happiness is *the* goal in the sense of being the most choice-worthy (and the most inclusive) of the major goals in life. This doesn't mean there can't be others, such as meaning; however, *the best kind of meaningful life is one that has as many of the ingredients of happiness as possible.* In this way, a life of meaning becomes incorporated within our sense of what is the most desirable life, and avoids the simple and stark binary choice between the two.

FIG 7 THE CRITICS' BINARY CONCEPTION OF MEANING VS. HAPPINESS

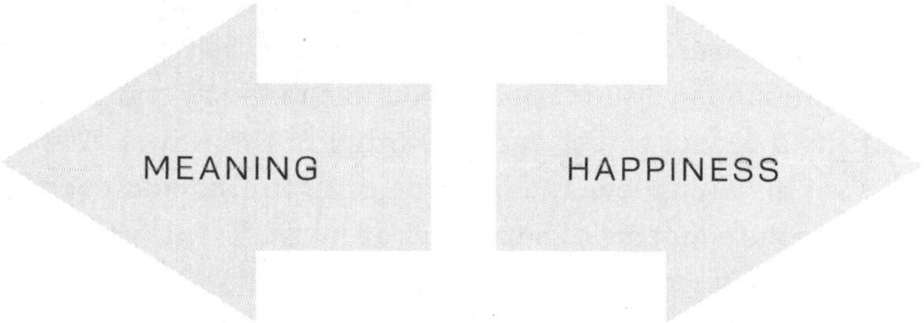

MEANING   HAPPINESS

... where "never the twain shall meet," so to speak. Instead:

HAPPINESS

MEANING

Often when we speak of "a meaningful life," we encounter cases (like those mentioned above) where there is dogged, disproportionate emphasis on one overall goal, be it the security of Israel, democracy for South Africa, or outstanding artistic or philosophical achievement. Yet, these are only the highest profile cases, and there's nothing to say that people who don't pursue lower-level goals (such as raising good kids or crafting a decent career) lack meaning in their lives. As I've said, in my own view, the best meaningful life achieves as many of the elements of happiness as possible. Failing that, it involves focusing on the achievement of goals whose criteria we've already laid out above in connection with lower- or mid-level goals: intrinsic, not extrinsic; authentic, not inauthentic; approach-oriented, not avoidance-oriented; harmonious, not conflicting; activity-based, not circumstance-based; and flexible and appropriate, as opposed to rigid and inappropriate. Ben-Shahar opines that the most meaningful goals will always turn out to be those that involve and spur "personal growth, connection to others, and contribution to society at large."[101]

These thoughts about a life of meaning are of special concern to the chronically afflicted. They provide a sense of orientation and satisfaction even when a full life of happiness cannot be achieved. One thinks in particular of cases where the illness or injury in question literally robs a person of the capacity to feel physical pleasure (e.g., because of chronic pain). It's important to understand that, in such instances, it's not as though one is failing in having a meaningful, or indeed even happy life. One may still pursue a happy life *to the fullest extent possible*, taking comfort and satisfaction in: a) knowing that one is doing one's best; and b) while not as pleasant as one would wish, one's life can still resonate with purpose and meaning, over time learning to take a higher-order kind of mental pleasure and satisfaction in purposeful structure and achievement.

One final remark: there's another kind of life that experts have described as importantly different from a life of happiness. It's closer to a life of meaning, and may even be a species of such. It's the pursuit of some kind of extraordinary experience, or achievement, or excellence. Think of some genius inventor devoting his or her entire life to creating an important new invention, such as the lightbulb or the vaccine for polio or smallpox, sacrificing all else—including personal happiness—for its sake. This has, in most recent times, been described as a "life of flow." We'll discuss this next chapter, as it connects deeply with pleasure, and will complete our reflections on pleasure in particular and its place within a life of happiness.

CHAPTER 3

Pleasure

We've spoken much of pleasure in the preceding chapters. Here's a quick run-down of the most important items:

- Those who pursue goals, and have deliberate direction, experience more pleasure and happiness than those lacking clear orientation.

- Those who can't, for various reasons, feel pleasure or experience a lasting preponderance of good feelings over bad can still pursue a life of meaning, which offers as much of a life of happiness as can be achieved under the circumstances.

- Hedonic adaptation is potent and real, and we need to be mindful of it as we go about trying to increase our pleasure and happiness: frequently, we adapt to the new, pleasant thing, and it soon ceases to offer us the same boost in pleasure as it first did.

- There *are* strategies we can follow, however, to combat hedonic adaptation. First, we can spread out the timing of our consumption in experiencing sources of pleasure. Second, we can seek out, and keep ourselves open to new sources of pleasure. Finally, we note that there are delightful things resistant to such adaptation, which range from small things like breakfast and sex, to larger things like long-term commitments, to complex positive experiences and enterprises such as mastering a skill, crafting a career, or developing a great marriage.

For those with chronic conditions, pleasure is both a source of *special solace* and *special challenge*. It is a challenge in the obvious sense that the condition, injury, or disorder in question probably is a source of pain, and/or it may hamper one's pursuit of pleasures readily available to unafflicted people. It may thus be difficult, and a source of frustration, to experience pleasure with the same focus and success as those unburdened with any such condition. At the same time, pleasures can also offer some of the most readily available sources of happiness for those with chronic conditions—quite clearly in comparison to some of the more complex internal and external goods mentioned in the Introduction. For example, regarding a complex internal good like positive thinking: there's much evidence that sustaining positive thinking patterns can be quite difficult for those with functioning challenges, and is extremely difficult to display especially in the immediate aftermath of an injury or diagnosis.[102] Compared to something like that, savouring the taste of a chunk of cheese, or the sound of one of Beethoven's sonatas, is child's play—and a very reliable short-term pay-off in terms of pleasure. Or consider a complex external good, like having a satisfying job or career that provides sufficient financial resources to afford one's goals and obligations. Compared to everything it takes to realize that, watching your favourite TV show while wolfing down a slice of delicious hot pizza is likewise much easier—and is a more reliable pleasure pay-off for those whose challenges might make the more complex and demanding elements of happiness harder to achieve. Pleasure is thus something of a paradox for the chronically ill.

Evolution's Great Gift
(and Aristotle's Excellent Definition)

Evolution has hardwired us to pursue pleasure. There's no deny-ing this; even Aristotle claimed this to be an inescapable feature of the human animal: we want pleasure (and we don't want pain).[103] Further, the process of evolution has hardwired us (or, at least, the overwhelming majority of us)[104] to find reliable plea-sure in things that maximize the odds of our survival, both as individuals and as a species. Hence the rudimentary yet intense, almost unbeatable basic sources of pleasure: eating, drinking, sleeping, and sex. (Sex is merely one of the most dramatic kinds of physical movement—and use—of our bodies; it's clear that, even more than sex, we biologically need, and get pleasure out of, regular physical movement.)[105]

Other vital biological needs and drives come with distinc-tive kinds of reliable pleasures, which are often overlooked when compared to the above. Consider breathing, as vital as any function we have. Breathing, like sleeping, does not provide an *intense* pleasure, but any interference with it (e.g., asthma, bronchitis, coughing, pneumonia, emphysema, lung cancer, etc.) immediately brings substantial pain and discomfort. And recent research has found that deep, rhythmic breathing and being flush with oxygen can, indeed, provide a noticeable short-term pleasure high, followed by a robust sensation of overall well-being as the oxygen floods into one's tissues, organs, and muscles.[106]

Pleasure theorist Paul Rozin has argued that the most primal and reliable sources of pleasure are those that involve interac-tions between the body and the environment—whether through ingestion (food, liquid, oxygen) and/or expulsion (carbon diox-ide, going to the washroom, orgasm). The original purpose of these interactions was a kind of vigilant monitoring both of self and world, for the elemental evolutionary purposes of raw survival, reproduction, and successful biological functioning. As these more basic kinds of "in/out monitoring" became more reliable, and as further needs and advantages were called for and naturally selected, we were able to develop more sophisticated forms of monitoring and exchanges with the environment (notably hearing, seeing, and language). Our brains grew apace with the need for, and success of, these adaptations. For each of the basic senses, there's a distinctive and strong associated pleasure, which is possible—to an extent—to cultivate and develop.[107]

Aristotle provides an excellent overall definition of "pleasure in general" as precisely the enjoyable sensation that follows the unimpeded and successful exercise of a natural faculty or power. So, think of *any* kind of natural faculty or power we might have—and not just the basic five senses of touch, taste, sight, smell, and hearing. There's pleasure associated with its successful use and deployment (and a corresponding pain associated with any impediment to such deployment). Aristotle goes on to say that it's not just narrowly "natural" faculties and powers that are relevant here. He has an expansive sense of what is natural: essentially, whatever contributes to the full development of the human person. Thus, crafts, skills, and highly refined artificial activities—and even social institutions—count as natural in that they play their part *in fulfilling our nature*, and striving for the fullest possible realization of our potential.[108] Thus, there are pleasures associated with, say, reading, carpentry, investing, and home decor, as well as with being a successful businessperson, or parent, and so on. These are often referred to, nowadays, as "the higher pleasures," which contrast to the "lower pleasures" of the senses. Though this distinction may sound elitist, it doesn't have to be: Martin Seligman points out that the "higher/lower" variation can refer to the fact that there's just more going on with higher pleasures than with lower, which, being based in the senses, don't involve much deliberate thinking. Meanwhile, the higher pleasures usually involve multiple senses plus other capabilities, almost always require deliberate thinking and focused attention, and, while less intense, can be more meaningful and longer lasting.[109] To illustrate:

FIG 9 PLEASURE AND ITS PARTS

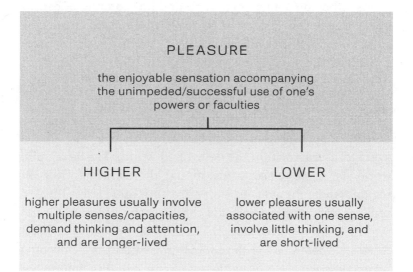

PLEASURE

the enjoyable sensation accompanying the unimpeded/successful use of one's powers or faculties

HIGHER

higher pleasures usually involve multiple senses/capacities, demand thinking and attention, and are longer-lived

LOWER

lower pleasures usually associated with one sense, involve little thinking, and are short-lived

What is *the actual purpose* or point of pleasure, whether lower or higher? Both Aristotle and evolutionary psychologists like David Buss have views that overlap considerably. For researchers like Buss, pleasure is the savoury reward/potent incentive that the process of evolution has planted in us over thousands of years, to do the sorts of thing proven useful for our survival and reproductive fitness. Likewise, Aristotle views pleasure as a kind of reward for successful action, and an ongoing incentive to keep us performing such actions, whether they are the lower kind (e.g., eating nutritious food) or the higher (e.g., making beautiful music). In both cases, pleasure is Mother Nature's prize for doing well and becoming better—and for avoiding pain (which is nature's signal that one is heading down the wrong road).[110]

But: Evolution's Big Burden (Always the Pursuit, Never the Completion)

We'll speak in detail next section about how to cultivate and intensify pleasure in its various forms. But first, one final thing needs to be noted about evolution and its profound effects on how we experience pleasure. We're hardwired to pursue pleasure, and nature has gifted us with basic drives and sensory capacities that enable the experience of pleasure. *We are, in this sense, literally built for happiness.*[111] It's probably a related fact that, when researchers ask people how happy they are on a scale of one to ten, the majority of people will say they are pretty happy, averaging around seven. This is a very reliable average, at least within the developed world. (The developing world also comes close to this, though there are countries and regions where the average scores are noticeably lower.)[112] Now, some researchers have argued that perhaps people are inflating their self-reported happiness scores, especially in North America where there is clear social pressure to say that you're happy (lest you seem like a "loser"). Some call this "impression management," as one tries to influence how others perceive them (e.g., the upbeat nature of most Facebook posts). But others, like Daniel Nettle, have suggested that, even factoring in impression management, it's still quite plausible—for reasons of evolutionary psychology—for such numbers to be accurate. Why? Because evolution wants us to be content with our lives. Consider: if our ancestors were totally miserable and utterly hated this planet, then it might be fair to conclude that none of us would be here today. We all might have jumped off a cliff a long time ago, and *homo sapiens* would be permanently out of the Darwinian sweepstakes for survival of the fittest. Evolution has built into us the means and even the inclination to be satisfied with what we've got. *It wants us to continue on.*[113] That's quite good news, which we can take advantage of in numerous ways. (In fact, researchers have proven in lab experiments what they call "the mere exposure effect," which relates to how people explain their likings and dis-likings. It's actually *not* true that "familiarity breeds contempt." In fact, a reliable way of getting most people to like each other is . . . to get them to spend time together; relatedly, a reliable way to get people to like some material thing is . . . simply to give it to them and let them have it for a while. Psychologist Christopher Peterson concludes: "[P]eople are pleased with what they have, and with what is familiar.")[114]

The catch, though, Nettle notes, is that evolution probably *doesn't* want us to be completely happy and satisfied. Why not? Because then we'd spend all day rubbing our tummies, staring at the ceiling, and daydreaming. Nothing would get done, and the species would fail to advance in preparation for the next big evolutionary challenge. So, most people's self-reported happiness score is what turns out to be a surprisingly realistic seven out of ten: mainly happy, and glad to be here, but never totally happy. This encourages us to keep trying new stuff, to see if we might become even happier. Indeed, in the surveys across cultures, almost no one reports a ten, presumably counting against the notion of rampant self-inflation with these scores. A number of countries regularly score in the high eights, or even just over nine (Nettle: "the positively nauseating Swiss"), but that really seems the upper limit. In truth, it's an interesting task even to consider what a perfect ten out of ten on a life-happiness scale might be. I think most of us can imagine—quite well, in vivid and unfortunate detail—what a zero or one might look like. But a perfect ten, with absolutely no room for improvement? It's difficult to conceive, though presumably Aristotle would say that the overall picture we're examining in this book is as close to "a human ten" as we can imagine.[115]

One very important asterisk to add in connection with the seven out of ten: it is only a general average. Important findings from England suggest that the average answer of those who self-report a chronic condition, illness, or disability comes in around just over six out of ten—*a full point lower than average.* This might sound small when listed as "one point," but don't forget that, on this scale, it means 10 percent: *the chronically afflicted are, on average, ten percent less happy and satisfied with their lives than the average person.* Nettle concludes: "Although people with acquired disabilities or health problems show very considerable adaptation, the adaptation is often not quite complete, leaving a shadow in their happiness judgments.... Serious health problems can leave a lasting mark."[116]

So, the burden that evolution has bequeathed to us is that we probably won't ever be completely happy and satisfied with our lives. We'll always be able to imagine *some further addition* that would make life better, which in turn drives us forward and doing productive things. The other let-down that evolution has given us, in more narrow terms of pleasure, is that while it has enabled us to pursue and experience pleasure in all kinds of ways, the "pleasure system," and relevant circuitry in the brain, tends to be decidedly short term. We know this from our own life experience, and this is confirmed through laboratory experiments: the release of pleasure-inducing chemicals cannot continue indefinitely. It is a short-term program that gets spent and then needs recharging during a "refractory period." (This fits with evolution's ultimate plan for us to get up and do something productive and future-focused.)[117] We can try to prolong and intensify our pleasures, for sure; to an extent, this can and does work. But in the end, it's still a relatively short-term payoff we're looking at—and so, *if we want abiding joy and positivity in life, it has to reside in things above and beyond mere pleasure* (such as the achievement of difficult and positive goals; the cultivation and development of internal goods of moral character and mental and emotional hygiene; and external goods of rewarding relationships, a satisfying career, and helping to construct a decent society).

Enhancing Pleasure

Pleasure's not perfect, but it feels great. It's part of happiness, and of course we'd like to get more of it if we can. But can we? Yes! Apart from a) spacing out pleasures, b) engaging in pleasures that are resistant to hedonic adaptation, and c) making a deliberate effort to add to the diversity of one's pleasures, researchers have found many other techniques and strategies to enhance one's experience of pleasure in general (whether lower or higher):

1) Capitalizing on Common Quirks

Distinguished researchers such as Daniel Kahneman have discovered some interesting quirks in our typical experiences—especially memory recall—of pleasant things. Some have delighted in stressing the apparent irrationality of these quirks, while others—such as Sonja Lyubomirsky—have instead advised us to incorporate such knowledge into how we set up and plan pleasant experiences.[118] Two big quirks in particular to note are:

- **The Endowment Effect**. Researchers have noted that, when people are given things, they get more pleasure out of the fact that they've been thusly "endowed" (as opposed to when they have to buy such things for themselves, or somehow own or possess them already). A funny experiment showing this involves two situations. In the first, an experimenter gives the subject a choice between receiving a small, cheap good (like a pen or a coffee mug), or receiving the equivalent amount in cash. In the second situation, the subject is given the good outright, for free, and then asked what amount of money would be needed for the experimenter to buy back the good from the subject. In every case, in the second situation the subject wanted significantly more money—usually double—than they would've accepted in the first.[119] While amusing, people like Lyubomirsky have suggested that we use this common quirk to our advantage by making a deal with our loved ones, offering each other random, small-scale surprises and gifts on a regular (yet not predictable) basis. (Birthday and holiday gifts don't count.) Bumps in happiness should follow.[120]

- **The "Peak-End" Rule, and "Duration Neglect."** Our memories of how pleasant experiences are or were are generally not composed by adding up the moment-by-moment pleasures so much as our experience of: a) the peak, most-pleasant moment; and b) the level of pleasure at the end of the experience. In other words, we typically neglect (or discount) how long a pleasure or pain endures, focusing instead on how it ends and the quality of its best moment. For example, experimenters asked people to submerge their hands in cold water and then rate their level of discomfort. Results showed that people preferred to have the experiment end with the water slowly being warmed up, even if the overall length of the experiment was increased as a result (involving more painful moments with their hands under the water). Those whose hands were under cold water for five minutes, with the water staying at a constant cold temperature, reported a less-pleasant experience than those whose hands were under water several minutes longer, but where, during the final minute, the water was warmed up.[121]

It's a fascinating experiment, and no doubt confirmed by common sense. Consider your memories of past romantic relationships. If you're honest with yourself, I think you'll find yourself ignoring (or substantially discounting) the sum total of overall pleasures you enjoyed with a specific person or persons over the months and years. Instead, I'd wager that you focus on three things: 1) the highest high (the peak) of the relationship; 2) the lowest low (the trough, the very worst moment); and 3) how it all came to an end. If it ended mildly (with mutual respect or even friendship), and the low was not so bad, you probably have fond memories of that love; whereas if the low was bad and the ending bitter, then the sum total of good moments (even if there were plenty) will not be enough to change your mind that the relationship was a dud, and to this day fills you with pain and regret. (This sort of phenomenon might also be witnessed when considering jobs one has had, especially for a longer period of time.)

Experts suggest using the peak-end rule to design experiences to ensure maximally pleasant recall of them later on. Consider, Lyubomirsky says, how one might design a dinner party, or a vacation, with the peak-end rule in mind. Quality over quantity would be the rule (since we neglect the overall sum), with special thought paid to both designing the very best moment as well as the very last moment (ideally you'd want them to be separate, to double the effect). So, for instance, with a summer vacation to Paris, it would make sense to try to rank your two top "things to do," and perhaps do one toward the start of the trip and the other on the last evening. (E.g., early on, you could do a walking tour of Montmartre, lingering over lunch and the art market. And then on the last evening, enjoy a twilight picnic on the huge lawn in front of the Eiffel Tower, complete with red wine and cheese.)[122]

2) Being Open to Beauty and Excellence

This one might seem unusual: Aren't we all attracted to beauty? Don't we all love excellence? Well, in theory yes, but there's surprising evidence that people can shut themselves off from these things, especially if they involve others who intimidate them with their stand-out beauty or with a spectacular display of skill (e.g., singing or athletic prowess). Learning to appreciate beauty or talent on its own terms, without defensively wanting to judge it or somehow "take it down a peg," opens one up to many more pleasures. And let's not forget nature: many studies have shown that, when it comes to ranking beautiful things, nature in general scores among the highest for most people. Every day, Mother Nature provides us with a parade of wonders from which to take joy and delight. From blades of bright green grass to sunshine in the sky or the gentle babbling of a brook, nature provides much to savour and appreciate. Studies show that people who live near parks and/or make daily (or at least weekly) effort to spend time outdoors not only report significantly less stress and increased happiness, they even on average live longer![123]

3) Mental Transportation

This is a visualization technique to help one feel pleasure when trapped in an otherwise bad or boring situation, such as an unimportant office meeting. You try to imagine yourself, in vivid detail, in a situation that always brings pleasure and makes you feel exhilarated, free, and/or relaxed. Imagine yourself, for example, enjoying a beach someplace bright and warm, or playing cards and sharing a laugh with your friends, or reading your child a sweet bedtime story. For the chronically ill in particular, this can be a skill worth cultivating, as almost anyone can engage in such acts of imagination. In studies on mental transportation, wherein subjects were instructed to engage in such an activity at least twice a week for six weeks, huge rates of success were reported: only 2 percent claimed it did nothing at all, whereas the rest claimed it had at least some—and sometimes large—beneficial effects on their daily happiness.[124]

Lyubomirsky tells a remarkable story of "group mental transportation" used by some Jewish prisoners at Auschwitz. This group was a pack of "foodies" and, to mentally transport themselves every now and then, would get together either during break time or sometimes even during work (depending on the task), and they'd conjure up—in step-by-step detail—an instance of them all going out together to enjoy a very fancy meal at an expensive restaurant in Paris. They would imagine everything: what they'd wear, the people and things they'd see on the streets, the tuxedo of the maître d', the smell and chatter and ambience of the place, each delectable course of food, and each savoury flight of wine. She concludes: "Remarkably, these individuals were able to experience 'pleasures of the mind' even under conditions of severe deprivation. With practice, we all can learn how to luxuriate and transport ourselves, using our five senses, no matter how ordinary or unstimulating our current setting."[125]

4) Nostalgia

This could be used as an example of mental transportation (i.e., recalling a happy past memory instead of a fictitious one to transport yourself), but it can be done under any circumstance. Studies show that people who go out of their way to recall, in detail, some of their favourite past moments report higher happiness than those who don't linger on the past. This is especially true for older people, and obviously could be useful for the chronically ill—especially if the memory involves a pre-afflicted moment, or a past moment where you enjoyed a small triumph in your ongoing struggle (e.g., a negative result on a blood test). Some experts even define nostalgia, alongside gratitude, as "pleasure, as it applies to the past."[126]

5) Celebrate Good News

Too often, people fail to celebrate their achievements, whether small or large. They often talk themselves out of it, stressing the cost, extravagance, or impracticalities of such celebration. Studies show that you should not make this mistake: it's one thing to be humble about an accomplishment, but quite another to treat it as if it's just another day and move on to the next thing. Relishing an achievement *is* important, and *does* make one happier. Doing so can draw one's attention to appreciating something good, solidify one's identity, and make one feel efficacious; and the celebration adds something new and diverse to one's typical routine. Thus, the next time you (or your child, your friend, or significant other) do something special celebrate it in a way proportionate to the achievement. As said in the film *Hector and the Search for Happiness*, a part of happiness is "knowing how to celebrate!"[127]

6) Savouring

Some experts feature savouring as its own kind of thing or skill, while others suggest that enhancing pleasure is a facet of savouring. Researchers have found that those who make it a habit to savour a thing or experience are: a) less depressed, b) display more optimism in their thinking, and c) report being happier than those who don't take the time to savour things.[128] Experts suggest there are several components to successful savouring:

- **Mindfulness and Absorption**. This refers to paying heightened attention to the details of a situation, and the overall "feel and texture" of the moment. Eastern traditions of thought, especially Buddhism, make much of this skill, and usually attach it to forms of meditation.[129] (Zen is fond of fables, and one on mindfulness involves a student monk-in-training who has prepared for three years, intensively studying the doctrines of Buddhism. He opens his master's door and steps through to begin his final exams, and his master says that he has just one question. The student replies, "I'm ready." The master asks him, "On which side of the door was there a bushel of flowers?" The student, not having noticed, failed, reportedly resulting in three more years of study. Mindfulness doesn't have to be attached to meditation, though, and can refer to any kind of deliberate focus that is determined to register mentally the full details of the moment and the pleasant feelings one experiences at that time. Peterson reports that this may involve a deliberate kind of "slowing down" of the typically fast-paced Western mind in order to extract the full feeling and flavour of the moment, whether it's the taste of an apple, a walk in the rain, petting your pet (or your lover's hair), or putting on head-phones to listen to and absorb more fully the music of, for example, Drake, or Ravel's *Bolero*.[130]

- **Sharing Pleasure with Others**. Studies show that a joint experience of pleasure only increases the moment. People in general tend to have heightened attention and perception when in social situations, putting this hand-in-hand with absorption (which need not be thought of as solitary, as it's often portrayed). Singing together, dancing together, joking around together, playing sports together, dining out, going to a party, visiting an art gallery, going to a concert, taking a cooking or wine-tasting class, or—above all—taking a trip are all great moments, ripe with opportunities for sharing pleasure.[131]

- **Take a Keepsake**. To heighten one's pleasure, as well as aid one's nostalgic memory later on, it's fun and advisable to take a keepsake or souvenir of an event: whether it's a selfie of all your friends bunched up together or a self-made panoramic video, or perhaps a purchased souvenir or physical keepsake. It's cool and fun to look at, and touch, such things later on— they can bring back wonderful memories during necessary "micro-breaks" from either work or home duties. I myself have a few "memory boxes," which are glass-enclosed trophy cases containing various meaningful mementos. These range from: my very first stuffed animal ("Bowser" the lion), which I won at the local fair when I was five (bursting balloons with darts!); a "student of the year" plaque I won in high school; rocks from such places as Stonehenge, the Grand Canyon, and the Acropolis; driftwood from the coast of California; and the cork of the most expensive and insanely delicious bottle of wine I ever bought ($300 at the Plaza Hotel in New York).[132]

- **Write it Down.** Once the flush of things has calmed down (and if the event is significant enough), I have found it very useful to jot down detailed notes about the thing or experience in question, usually with lots of descriptors and an eye not just for detail but, moreover, a sense of how I was feeling and what I was thinking in the moment. But don't let such writing spoil the moment—savour it in real time. And don't leave the writing too long, such that you can't accurately recall. Also—as Lyubomirsky says—don't expect the actual writing to offer you much pleasure: what you're doing is creating a vivid record that will help you re-live a moment in the future.[133] For example, I always keep a travelogue of my big trips—usually writing them during the long flight home, when there's little else to do—and break down my experiences day by day. I absolutely love reading these three to six months down the road (looking at pictures at the same time), completely relishing the details of my happy memories.

7) The Great Day

An almost foolproof method of augmenting one's pleasure—and indeed of keying into *which* things and experiences make one happier in general—is to imagine, list, and plan out a great and happy day. This, as Seligman notes, is a much better strategy than the unsustainable and clichéd advice to "live this day as if it's your last."[134] (There's an episode of *The Simpsons* where Homer is told to do this, and so he promptly sits down on the curb in front of his house and starts sobbing and wailing, yelling "Oh my God, I'm gonna die!") This activity is fun to do, even just as an intellectual exercise—it usually provides further insight into the things that most make you happy. And, if followed through, you will no doubt gain a clear happiness boost from the process. Even if you have to tell yourself that it's a special treat, just to reserve one great day for yourself to do whatever you'd most like, you should go for it and reap the rewards—it's an investment in your well-being. The other great thing about such a method is that it's *accessible to everyone, including the chronically afflicted.* It doesn't have to involve some kind of implausible activity, if such a thing is not actually achievable for you (e.g., sky-diving); it's relative to what would boost your mood right now. For instance, yesterday I saw a story on a news program of an elderly man, bed-ridden in the hospital, dying from leukemia. He'd said his final goodbyes to all his family and friends, and then asked to have his guitar, so that he could "go out" while strumming and humming. Well, he got such a kick out of this that he just kept at it, and the next morning everyone brought in an instrument of their own. They ended up having a jam session that lasted for days, culminating in a boisterous St. Patrick's Day bedside sing-along over a week later. *No matter where you're at in life, there's a set of things that, for you right now, would make for a great and happy day.* List them. Do them. Reap the rewards.

Twelve Pleasure Enhancements, Specially Targeted at the Chronically Ill

I wanted to craft a special section for this subject, even though I think that the above can be tailored quite clearly to the chronically afflicted. I'm going to err on the side of stressing good things that seem available to (almost) anyone, but I certainly don't want to convey the impression that only these "low-impact" things apply. Only you know what you're capable of—what truly gives you pleasure, and what would work best for you given your circumstances. (There's something to be said, though, for pushing the limits of that, as often we're capable of much more than we typically think). Still, here are some nearly fail-safe pleasure promotion strategies:

1 **The Great Day**, as just described.

2 **Daily mental exercises**: positive nostalgic reminiscence, or imaginative mental transportation. Try one of each for at least five minutes. And *keep at it*. The more you try, the better you'll get at crafting a mental picture, honing the details of the memory, projecting yourself into the moment, and enjoying it.

3 **Mindfulness and absorption**: especially focused on deploying the five senses, and using them to extract as much information and sensation from a thing or experience as possible. Try combining this with a deliberate "slowing down" of the mind. Often, combining this with a meal is practical, as multiple senses come into play. Plus, we've all got to eat, and this can enhance the experience of the meal to boot. Make mealtime a special time for sensation and, hopefully, companionship, which will only heighten attention and perception.[135]

4 **Nature**. Ideally, go out and be in nature, at least once a day for thirty minutes, and during different times to appreciate the different forms of day and night (thus adding variety). Consider combining this with absorption, as concentration on natural things (e.g., clouds, running water, wind blowing through leaves on trees) is deeply relaxing and gratifying. If for some reason you can't actually get outside, consider the

small joys of plants (or making a terrarium for yourself),[136] or buying a small indoor rock fountain. Or buy and build (and gaze at) an aquarium filled with pretty, brightly coloured fish. Or, at the very least, orient your bed so that you can see the sky and partake of natural light.[137]

5 **Special Breathing**. Almost everyone can breathe. *Don't underestimate how good and relaxed proper breathing can make you feel.* Try the following exercise on a routine basis:

- Breathe in through your nose—a deep breath in which your stomach comes out (as opposed to your chest moving up). Breathe in on a count of three or four—whichever is comfortable.

- Immediately breathe out (don't hold it), but when you exhale, do so slowly, to the same three or four count, and exhale through your open mouth.

- Immediately repeat anywhere from at least four times in a row to as many as you like. This exercise, or any variation thereof that best suits you, is guaranteed to provide a short-term feeling of relaxation and well-being.[138]

In Chapter 8, I'll detail how to combine such breathing techniques with cognitive techniques like meditation. Meditation and similar techniques have been shown in many experiments to be some of the most reliable and substantial happiness-boosters out there,[139] right up there with gratitude, physical exercise, and the "three happy things" daily ritual. Speaking of which . . .

6 **End-of-day Gratitude Ritual**: considering and naming three concrete things or events that made you happier that day.

7 Rhythmic touching. A great many of the chronically afflicted can receive a massage, which most people find both relaxing and pleasant. But if receiving a massage from others is too expensive or not practical, one can learn—as amusing as it may sound—to massage oneself in a rhythmic and small-scale way, offering almost a micro-break of "mini-pleasure." Rubbing the inside of one's index finger with the inside of the thumb in a soft circular motion for ten seconds is one such example. (A related technique for relaxed focusing: pretend that you're holding a potato chip between your thumb and two closest fingers. Hold this posture while you relax and focus. Combine this with the special breathing exercise just mentioned.) Or grow your nails a bit and gently drag the nails of one hand in a circular pattern on the inside palm of your other hand for about thirty seconds. Or do the same on the interior of your forearm, from the inside of your wrist to the crook of your elbow. You'll be pleasantly surprised. Experiment from there, but note that medium-speed, circular motion is almost always the best. Consult the sources in the note for more specific techniques of self-massage.[140]

8 Visual variation on beauty/excellence. In addition to breathing, self-touching, and thinking of three positive things a day, most people can see to some extent, and do so even in spite of very painful chronic conditions. Thus, tutoring and cultivating visual pleasures is a real source of solace or stimulation, depending on one's mood. Pay attention to what pleases your eye, and surround yourself with such things, be they flowers, art, family photographs, home decor magazines, or even just watching "the beautiful game" (soccer) on TV. And don't underestimate the pleasures of reading, which combines the stimulation of imagination with the love of language, which we are hardwired by evolution to appreciate and respond to. Further, researchers have found that the eye tracking of sentences as you read literally induces a relaxation (and even sleep-inducing) mechanism within most people's brains.[141] Which ties into ...

9 **Sleep**. Everyone needs sleep, right? It's a vital pleasure-promoter, at least in the indirect sense of allowing one to feel rested enough, alert enough, and efficacious enough to be receptive to the other pleasure-boosters listed here. *Sleep is a key helper for the chronically afflicted, allowing an escape from pain as well as the best opportunity for recharge-and-rebuild.* But there's plenty of evidence that people don't get enough sleep, or suffer from fractured sleeping habits. Good "sleep hygiene" habits include:

- no daytime napping

- plenty of exposure to daytime natural light

- exercise during the day (preferably earlier in the day)

- avoiding stimulants too close to bedtime (like caffeine, alcohol, nicotine, and even just too much food/calories)

- having a regular-ish bedtime (in particular, not wildly different work week and weekend sleep schedules)

- having a soothing bedtime routine (consider the gratitude ritual, touching, breathing, reading, as mentioned above)

- associating your bed with sleep and relaxation. Do not do work on your bed, watch TV, or endlessly surf social media while there.[142]

10 **Gentle stretching**. One should strive to be as active as one's condition allows. *The more exercise the better,* in terms of everything: impact on mood, condition, sleep patterns, etc.

(With my epilepsy, I found that one of the very best things for me, including prior to receiving the proper diagnosis, was—and still is—a rigorous workout, especially using a stationary bike first thing in the morning after breakfast.) Some physical movement every day is an absolute must, even if—for those restricted in their capacities—this means only gentle stretching in bed while waking up in the morning. *Your body wants this, and will respond to it positively.* Other excellent low-impact exercises include walking and swimming—and if you've never tried yoga, you don't know what you're missing.[143]

11 **Musical Interlude**. The relaxing and healing power of music has been well documented, and is accessible to everyone but those with total hearing loss. This is true not just for short-term mood boosts but even in terms of measurably enhancing natural pain blockers and aiding in recovery from very serious things like brain injuries.[144] There are so many wonderful genres of music out there. Invest in a decent pair of headphones, close your eyes, and have fun experimenting with different genres—open your mind to fresh sounds, and familiar rhythmic joys.

As Lyubomirsky points out, and no one has stressed more than Aristotle, none of these sorts of things—regarding the enhancement of pleasure—will make more than a dent in your current mood and/or state of being unless you work at incorporating them into the structure of daily life. Even when your condition derails the schedule of a given day or week, there needs to be thought, attention, and effort given to turning these things into actual habits—regular parts of your life—as opposed to occasional stress releases, like going to the sauna, or pounding a punching bag, or getting drunk. Aristotle once said that who we truly are is how we habitually behave—what you do on a routine, repeat basis *is* the nature of one's identity, and more than anything else, especially mere hopes and dreams, *habitual practice and regular behaviours are what come to shape one's quality of life, and degree of happiness, over time.*[145]

Pleasure's Proper Place

Much of this chapter has been devoted to the subject of how to get more, and better quality, pleasure in one's life. We noted from the start how nature has hardwired us to go after pleasure in the first place. But before we go off the deep end—wallowing whole-hog in hedonism—let's restore some balance by coming back to the important issue of the proper role that the pursuit of pleasure should play in our overall pursuit of happier lives.

Psychologist Christopher Peterson has important insights in this regard. He urges us to reflect on the following: some of our very best moments in life, both as individuals and as a species, have come during times that *did not involve any pleasure at all.* Think of your most heroic moment, for example, when you stood up for what was right even though you were scared to do so. Heroism, properly understood, really doesn't involve any pleasure in the moment. Yet one can often look back on such moments with great pride and a sense of accomplishment. Speaking of which, we can think of many examples involving collective action that didn't involve any kind of pleasure yet were enormous "break-through" moments that ended up improving everyone's lives: winning an important war, for instance, or seeing through a risky series of protests that spurred on pro-rights changes in social and political institutions. Recall the example from the end of last chapter—the case of a driven, brilliant inventor who sacrifices pleasure (and sometimes basic comforts) during their relentless drive to create a new invention or stumble upon a new discovery that ends up making things better for everyone.[146]

Just as many of our very best moments in life can involve no substantial component of pleasure at all, I extrapolate that some of our very worst moments in life can involve us doing nothing but gorging ourselves on our own private pleasures. I invite you to think of some of your most shameful moments that you deeply regret. I'd wager they involved you pursuing one or several personal (often lower) pleasures in a completely self-absorbed and out-of-control kind of way. (Not coincidentally, reflect on how many of the so-called "Seven Deadly Sins" refer to the disproportionate pursuit of some kind of pleasure.)[147]

These reflections suggest that the relationship between pleasure (in particular) and happiness (in general) is not as straightforward and simple as it may seem. There's no denying that the happiest kind of life is going to involve some consistently felt pleasure, which truly seems *a necessary component* of what we mean when we talk about happiness. Clearly, though, on its own, pleasure is not sufficient for happiness, as: a) it's too short-term; b) there are other (more complex and demanding) goods in life that we also want; and c) the pursuit of nothing but pleasure can lead to mistakes we regret, and even end up harming us in serious ways. Once more, Aristotle rides to the rescue with his doctrine of the mean and his insistence on moderation in all things.

Between Hedonism and Stoicism

During Aristotle's lifetime, two other ancient Greek philosophers developed firm views about pleasure, which now provide helpful and informative contrast. One is Epicurus (341–270 BC, after whom the term "epicurean" was coined); the other was Zeno of Citium (334–262 BC), who gave his lectures outside on a porch (a "stoa," in Greek, hence why Zeno and his followers were labelled "Stoics").[148] These philosophies, and their more radical modern derivatives, constitute clear end points on a continuum regarding the relationship between pleasure and happiness:

FIG 10 PERSPECTIVES ON THE RELATIONSHIP BETWEEN PLEASURE AND HAPPINESS

Epicurean/ Hedonism	Aristotelian	Stoic
Pleasure is happiness	Pleasure is only a part, and not the whole, of happiness	Pleasure is not even a part of happiness
(i.e., pleasure is both necessary and sufficient for happiness)	(i.e., pleasure is necessary but not sufficient for happiness)	(i.e., pleasure is neither necessary nor sufficient for happiness)
biased toward short-term, present pleasures	recommends blend of past, present, and future pleasures	only cares about future pleasures, if at all (Ben-Shahar's "Rat-Racer")
sensory pleasures only	mixture of sensory and "higher," contemplative pleasures	the senses are in many ways to be ignored or overcome; only contemplative "pleasure" of knowing you're doing the right/best thing

Epicurus' views sound shockingly modern for an ancient Greek philosopher. He thought that the universe is composed of nothing but atoms moving randomly through space: sometimes coming together for a time to form a thing or creature (like a human being), sometimes not. (This was in contrast both to Aristotle, who thought that all natural substances have essences they are trying to fully realize, and the Stoics, who believed that the universe is a structured and ordered whole in which every part plays a pre-ordained role.) As a result, Epicurus believed that there is no intrinsic purpose or meaning, either to the universe as a whole or to human life in particular. The only thing we know for sure about human life is that we are creatures who like and pursue pleasure, and who dislike and try to avoid pain. This is as basic an axiom as anyone can assert about human beings (apart from the fact that we're all going to die). "Pleasure," Epicurus said, "is the starting point and goal of living blessedly." And by pleasure, Epicurus did not mean anything fancy or complex. Rather, he straightforwardly said that, "all good and bad consists in sense experience." Thus, pleasure is an enjoyable, positive sensory experience, while pain is an un-enjoyable sensory experience (e.g., the contrast between hunger and then alleviating said hunger by eating something delicious and filling). That's it, for pleasure and for happiness. Happiness is actually identical to pleasure—pleasure is the most we can hope for in terms of human happiness.[149]

It's important to note, however, that Epicurus himself didn't really embody what the words "epicure" or "epicurean" have since come to mean (i.e., taking decadent delight in non-stop short-term sensory pleasure). He's not a hedonist in the modern, more radical sense of the term.[150] While Epicurus *did* believe that pleasure is really the best we can hope for out of life, he himself recommended *a prudent, risk-averse approach* to pleasure that emphasized making the most out of reliable, small-scale pleasures like chatting with friends and having nice dinner parties. He went out of his way to stress that he did not recommend "the pleasures of the profligate."[151] But, we might ask, why not? If all we can count on in this life is pleasure, then why not go for some risk-prone, aggressive pleasure seeking? Why not put all the focus on short-term sensory delight and pleasure maximization, so to speak? Here his personal situation sheds light, and may be of interest to the reader. Epicurus long suffered from painful kidney disease, and died of a severe attack of impassable kidney stones and out-of-control diarrhea. This is to say that, until the end, he managed a chronic condition very much of the sort here described. Knowing this, we can see how someone like that, given the choice, was probably going to be a risk-averse and conservative kind of hedonist, as opposed to a risk-prone and aggressive one. There's too much risk and potential painful downside to the aggressive option: far better to wager on the smaller-scale, more achievable pleasures on a more consistent basis. Further, his condition involved chronic pain, which simply made him physically less able to go for more aggressive, risk-prone pleasures like wild sex, drunken parties, sky-diving, motorcycle racing, snorting cocaine, joining a fight club, or taking off for some exotic, far-flung travel.

There may be much to Epicurus' approach that appeals to, and inspires, the reader and those sharing similar chronic conditions: a life managing constant pain spent accumulating whatever small-scale pleasures can be had, all adding up to as happy and pleasant a life as can be expected under the circumstances.[152] It's not just that, though. There's much contemporary evidence that, for many (or probably even most) people, being mindful of small-scale pleasures, and doing what one can to maximize them and appreciate and savour their experiences, does indeed add up to a happier life overall than the experience of a few "big bumps" of happiness, such as what might be experienced by those who sacrifice many small-scale pleasures in the name of working very hard and chasing after a few huge goals. Almost all positive psychology literature underlines what Epicurus taught his disciples so long ago: don't underestimate the cumulative power of many (hopefully daily) small-scale pleasures on one's overall mindset and perception of happiness. It's a classic tortoise-and-hare situation: *all those little "tortoise moments" of tiny pleasures add up to being more, in the end and over a lifetime, than the huge dramatic spurts of the hare.*[153]

Contrast Epicurus' beliefs and approach with those of the Stoics. Epictetus, for example, starts off his *Enchiridion* by proclaiming that:

> Some things are in our control and others not. Things in our control are opinion, pursuit, desire, aversion, and, in a word, whatever are our own actions. Things not in our control are body, property, reputation, command, and, in one word, whatever are not our own actions.[154]

The Stoics believed in the universe as a purposefully structured whole (i.e., the furthest thing from a mere aggregate of atoms randomly moving through space). Happiness for them is best understood as a kind of peaceful serenity in which one bows to one's fate and place in the universe. We've seen shades of this attitude, two chapters ago, when discussing the "laid-back philosophical objection" to the idea that happiness can be consciously pursued as a goal. Recall the notion that happiness is like a butterfly that can't be chased after; rather, you must focus on other things, and let happiness land gently upon you. The Stoic view is even more radical, and it's not clear that happiness as we understand it is even part of their agenda—much less mere sensory pleasure. Epictetus, for instance, urged people not to pursue "luxuries," or even to indulge in laughter. At one point, he proclaimed that "silence should be the general rule; let only what is necessary be said."[155] Not exactly a party! There is much talk of *necessity* in the Stoic worldview, and of it being the role of our rational faculty to: a) understand this necessity of nature, and b) bring the rest of our body and emotions in line with the natural course of the universe. Epictetus summarized: "Whoso nobly yields unto necessity is wise and skilled in things divine."[156]

Stoics preferred to speak not of pleasure, or even happiness, but rather of tranquility, nobility, and "blessedness." It consists of adjusting oneself to one's place in the universe, and being able to appreciate that. As Epictetus said, life "is like a banquet. Don't ask for things to come, just let them come." Even more dramatically, he advised us repeatedly to "desire not what you want to happen . . . but what actually does happen."[157] These views are akin to forms of Buddhism, and pre-date Reinhold Niebuhr's famous (circa-1930) prayer on serenity, often repeated as:

"God, grant me the serenity to accept the things I cannot change,

the courage to change the things I can . . .

and the wisdom to know the difference."[158]

Thus, unlike with Epicurus and contemporary hedonists, it's clear that ancient Stoics did indeed have much in common with what, and how, we use the word "stoic" today: as someone who bears struggle and ill-fortune with a kind of quiet, uncomplaining, and determined fortitude; as someone who can forego most, if not all, short-term sensory pleasures and still get on with what they have to do. (It may interest readers to know that Epictetus himself was a slave for most of his life, hence a determined fate was his reality. Further, he was crippled in one leg for his whole life, and referred to this repeatedly in his writings—and, no doubt, is one of the reasons why he curiously included "body" in the list of things over which one has no control.)[159] For Stoics, it's more about virtue, and controlling one's passions and feelings, than about giving in to them for the sake of one's own personal happiness. It's about achieving a long-term, future-focused goal of having lived a life full of tranquility and noble, worthwhile behaviour of which one can be proud. The contrast to the present-focused, sense-indulging hedonist could hardly be larger.[160]

Ben-Shahar's Pleasure Personality Archetypes

Tal Ben-Shahar, in *Happier*, agrees.[161] He sketches out what he calls four contemporary, updated "archetypes" of attitudes toward happiness in general and pleasure in particular. These are:

1 "The Hedonist," who is all about short-term sensory pleasure, with little thought for potential future consequences.

2 What Ben-Shahar calls "The Rat-Racer," who sacrifices short-term pleasure in the name of working extremely hard to get ahead and claim lots of material and social rewards and advancements, in the hopes that one day they can "truly be happy." These people are entirely future-focused. (However, they are importantly *unlike* Stoics in the classical sense, as Stoics wrapped their attitude around a conception of duty, personal adjustment to the flow of fate, and subsequent tranquility of mind. The Rat-Racer—a more familiar figure in today's North America—is a much more self-centred character, more about *deferring* pleasure for oneself until the future, when one hopes the experience will be even greater.)

3 "The Nihilist," who believes that happiness and pleasure aren't really possible—a true and radical skeptic (as we briefly mentioned two chapters ago).

4 "The Happy Person," who is very much like Aristotle's balanced, moderate person, pursuing a blend of short-term and long-term pleasure, and seeking pleasure and good feelings in terms of each of the three basic "time-slices": past, present, and future. (The pleasures of the past include nostalgia, fond memories, appreciation, and contentment. Those of the present notably include sensory experience, joy, and satisfaction.

And those of the future include planning for, and excitedly anticipating, positive experiences and worthwhile achievements down the road.)[162]

Ben-Shahar, to illustrate the different attitudes and approaches of each of these "happiness personality archetypes," talks about these four kinds of people going into one of his favourite places: a hamburger restaurant. The Hedonist, of course, will order the most tasty, decadent bacon cheeseburger and relish wolfing it all down, chasing it with their favourite beverage. The Rat-Racer, by contrast—mindful of all those calories and the more important long-term objective of fitness and health—will instead order and munch on the tasteless veggie burger, and only derive a kind of pale, indirect, contemplative pleasure from knowing that they are doing the right thing for their body over the long term. The Nihilist, of course, will order nothing and complain about everything. Finally, the Happy Person will probably do something like order a still tasty but much healthier turkey burger, or a juicy chicken breast sandwich, and try to carve out a blend of short-term sensory taste and indulgence with still-real concern for long-term health and well-being.[163]

Ben-Shahar goes on from there to point out how there's really only one of these options and archetypes that has any real, substantial hope for consistent, lasting happiness: the final one. The Hedonist may indeed get plenty of sensory pleasure. But, as I'm sure we all know from at least some personal experience, the long-term painful consequences of such relentless pursuit of short-term stimulation are real and unavoidable. The Hedonist—maybe not Epicurus' cautious hedonist, but certainly the contemporary, head-long hedonist—lives a life of too great a risk and too little regard for the well-being of their future self. The problem with the Rat-Racer is that, though they may go on to experience out-size success—especially in career and in connection with material comfort and financial well-being—we've seen from our previous investigations into hedonic adaptation that such gains by and large get adapted to, and only raise one's expectations for more. We've also seen that there exists plenty of evidence that, when one achieves a goal, it actually tends to be less satisfying than its pursuit. Relatedly, one wonders whether—after all that time spent deferring pleasure and look-ing for happiness in the future—the Rat-Racer doesn't actually condition himself or herself to be this way permanently, thus the promised day of "true happiness and bliss" never really arrives. This leaves the options of either nihilism or happiness, and of course nihilism is far too bleak to serve in any meaningful way as a guide to life. A true nihilist likely suffers from severe clinical depression and thus stands very far removed from happiness.[164] These considerations leave the one, moderate, balanced option as the most promising one for a pleasing—and a *sustainably* pleasing—life. Aristotle would be proud.

Back to Lessons from Stoicism and Hedonism: Special Concerns for the Chronically Ill

a) Stoic Endurance

We referred to the fate of Epicurus as having kidney disease, and then observed how his chronic condition tempered his under-standing of, and recommendations for, hedonism. It is worth noting, for the sake of balance, how many sick and troubled people have found solace in Stoic philosophy. One of the most famous proponents of Stoicism was the Roman Emperor Marcus Aurelius, who ruled from 161 to 180 AD—nearly twenty years. He even wrote a book on Stoicism, titled *The Meditations*, which is still studied today.[165] Aurelius obviously lived a very privileged and powerful life, as a long-serving and well-liked Emperor of Rome. During his life, however, the Roman Empire was starting to fall apart, especially in the west, owing to challenges from Germanic tribes. Aurelius spent much of his time as emperor away from Rome, leading the fight on the battlefield against the many, and very violent, Germanic groups. He could have enjoyed a safe and luxurious life in the heart of Rome, but instead chose to live a difficult life on the road, with minimal creature comforts, in seemingly endless military campaigns. In his writings, it's clear how sad and exhausted he was rendered by this constant struggle, conflict, and fighting. He desperately missed his wife and their thirteen (!) children. Yet he carried on because he felt, deeply, that it was his duty—especially as emperor—not to give up, and to try to save the Empire from destruction, to preserve civilization in the face of uncultured barbarity.[166]

Though he himself did not suffer from chronic illness, there's much in Aurelius' example that can inspire those who *do* suffer from such: in particular, the dogged determination to carry on, with quiet courage, in spite of serious challenges. I myself think that, overall, the Stoic attitude is too grim and gives up the ghost too easily when it comes to enjoying small-scale pleasures and trying to change what one can to improve their health and happiness. I mentioned these at length when speaking, two chapters ago, about the "laid-back philosophical objection," and its passivity and fatalism. Such an attitude did not, at all, work for me—and I note once more, with interest and skepticism, Epictetus' inclusion of "the body" as one of those things he claimed resided outside of one's control. Surely, these days, we know better than that, and how things like proper nutrition, exercise, good sleep hygiene, and locating and following expert medical advice, can literally do wonders for one's body and health. That said, there are some aspects of the body that clearly *are* out of our control: that we age and will die, have biological needs and are slaves to gravity, and so on. I think in particular here of those who are at the end-stages of some of the worst terminal conditions and disorders. I think that such people, *when it's clear what's going to happen*, could profit mightily from adopting a Stoic attitude and focusing not on "raging against the dying of the light" but, rather, on accepting one's fate, and trying to cultivate tranquility and peace of mind while succumbing to the rhythms of nature and the flow of the universe.[167]

Perhaps the most recent, and spectacular, example of someone professing faith in the tenets of Stoicism, and using these to endure a terrible ordeal for years on end, is that of Vice Admiral James Stockdale. He is best known as the US Vice Presidential candidate in 1992, running alongside independent presidential candidate Ross Perot in the election that saw Bill Clinton win his first presidency. Stockdale went on to become one of the most highly decorated officers in the entire history of the US Navy. In 1964, he was shot down while on mission during the Vietnam War. He was taken as a prisoner of war (POW) and held in captivity for seven and a half years. His leg was crushed during the original crash of his plane, and he was denied medical treatment for it throughout his imprisonment, during which he was routinely tortured, beaten, and starved. He was an enormous fan of Epictetus, especially *The Enchiridion*, and credits its lessons with being able to detach mentally from his brutally injured body, and to focus on enduring and never giving in to his cruel captors. When he was finally freed, American troops discovered that—out of last-minute spite—his captors had re-broken Stockdale's leg, wrenched both his shoulders out of their sockets, and had broken his back. He could not stand up, and it took many months of healing and rehabilitation before he could even walk again. Yet he did; he recovered, and went on to numerous senior leadership positions within the US Navy, including Vice Admiral, before ultimately serving as VP candidate. He died in 2005, after a long bout with Alzheimer's.[168]

b) Hedonism Run Amok: The Allure of Substance Abuse

If the Stoics provide certain important lessons about detachment, courage, and endurance, there's another big reason to reflect critically on hedonism, especially the more radical modern kind. I've always thought that one of the "dirty little secrets" of those who deal with chronic conditions is the alarmingly high rate of drug and alcohol addiction, and substance abuse in general. Unafflicted people might be shocked at this, too; however, there are many reasons why it can become very tempting to first indulge in, and then (perhaps) fall victim to, such abuse.

First, and as previously mentioned, many people succumb to some form of depression upon initial diagnosis. And we know that there exists a strong correlation between any kind of depression and substance abuse. Second, those with injuries are often prescribed addictive painkillers to help them tolerate the pain, and this can lead to addiction. Third, be it for depression or for pain, sleep aids are another common prescription for those with chronic conditions, and, depending on the form, they can be highly addictive. Fourth, there's a desire to escape—if only briefly—from the condition, its pain, and its limitations on one's life. Lots of kinds of drugs and alcohol—at least initially—allow for that kind of temporary escape and (false) sense of empowerment. Fifth, chronic conditions can render one systematically fearful—about the condition, about the future—and, likewise, drugs and alcohol can provide a temporary means of dampening said fear. (It's older British slang to refer to an alcoholic drink as "a nip of courage.") Sixth, as mentioned, chronic conditions often spur one toward greater introversion and loneliness. Substance abuse, as sad as it sounds, can help pass the time and dull the edge of such loneliness and "solitary confinement." Finally, and especially if one is philosophically inclined toward hedonism in the first place, one might simply figure: "Why not? I'm sick/injured. Life sucks. I already take a bunch of pills, what's a few more? And the booze provides a warm glow, even if my doctors strongly discourage alcohol. I might as well get my kicks while I can."[169]

Though it sounds perverse—and it is—those who are chronically unwell often engage in addictive behaviour for reasons such as these, which end up in the long-term rendering them even worse off than before. I've seen it happen too often, and have the following objective data to share. In the US, it's thought that, in the general population, about 9 percent have a substance abuse problem requiring medical treatment (incidentally, the same government source says that only 1 percent actually receive such treatment, for myriad reasons).[170] By contrast, and though exact numbers vary across studies, all experts agree that substance abuse problems among the chronically afflicted are significant and much more prevalent than in the general population, likely somewhere between 20–33 percent of that specific group. The 20 percent figure (or one in five) is quoted more for those with chronic *physical pain* conditions, whereas the whopping 33 percent figure (one in three!) is for those with chronic *mental health* conditions.[171] Thus, *the population of the chronically afflicted is at least twice as vulnerable to substance abuse as the general population*, and maybe as much as three-and-a-half times more vulnerable. Presumably, this is so for reasons listed above—though experts go beyond the merely personal and psychological reasons I mentioned (to give readers a deeper sense of where the chronically ill may be coming from in this regard) to enumerate further genetic, environmental, social, and even economic factors that raise the likelihood of such so-called "co-occurrences" or "co-morbidities."[172]

Such addictions, of course, are destructive over the long term, and all the temporary relief that such substances provide is just that. This is the insidious problem with addiction: in the short term, the calculus of "what to do" is almost always going to side in favour of taking the hit, or the pill, or the drink. Especially if one is a hedonist—the temptation can rapidly become overwhelming and irresistible. But each short-term "hit" has not only immediate consequences (the buzz, problems with judgment and bodily control) but also contributes to long-term consequences that include: a) permanent physical alterations, notably brain and heart functionality; and b) almost certainly a worsening of the very condition from which one is trying to escape. To summarize, *indulging in substance abuse only makes matters worse.* (And, of special interest, the medical community now models addiction after any other chronic condition, such as heart disease or diabetes: it alters bodily function; it requires treatment; and, if untreated, serious and permanent negative consequences will follow.)[173]

Psychologists in the 1950s used rats to conduct a now-famous experiment about pleasure; however, the experiment didn't go as expected, and instead became a landmark study in how we understand addiction and its consequences. The rats had tiny electrical wires put into brain regions most centrally associated with intense sensory pleasure. Control of the electricity was given to the rats themselves, in the following form: they could push down a lever and receive a jolt of electricity right to the "bliss spot" of these pleasure centres. The result? The subject rats just sat at the pleasure lever and pressed it—some up to 700 times an hour! They preferred hitting the pleasure centre with electricity over food, drink, sleep, sex . . . and ultimately even life itself, as many dropped dead of exhaustion from all the lever-pushing combined with the deprivation of their vital needs. This doesn't teach us so much about the nature of pleasure (except to confirm its association with electrical stimulation to certain brain regions) as it does the very dangerous and utterly perverse consequences of addiction to intense short-term stimulation. The perversion and illogicality are laid bare, as the rats were willing to kill themselves—destroying all potential at future pleasure—for the sake of a very temporary yet intense short-term pleasure. The stimulation, it's thought, creates an intense craving that must be immediately satisfied. This compulsive craving can get "carved into," and completely dominate one's short-term decision-making capacity to the detriment of everything else in life: one's health condition, career, finances, relationships, and ultimately (sometimes) even one's very survival. Breaking the cycle of compulsive cravings—or, ideally, never jumping on that hamster wheel to begin with—thus becomes the crucial thing.[174]

Now, I don't want to come across as preachy, judgmental, or too much of a scare-monger. I'm talking here about genuine abuse and addiction, not the controlled, moderate enjoyment of a legal substance—such as a nice glass of wine with dinner. There are also high-profile controversies regarding whether some substances, though quite addictive, might actually be helpful for certain health conditions. For more information, the reader is referred, for example, to the literature on medical marijuana.[175] All I'm keen to stress here is this:

- Those with chronic conditions need to know they are at substantially higher risk for substance abuse than the general population. Pre-emptive measures should be taken to prevent this (such as trying to create a happier life through all the other methods recommended in this and other books, like Lyubomirsky's *The How of Happiness*).

- If the hedonistic and recreational use of a substance turns into abuse and addiction, it is guaranteed in the long term to cause you pain (and thus be at odds with your hedonism). Not only will your chronic condition worsen, you will be rendered substantially unhappier across a range of vital regions, such as your career, your relationships, and your own peace of mind and mental health.

- Know whether the medications you take for your condition are themselves addictive and/or will interact negatively with drugs or alcohol. (Don't ignore such soft-sounding warnings as "don't drink alcohol in excess with this medication." Become informed about what defines a moderate and acceptable level of alcohol—it's lower than you think.[176])

- Know the signs of true addiction. If you keep on taking a substance even when it no longer gives you pleasure (compulsive craving), or moreover even after you realize that it's hurting you and your life, this is a very bad sign. Here's a good rule of thumb: *try not taking the substance in question for two weeks.* Not one drop, pill, or anything. If you *can't* achieve even this, consult a doctor immediately for treatment; if you *can* achieve this, take careful note of how great your body feels, by comparison, at the end of the two weeks. That's your body telling you the true effect of the substance upon it, and how much better—happier, energetic, resourceful—your life will be without it. Above all, be honest with yourself: if you even suspect that you may have a problem, you probably do. Do whatever it takes to not get trapped in the downward spiral of addiction. What you want to achieve, of course, is a happiness that is sustainable, not temporary; happiness in a positive upward spiral, not a destructive downward one; and *happiness that is achievable to, and felt by, your normal, unimpaired self.*[177]

Flow

We can't leave off a chapter about pleasure on such a note of warning! There's another important subject here, which provides a nice bridge between the two seemingly separate subjects of substance abuse and satisfaction at work. That of flow: a term coined by Mihaly Csikszentmihalyi who, in the 1960s, was studying the creative process, especially as exhibited by acclaimed and successful artists.* He was intrigued by how, during the process of creation, artists would often disregard

---

* One immediately thinks, e.g., of Michelangelo, up on his scaffolding for four years, inches away from the ceiling of the Sistine Chapel, labouring away at the massive, colourful, and dramatic sets of paintings, such as *The Creation of Adam.*

even the most basic comforts of sleeping, eating, drinking, and relaxed physical posture. They would be in intense absorption, and be utterly "taken in" by the process of creation. Yet when finished, the artists wouldn't really celebrate the finished product; often they would simply take the physical rest they needed and see to their biological needs, and then get back to plotting out and creating another new piece of art. What intrigued Csikszentmihalyi so much was this fascinating, apparent disconnect between the lack of pleasure during the process of creation, and total absorption and concern about "getting it right" in bringing the work into existence. Often, afterwards, the artists would indeed come to speak of the process of creation as pleasant—and almost always as very worthwhile—but, in the moment, there was not much pleasure reported at all. Csikszentmihalyi concluded that such a process must be intrinsically rewarding for the artists, describing such moments as having "flow": 1) the person is kind of "carried along" or "carried away" by the process of creation, as if by a flowing river; and 2) there is almost a kind of merging (psychological or attention-based) between the person and what they are doing—between self and environment—during these times, thus they can be said to sort of flow together, or into each other, for a time. Flow has thus been defined as intense absorption into, and engaged involvement with, the activity and experience of the present moment.[178]

Over the years, Csikszentmihalyi and others have more fully described these sorts of experiences, which don't have to be confined to individual artistic creation. To count as a genuine flow experience, it's thought that the following things must be true:

- Practically all the individual's attention is deeply focused on the activity. The attention is highly absorbed by the activity and experience.

- As a result, the individual tends to lose track of: time, himself or herself as a social actor, and the immediate environment in general. There is a disregard for anything but the task, often even including one's normal needs. During flow, it's as though "time stops"; once over, the sense is that time has "flown by."

- The activity tends to have a very clear and concrete goal, be it the creation of a work of art or a piece of writing, the correct performance of a scientific experiment, making the shot and winning the game, or what have you. It is not an open-ended activity.

- There is a kind of matching between the skill of the person involved and the challenge presented by the activity. The activity cannot be too demanding—lest the individual experience frustration—nor can the activity be too easy, or else the individual will become bored.

- There is very much a sense of control and efficacy experienced by the person involved, since their skills are up to the challenge of the situation. The activity has an invigorating effect on them.

- Though people in flow experiences do not report pleasure in the moment—they are too involved in the activity to notice—they report such experiences afterwards as having been extremely worthwhile. In their descriptions, they use words like "extremely satisfying," "highly engaging," "thrilling," and "very worthwhile," as opposed to ordinary words describing the sensations of basic sensory pleasures.[179]

Csikszentmihalyi was convinced that a life filled with flow experiences is a better and much happier life than one without, even taking into account the fact that these experiences themselves seem to lack pleasure in the moment. Why? Well, we can see how some of the flow criteria above hook into the findings of established happiness research, which we've previously discussed: absorption into the present moment; the pursuit and attainment of a clear, concrete goal; engagement instead of withdrawal; the sense of control and efficacy; and the after-the-fact evaluation that one's time has been well spent, and with positive results. "Flow" experiences can quite plausibly be described as providing a kind of "natural high," with intense engagement occurring in the moment. But the results, of course, are so much better than those of indulging in addiction. Those tempted to go down the road of addiction should instead go down the one recommended by Csikszentmihalyi.[180]

He also suggested—in a way that actually anticipated the broaden-and-build theory mentioned in Chapter 2 (in our discussion of the benefits of positive emotions like happiness)—that repeated flow experiences confer upon the individual in question a kind of "capital formation" experience, both in terms of skill development as well as psychological buttressing. You are "socking away savings" for future use, so to speak—in terms of both skills and confidence. Whereas pleasure is short term, comparatively passive, and in the moment, engaging instead in flow experiences is a longer-term commitment, definitely requires activity, and builds in oneself a sense of confidence—plus a heightened skill set—which one can then have and deploy for future occasions. These speculations were confirmed in some interesting studies done on teenagers followed through their high school years. It was found that those who routinely engaged in "high-flow" activities, such as sports and music, fared much better by the end of high school—in terms of grades, graduation rates, college acceptances, self-described levels of happiness—than those routinely engaged in "low-flow" activities such as watching TV, "hanging out" at the mall, and playing endless hours of video games. Thus, Csikszentmihalyi and others like Peterson have warned of the dangers of so-called "faux-flow," or "junk flow," activities: activities that might superficially look like flow experiences (especially in terms of time quickly passing), but which fail to meet other crucial conditions—notably requiring skill—such as a sense of invigoration and achievement at the end. And, as one final note, if anything counts as "junk flow" then certainly substance abuse would fill the bill: it takes no skill, produces a sense of escape but certainly no sense of control and efficacy, and there is no sense of invigoration or proud achievement at the end.[181]

So, how does one get more flow into one's life, especially if one has a chronic health condition? Lyubomirsky has some helpful tips. First, *notice the sorts of things that give you flow*, or flow-like experiences. A very interesting experiment tested this on a group of people by giving them beepers, and whenever the beeper randomly went off people were asked about what they were doing and whether they were experiencing flow-like conditions. The result? Most people reported experiencing more flow-like conditions at work rather than at home, during their leisure time. This is surprising as—given its connection to pleasure and fulfillment—flow probably conjures up thoughts of ecstatic engagement with freely chosen leisure tasks: true labours of love. But, as Lyubomirsky points out, when one considers how lots of people seem to use their leisure time, it usually does not satisfy the typical conditions for flow. For instance, many in North America use their leisure time in undemanding ways that are more about decompression, "vegging out," and passive relaxation than they are about finding a new challenge that matches their skill level. Conversely, many of the flow criteria laid out above can, indeed, be found at work: challenging tasks that demand one's attention and skill; clear, concrete goals; active engagement rather than passive consumption; and so on. The first step to more flow is taking note of which kind of activities actually offer flow opportunities. They don't all have to be work-related—one simply needs to think through which kinds of leisure activities are more likely than others to offer such chances. (Lyubomirsky labels them "smart leisure.") For example, rock climbing is probably going to rank higher on that list than watching TV; and taking an adventuresome vacation (like learning to surf in Hawaii, or to cook in Italy) is going to rank higher than fiddling around all evening on Facebook.[182]

The pursuit of flow may pose challenges for the chronically ill, as it stresses active engagement and rising to the occasion by developing and deploying one's skill. If you're tired, or have chronic pain, this may seem formidable. But fear not: flow can be experienced across a wide range of activities, and is by no means reserved for out-sized physical, mental, or creative challenges. Indeed, *the more one is open to new and different experiences, the more likely one is to experience flow.* Those new and different experiences provide opportunities for the development of new skills, and increasing the level of one's skills. So, the pursuit of flow recommends, as does the battle against hedonic adaptation: diversity, variety, and new experiences. These truly are the spice of life, and afford endless opportunity not merely for passive pleasure but also for the active pursuit of flow. According to Lyubomirsky: commit to learning until the day you die, and you will never run out of opportunities to experience flow.[183]

The second thing to note, by way of special advice for the chronically ill, is that experts have come up with something called "micro-flow." This refers to lower-impact, lower-effort, quick-timing sorts of activities that nevertheless meet the criteria for flow, albeit on a brief and small scale. These activities are both more achievable for the chronically afflicted and serve as excellent, refreshing "micro breaks" from other tasks. Doodling a good cartoon caricature has been offered as one such example, as has been constructing a quick Haiku poem, or a piece of origami or knitting, or doing a Rubik's Cube or crossword or Sudoku puzzle. Lyubomirsky describes an interesting case of a student of hers using the following technique while stuck in traffic: he turns on some music that has multiple layers to it. He then follows one of the layers—say, the bass line or the drum beat—throughout the song, and focuses on tapping his fingers and feet solely to that isolated line. He finds that it meets all the criteria for flow, even though it only lasts a short while, and finds it an excellent stress-beater when caught in the doldrums of rush-hour traffic.[184]

It's both fun and instructive to remember past times when you've experienced flow, as well as to make a list of the things that give you both flow and micro-flow. Also, list some things you suspect *might* be plausible future flow candidates (i.e., things you've always wanted to try but never have that meet flow criteria). I still vividly remember the first time I experienced true, unforgettable flow. It was in Grade 8, and I was running the 400–metre race. It's a difficult race: one full lap around the track. It requires strategy and self-knowledge: it's not a full-on sprint like the 100 or 200, nor is it a paced, long-distance run like the 800 and above. You've got to know whether to run fast then slow—or, rather, to pace and then finish hard. Based on previous struggles, I had formulated my plan: quick start, but then strong pace, reserving myself for an all-out sprint for the final 100 metres. I can still remember the exact moments of that race like it was frozen in time: I had a profound awareness of my body's exertion, deep breathing, and the mental alertness of knowing I was going to stick to a plan and see what happened. The result: I came in second. While the objective results weren't so amazing, what's so memorable for me is that it was a total moment of flow. Unforgettable. And I would never have traded that experience for the first-place position. Since then, I've experienced flow regularly during intensive workouts, sex, lecturing, hearing a great lecture, artistic appreciation (especially of painting or music), reading, writing, adventuresome travel, time in nature, moments with my son (especially involving sports or trying to make each other laugh), and, at times, during stimulating conversations and/or dinner parties.

Conclusion

This is the end both of this chapter and this section, which has been concerned with introducing us globally to happiness, as well as focusing intensively on pleasure as a necessary but not sufficient condition for such. We are built by nature for both happiness and pleasure. There are two vital things to note here: 1) most of us are mainly happy to be here, and can find enough pleasure to want to continue life's journey; but 2) practically none of us will ever see ourselves as perfectly and totally happy. We need to be mindful of both truths as we go about planning how to gain more happiness and pleasure in our lives. We can do so, pleasure-wise, by being mindful of the latest research regarding how to enhance pleasure, which I capped off by listing a dozen things of special interest and promise for the chronically ill. Yet, as we go about pursuing pleasure and its enhancement, we shouldn't forget the proper role of pleasure: as being between the extremes of hedonistic sensory indulgence and stoic self-denial. Flow, in many ways, is both a capturing and intensification of pleasure, but also represents a transcendence of pleasure and its blending into more enduring strengths and unforgettable experiences that need to be part of a full and satisfying life. Next, we turn to the external and internal goods, and examine their place within happiness.

The External
Goods

CHAPTER 4

Work and Income

We've completed our initial meditations on the nature of happiness in general, why it is both possible and desirable to pursue it, and on one large, truly necessary component of it: pleasure. Recall from the Introduction that we are using Aristotle's overall conception of happiness to guide our reflections and contemporary research. This schema proposes that there are three parts to happiness: 1) pleasure, 2) the so-called "external" goods, and 3) the so-called "internal" goods.

Having dealt with pleasure, we now turn to the external goods. But what do we mean exactly by the term external—especially when, in the final analysis, we are talking about our own personal happiness? The term shouldn't be taken too literally, nor should the distinction between internal and external be interpreted too sharply. It's just a convenient way to provide a readily understandable overall schema or conception of happiness. That said, what Aristotle meant by internal was that it had to do with your interior life: your emotions, your thoughts, your moral values, all leading into your behaviour. So, the internal goods refer to those components of your interior mental and emotional life that contribute to your happiness. There are many of these, of course, and they turn out to be absolutely crucial—as vital as (or even more than) pleasure—in one's overall experiences of happiness or unhappiness. Contemporary research repeatedly comes to the conclusion that happiness is, in so many ways, an issue of mind over matter. This is why the internal goods will be left for the final section, in acknowledgment of just how important they are: we'll build up to them. As Abraham Lincoln once said: "Most people are about as happy as they make up their minds to be."[185]

That said, it would be a severe exaggeration to pretend that it's all mental, and that nothing from the material world impacts happiness—or, indeed, that the material doesn't, in its own significant way, *influence* the mental. If one has had a certain upbringing, for example, then one is much more likely to think in certain ways. The same holds true if one is born into one kind of society versus another. Most obviously (and of especial relevance for us), if our material bodies are harmed, injured, or malfunctioning in certain ways, this has indeed been proven to affect how we think and feel, and to put limits and constraints on the degree to which we can simply "look on the bright side of life."[186] So what we mean by external, in general, is all those things in the material and social world that have been shown to have large impact on one's happiness. For this second section, I have—following both Aristotle and contemporary researchers—selected the following external goods as most important for our purposes: a) work and income; b) how our societies are shaped by the most powerful social institutions; c) how we relate to other people (and they to us); and, finally, d) the impact of our bodies on our interior life and outlook. I leave the body for last because it underlines the artificiality of the word external (since no one is external to their own body), and because it makes for an excellent connection to, and transition into, the interior world of thoughts, feelings, and values. The body, after all, is where we have such things.

Sigmund Freud reportedly said that there are two secret ingredients to happiness in life: love and work.[187] Let's leave love for an upcoming chapter; for now, we turn our attention to the world of work, and the related status of income generated. How important are these things for our personal happiness? What special challenges exist for the chronically afflicted? How might they be overcome?

The World of Work

Let's start with the concrete issue of work, and then we'll "make our way out" to the more abstract issue of income, which in turn will set the stage nicely for a discussion (next chapter) of those social institutions most likely to conduce widespread personal happiness.

According to Tal Ben-Shahar, only 50 percent of Americans describe themselves as happy with their work. This finding has been confirmed in more recent studies. (By contrast, Canadians are among the happiest workers in the world, with 64 percent saying they either like or love their job and only 2 percent saying they dislike or hate their job, versus 15 percent of Americans who say the same thing.)[188] Given how important work is—as, usually, our major source of income, a prime source for personal identity, and in raw terms of how much of our life is spent at it— it is well worth considering how we can become happier while working. (Before doing so, I should declare that I'm well aware that a portion of my intended audience—those with chronic conditions—might be utterly unable to work, owing to their illness or injury. For now, we talk about work for those who, while perhaps having a chronic condition, are nevertheless capable of participating in the work force.)

Micro-Tips

Here are some quick tips for improving one's happiness at work:

- **Take micro-breaks, and know that they are justified.** Both self-reported happiness and objective productivity at work are maximized (on average) when one works in sixty-to-ninety-minute intensive bursts, followed by ten-to-fifteen-minute breaks (e.g., of conversation, a quick little game, listening to a song and singing along, watering your plants, meditating, etc.). One study showed that people who used their ten-minute break to watch a video of stand-up comedy improved their productivity by 13 percent afterwards.[189]

- **Make full use of your entitled time off.** A shocking 40 percent of American workers leave sick days and vacation days "on the table" every year. As noted in *Men's Health* magazine, that's like turning down free money, earned leisure time, and stress relief. From a happiness perspective, it makes no sense. And it's not just "stress relief": a 2013 Swedish study found that anti-depressant use declined among people when they started taking full advantage of the vacation days they'd earned. It's about self-respect and taking control, as well as time away and "re-charging the batteries."[190]

- **Be mindful of "work-life balance" in general.** If possible, pace out one's work in a sane way, and come up with rules that preserve balance, such as "no work emails on weekends." (Average self-reported happiness levels peak on weekends, and for most people usually in the morning.)[191] Band with fellow employees to urge your employer to see the many benefits of sound work-life balance policies, ranging from parental leave, to caps on hours worked, to potential for voluntary "task-swapping" and the like among workers. In particular, take note that—while working overtime some of the time is probably inevitable—research proves that each incremental unit of added income (beyond a threshold) contributes less and less to happiness, and takes more and more time away from other things that *do* augment happiness, such as quality time spent with loved ones.[192]

Kinds of Work

An influential study by Amy Wrzesniewski and colleagues[193] discovered that there are three fundamental ways in which people tend to interpret their jobs:

1) As a mere "job"

Those falling under this category perceive their employment as a means to an end, paying their bills and helping them meet the material requirements of the modern world. They reported no satisfaction with their work lives beyond this kind of survival instrumentality. Work is perceived of as a chore, and the only reason to do it is the extrinsic reason of getting the money needed to live. These people derive no personal fulfillment from their work and have limited expectations from it. They are simply "punching the clock"—working because they have to. What they'd rather be doing—what they really want to do—is enjoying their leisure time: their nights, their weekends, their vacations, and, eventually, retirement. The rock band Loverboy had a song capturing this attitude: "Working for the Weekend."

2) As a "career"

The best way to think of a career is that it is a more highly paying job, with greater prospects for advancement. People who see their employment as a career are identically motivated as those in the previous category: the motivation is all extrinsic, and focuses around money, material security, and prospects for advancement.

The work does not delight them, nor does it even have to interest them at all; what interests them is income, and the prospect of getting progressively more of it if they work hard and perform well.

3) As a "calling"

People in this category view their employment lives very differently. They are the one group that works not from extrinsic reasons but, rather, from intrinsic ones (i.e., they find the nature of the work they do to be intrinsically satisfying, and often say things like "I'd do this job even if I was only paid half of what I'm currently getting"). People under this heading often say it's a privilege to have the job they have, and very much look forward to coming to work, and conceiving and executing various projects. They do their work not because they have to (in order to pay their bills) but because they want to, with the job satisfying a deep personal need, value, or sense of self. So they *do* gain personal fulfillment from their work, and often display considerable enthusiasm and passion while at work.[194]

As you might expect, people who describe their work lives as a personal calling are much more likely to be happier with them than those who view things in terms of a job or career. And while it's generally true, as noted by Martin Seligman,[195] that those who are higher up in an organization are more likely to view their work as a calling (rather than as a job or career), a fascinating and important follow-up study by Wrzesniewski et al. showed that it's not merely power, or higher placement, or more social prestige that determines one's views in this regard. She led a detailed survey of the same group of workers: janitors and cleaning staff in a hospital. These were people who made approximately the same income as one another, and all stood in a similar position in the internal work hierarchy. Moreover, they usually came from quite similar socioeconomic and educational backgrounds. But Wrzesniewski and her colleagues found (to their surprise) that, even among the hospital janitors, there was a clear division between those who viewed their jobs merely as jobs versus those who viewed them as a genuine calling. Indeed, the researchers were surprised that there were *any* people within this group who viewed their job as a calling. But there were, and lo and behold, they reported quite high job satisfaction—certainly much higher than those of their colleagues who only saw themselves as occupying a job.[196]

How was it possible, you might ask, for hospital janitors to see their work as a calling? Wouldn't it be more plausible to side with those who just viewed their work as a job: routine, physically strenuous, exposure to lots of dirty and even dangerous situations, plenty of very gross things that need cleaning with powerful and abrasive chemicals, no real prospects for bonuses or substantial advancement, and little control? Maybe, but those who viewed their janitorial work as a calling described it quite differently. They saw themselves as an important part of a team that, all together, shared two objectives: making patients better, and having their stay at the hospital be as pleasant and helpful as possible, given the circumstances. These janitors did not see themselves as being at "the bottom of the totem pole," with the doctors on top and the nurses and technicians secondary, and so on. These janitors would often say things like, "Well, where would this hospital be without people to keep it clean? It would be not only grimy and smelly but also downright dangerous and filled with tons of germs and bacteria." They saw their work as purposive and meaningful, deserving of important recognition. They did not dwell on hierarchy but viewed everyone as playing a necessary role on a team. This group of janitors—unlike the first—also took the time to try to get to know patients personally, which they said helped motivate them to keep the hospital as clean as it needed to be. (You don't want to let people down when you know and like them.) And apparently, some within this group even saw it as their job to make sure the art hanging on the walls of patients' rooms was not crooked, and was even refreshed every now and then (i.e., rotated around from other rooms) so that patients would not get bored and would have beautiful things to look at every day—which, presumably, would help their recovery.[197]

The above case study provides a vivid example showing how much depends on *the interpretation of* the work one does as opposed to any essential, objective feature of the work itself. It also provides important, focused insights into happiness at work:

- seeing one's work as purposive and meaningful

- not being envious, or obsessing about hierarchy

- seeing oneself as part of a team—everyone plays a role, and these roles come together to achieve and fulfill the overall purpose of the organization

- taking full advantage of the social aspects of work, as opposed to withdrawing and mechanically and individually going about one's tasks

- looking for opportunities to add creatively to the ambit of one's job in ways that are consistent with the overall team goal (akin to viewing one's cleaning tasks as including the need to refresh and beautify the surrounding art)

Of course, these sorts of employee efforts work best if accompanied on the employer/manager side of the equation by:

- encouraging everyone to see their work as meaningful and purposive

- being both lavish and sincere with praise and recognition for a job—any job—well done

- effectively communicating a team ethos and orientation to everyone within the organization, and how they contribute to the overall mission

- minimizing work hierarchies (or at least not drawing attention to them), and reinterpreting them as necessary for the organization to run effectively

- encouraging and perhaps organizing social connections (or events) that are appropriate and enhance people's motivation

- encouraging and rewarding those who put forward creative new proposals for how to augment their own role(s) within the organization

With all that said, one must comment on the job/career/calling distinction, and the normative thrust of the idea that one should strive to find their calling. There are, after all, difficult situations where people simply have to pay the bills, and/or need to be grateful and stick with what they've got (e.g., if they have dependents), thus traipsing around looking for self-fulfillment in the labour force might seem self-indulgent, irresponsible, or unrealistic. Plus, it's probably also true that those fortunate enough to have had a reasonably decent upbringing and a strong education most likely have greater opportunities for finding work that is personally fulfilling. One needs to be mindful and respectful of these realities. That said, we are talking about what makes for happiness *in the workplace*. According to the research: either find a job that *is* a calling, or else push yourself to interpret your existing job in such a way as to make it *as much like a calling as possible*. In cases where satisfaction just can't be had in the workplace, happiness advice must focus on the leisure side of the life equation.[198]

Flow, and The Importance of Work

We saw at the end of last chapter how, to the surprise of researchers, most people who experience flow do so much more at work than in their leisure time. In part, this is because people can have a passive pursuit of leisure, which fails to meet the criteria for flow. But, as noted by Lyubomirsky, this fact may also be relevant in aiding people in thinking clearly and correctly about their work lives. Most people, when prompted, will say—overwhelmingly—that they'd rather spend their time doing leisure activities than work. Yet, most people find states of flow very positive, and are much more likely to experience such states at work. What gives? Lyubomirsky suggests: 1) we generally don't know how to spend our leisure time well; and 2) we've been culturally programmed to refer to work as a chore and necessity, and fail to give it the kind of credit that it may deserve in providing us with plenty of opportunity for things we know increase most people's personal happiness. Things such as: goals and structure, material resources, contributions to identity, social activities, and opportunities for reward and recognition.[199]

As stated in the Introduction, one of the more important recent findings in the happiness literature—especially that produced by economists interested in happiness—is that in today's society, *unemployment forms one of the most potent threats to a person's happiness*. Using data from around the world, experts like John Helliwell and Richard Layard have shown that being unemployed poses a short-term negative hit to one's happiness, which is tied for the second-most severe common cause of unhappiness, behind marital break-down but tied with a major health crisis.[200] These economists have also shown that the negative psychological effects of being unemployed endure for years. But it's not just the loss of income and resulting financial insecurity, though those *are* serious threats in themselves. It's also the loss of daily structure and goal setting, the loss of social activities and opportunities, the hit to one's self-esteem and identity, and fear for the future. Layard concludes: "... unemployment is one of the worst things which can happen to anyone... low and stable unemployment must be a major objective for any society."[201] *We should want everyone who desires to and is able to work to get it.* This raises vital issues about the role of social institutions in helping along personal happiness.

For now, we observe that having work is important for one's happiness in general (as Freud originally stipulated). And the more opportunities for flow to be had during one's daily work, the more fulfilling and satisfying it will be. So, we've arrived at two significant conclusions about how to make work increase one's happiness: 1) find your calling (as defined above), and 2) find work that enables you to experience flow on a regular basis. As stated previously, for me, during my health crisis, my work life was one of the very few things on which I could count. It organized my life, and from it I got a sense of satisfaction, achievement, and self-worth, even as everything else fractured and melted around me. And I do consider my job as a professor as a calling, and regularly experience flow in connection with my job—notably during writing, while lecturing at my own university, and during guest lectures at other universities wherein there is some travel involved as well.

I realize, though, that not all who are chronically afflicted are going to be able to say the same thing—and that numerous threats and sharp challenges lurk in this domain for those with imperfect health. I was lucky that my health problems didn't begin until I had completed the education and credentials needed to be able to land as rewarding a job as university professor. I was lucky to have supportive and enlightened coworkers who helped me and accommodated my illness (to the extent possible, consistent with my workload). Finally, one of the really nice things about being a university professor is the degree of autonomy one has. This no doubt enabled me to shuffle around tasks as required, in case of a sudden seizure and need for recovery. We'll come back again to this vital issue of control, as recent research has shown that it turns out to be perhaps THE most important thing when it comes to finding lasting happiness at work. For now, let's move in tighter on the specific issue of happiness at work for those with chronic conditions.

Accommodating Disabilities at Work

It's important to know—in addition to the general advice above regarding calling, flow, and work-life balance—about important and useful "accommodations" available to you, to render your work life more pleasant and do-able as someone chronically afflicted. Such accommodations can be split into those legally required and ones that, while not required, might nevertheless be requested and provided.

Obviously, legally required accommodations at work will vary from jurisdiction to jurisdiction, and are usually part of that jurisdiction's human rights act (designed to secure fundamental fairness in the workplace). Usually, in developed countries, *employers have some duty to accommodate injured or ill workers*, which is consistent with: a) the continued ability of the worker to work, b) regard for reasonable cost, and c) concerns about any impact on the effectiveness of other workers.[202] Disability-related workplace accommodations often include:

- making workplace facilities accessible (e.g., different door handles for those with mobility impairments, or ramps instead of steps)

- modifying general work schedules (e.g., "flex-time") and/or specific task schedules (e.g., longer notice before deadlines, allowing for longer breaks for those who might need them)

- restructuring the work (e.g., new tasks, swapping equivalent tasks with a willing other, or possibly "work-splitting" with a coworker)

- acquiring or modifying equipment, software, or devices (e.g., larger computer screens and fonts for the visually impaired, ergonomic chairs for those with chronic back pain)

- providing support services or qualified assistants (e.g., interns who need the training regardless)

- changing work locations (e.g., if someone has had their driver's licence suspended for a medical reason, such as seizure)

- retraining or reassigning employees[203]

That said, there can be misunderstandings about the magnitude of cost and/or burden in employers making these sorts of accommodations, resulting in an almost automatic reflex toward rejection, without considering details. The good news is three-fold:

1 Awareness about chronic conditions is vastly improving every day. And by "a certain age," it seems like everyone has to deal with *something*. So, it's not much of a stretch to claim that, over the course of a whole career, we all should have a keen self-interest in these sorts of accommodations being made generally available.

2 New technologies, specifically designed to help those with chronic conditions stay productive on the job, are also constantly being developed (e.g., in mid-2016, a high school student from Oakville, Ontario, won a prestigious technology award for developing a computer mouse that can be put

into one's mouth and controlled perfectly with one's tongue. She was inspired by wanting to help people who've lost fine motor control of their hands owing to MS or Parkinson's).[204]

3 Experts believe that the majority of physical accommodations can be made for less than $500 (e.g., different software, an ergonomic chair, extra lighting, bigger and brighter computer monitors, etc.).[205]

Still, those with chronic conditions are often reluctant to admit their conditions to their employer and/or ask for such accommodations. I myself had no choice but to come clean about what was going on with me, as my initial seizures were in public and required hospitalization. Over the long term, it's nearly impossible—and ill-advised—to try to keep things secret.* My disclosure was essential in getting the kinds of accommodation I required, and my employer was quite supportive. Here are some excellent tips for bringing up, in a successful way, the issue of chronic affliction requiring workplace accommodation (from the Alberta Learning Information Service):[206]

- **Take care of your own needs**, if possible, by providing equipment or technology (i.e., consider buying it yourself.). This removes a potential barrier for employers considering your request.

---

* One is reminded of a recent court case in Canada. A woman who long suffered from epilepsy had managed to keep it secret from everyone at her work at one of Canada's biggest and richest banks. One morning, she was informed that she was being promoted to a senior executive position at the bank. Overcome in the moment with emotion, she blurted out that she did have epilepsy and was so proud that this hadn't held her back. Upon returning from a celebratory lunch, she was promptly fired. She sued the bank for discrimination, as well as unjust firing, and won a large award.

- **Be open, honest, and clear when requesting an accommodation**. Give examples, so the employer can understand what's involved.

- **Explain your specific needs**. Don't expect your employer or coworkers to anticipate them (or to know anything about your condition).

- **Know how much it costs** to provide the physical accommodations you need and where they can be purchased.

- **Know what funding is available** (e.g., from the government and/or one's health insurance) for accommodations and show your potential employer how to access it.

- **Offer solutions and suggestions**. Emphasize what the accommodation will enable you to do. You'll be demonstrating the positive attitude and problem-solving skills you'll bring with you to (your effective continuance on) the job.

I would also add: *be prepared to have medical proof and written advice available, for any and all such claims for accommodation.* This, too: be a good employee in general, as the simple fact remains that employers are more likely to offer easy accommodation to those they view as clear assets and likeable people.

In addition to these sources, readers are strongly urged to research three useful things:

1 required workplace accommodations in their home country/ state/province/territory

2 any available local, state/provincial, or national government funding to aid with accessibility in the workplace (not just direct funding but also tax breaks, credits, and subsidies)

3 kinds of technology and accommodations most commonly requested and used by those with your specific condition (be it diabetes, depression, sore back, epilepsy, vision or hearing impairment, etc.)[207]

Ben-Shahar's "MPS" Process

One final "big picture" strategy proven to increase one's happiness at work—whether one is unafflicted or lives with a chronic condition—is Ben-Shahar's so-called "MPS Process": Meaning, Pleasure, and Strengths.[208]

In this process, ask yourself three questions and list the answers. These questions are:

1 What kind of activity do I find meaningful and worth doing?

2 Which sets of activities give me actual pleasure in the moment?

3 What kind of activity allows me to display skills and characteristics that I know are part of my own personal strengths?

The goal is to take said lists and build a kind of overlapping Venn diagram (see below), *paying special attention to the overlap* between the circles, and then to consider which careers allow one to engage in such activity. (Ben-Shahar notes how this process is not only useful for choosing a career in general but also in considering how to transform one's existing job into a more fulfilling one.)

FIG 11 VENN DIAGRAM OF THE MPS PROCESS

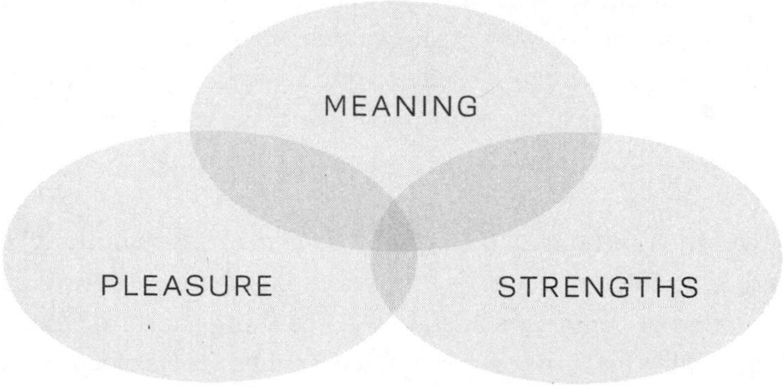

MEANING

PLEASURE   STRENGTHS

I enjoy my own job because it resides at the intersection of these three values. As I think about it, it's not the only possible career path here, but it's a very good fit nonetheless. For example, as corny as it sounds, I actually find the process of education in general—in terms of the creation and spreading of knowledge, and the eradication of ignorance—to be meaningful and purposive. I believe that ignorance is a terribly destructive force in our lives, and knowledge a wonderfully positive force for creation and empowerment. And, as mentioned above, in connection with flow, I also find both lecturing and writing to be quite pleasant—lecturing more so than writing, at least in the moment. I also have to do a lot of reading in my job, and have loved reading from early childhood, and I enjoy being around energetic, optimistic, and idealistic young people every day, teaching them and even mentoring them regarding their own careers and life paths. I also like having intelligent, cultured, open-minded, and accomplished colleagues and peers. Finally, being a professor does draw upon some of my strengths, including public speaking and being able to learn quickly and then explain things so that others understand. Now, as mentioned, there might have been other careers that could've drawn upon these strengths—perhaps I could have been a lawyer or a journalist or a full-time author—and there are aspects of my job that do not give me pleasure at all, such as grading exams. But it's a good fit, and one that has only grown stronger over the years.

It's well worth one's while to go through the MPS Process, whether in terms of career or particular tasks within one's existing job. It is both informative and instructive, and perhaps even heartening for the chronically ill or injured (especially those newly such), who may be struggling with a sense of inefficacy and/or confusion. The MPS Process can lead one either to confirmation or conviction as to how some things need to change. It's valuable for future planning, too, as these sorts of thing can change over time. Moreover, most of us have a great deal of accurate self-awareness about what we find worthwhile, purposive, and meaningful—and certainly about what gives us pleasure. But note that there exists evidence that objective self-awareness of our own strengths and weaknesses—while present—is not as strong as it is for the other two, and can benefit from sustained critical attention and reflection. In particular, there's evidence of some self-deception, which can exaggerate strengths (e.g., the vast majority of us think we're smarter and morally better than we really are); and there can be stubborn self-identifications, which can "lock in forever" some weaknesses (e.g., "I'm just no good at math").[209] Getting perspectives from others can be valuable in this regard, as are other objective indicators: what one has spent a lot of time on, is credentialed and experienced in, gets rewarded and praised for, and which deployment of skills results in successful completion of a given task or activity. Also, don't forget the incredibly wide range of strengths and weaknesses, which it's possible to consider given human complexity (we are: physical, intellectual, practical, emotional, social, moral, political, cultural, technological, spiritual, and so on). Have fun, and above all *look for repeated themes and intersections*—and don't be scared to pay special attention to weaknesses, as they can point to areas of self-improvement, yes, but also to possible zones where one can eliminate pain or frustration, thus growing in overall happiness. While it has been proven that exercising a strength tends to give us particular joy and satisfaction, there's no doubt that eliminating or reducing a weakness can both diminish a pain as well as serve as its own source of pride and accomplishment.[210]

Aristotle's Ideal Forms of Work

It may interest some readers to know what Aristotle thinks about the world of work and labour. There's no doubt that he thought work was important, and vital in fulfilling one's natural potential. To that extent, he agrees with Freud. At the same time, Aristotle lived a very privileged life and took for granted having enough income and resources to satisfy his basic needs (e.g., his father was the official doctor to the court of the King of Macedonia). Aristotle himself went on to become the tutor of Alexander the Great, who conquered and founded one of history's largest empires. Not only that, Aristotle was the student of the great Greek philosopher Plato, and went on to found his very own mini-university called the Lyceum. Aristotle enjoyed a nice marriage, had children, and died of natural causes around age sixty-two—a very nice lifespan for the time.[211]

Those personal facts, plus the context of Aristotle's world, are needed to keep his comments about work in perspective. Not only was he personally very privileged, he also lived in a world where all manual work, and work related to vital physical needs, was done by slaves. Slavery was the norm in the ancient world, and there was a sense amongst privileged Greeks such as Aristotle that manual work, household work, even the very task of making money was something for "lower classes" of people. Gentlemen, so to speak, just didn't do that sort of thing: "chasing the dollar" was for people who had to, and/or for "vulgar" people who couldn't set their sights higher. Not only that,

Aristotle's world was also highly gendered, and it was taken for granted that females would not be formally educated and were expected to see their proper place as in the household. Finally, despite their many incredible achievements, the ancient Greeks—compared to us—still had a primitive economy, which revolved around agriculture, real estate, basic household needs, some trading between city-states, and the material resources for (and consequences of) military activity.[212]

Factoring all that in, Aristotle argued that two forms of work are the best, most satisfying, and most fitting for the full development of human personality. Each has to do with the use of rationality and knowledge (which Aristotle saw as our highest and most special characteristic) but corresponds to the different forms of intelligence as Aristotle saw them. Corresponding to theoretical rationality (i.e., knowledge about the world in general, or what we might today call "book smarts") is advanced research: the creation of knowledge. Aristotle referred to this in general as "philosophy," though for him this was an umbrella term meaning "the love of wisdom" (literally from the Greek "*philo*"—friend or "lover of"—and "*sophia*"—wisdom). This was the career path that Aristotle chose. Not only did he spend time studying basically every subject then in existence, he himself created a few brand-new disciplines (such as formal logic) and made absolutely foundational contributions to others, including perhaps most centrally: biology, education, literary criticism, physics, and political science. Along with being one of the most important philosophers in world history, Aristotle is also generally thought to be the world's first genuine scientist, insisting on detailed, factual observations and descriptions of various phenomena ranging from plants and animals (his favourite) to the legal constitutions of various city-states and empires.[213]

Though Aristotle referred to his path as philosophy, we can abstract from that term and see that, today, Aristotle would likely recommend any sort of career or work that has, as its main function, the creation and spread of knowledge about the world and/or the discovery of new knowledge or theories for better understanding existing knowledge and observations. We can see many kinds of jobs falling under this description: from scientist to journalist, university and college professors down through every level of teacher, authors to broadcasters/podcasters, even the entire field of creative invention—especially of goods and services catering to our ability to better understand and manage the world (e.g., engineers, product designers, software developers, medical researchers and pharmaceutical developers, documentary filmmakers, and so on).

The second kind of best work—in terms of individual fulfilment and happiness—Aristotle referred to as "politics." Again, we need to keep in mind the primitive nature of the economy in his world, and abstract from there to get a wider picture of the nature of this work. If the creation and spread of new knowledge corresponds to a theoretical kind of human rationality, then politics in these terms corresponds to practical rationality (i.e., the deployment and use of reason, in daily life, to improve people's lives in an observable way—what we might call "street smarts"). Aristotle saw as the highest and most useful form of practical rationality being an excellent political leader, such as Pericles (494–429 BC).[214] Leaders like Pericles excel at practical rationality because they are able to achieve not merely happiness and full development for themselves but also they facilitate it directly and powerfully for many others. And if happiness is the ultimate objective for any one of our lives, how much better is it then for someone to contribute in a substantial way to the happiness of the lives of hundreds, thousands, or even millions of others?[215]

Reflecting here, we conclude that an Aristotelian conception would endorse any work or profession whose major aim is the wellness and happiness of others. The key here is the other-directedness of it. For Aristotle, this shows more capability and efficaciousness: you're able to "spread the love," so to speak, not merely creating happiness for one(self) and/or a very small number. We can acknowledge and appreciate that, and then note further that today's research shows, for example, that when people spend money on others, they report being much happier than when they are forced to spend it on themselves.[216] As we'll see in great detail when we get to Chapter 6, feeling connected to others, and moreover giving gifts to and helping others, is a deep, rich, and enduring source of happiness.[217] So, when we think of work that is directly in view here, we think of all the so-called "helper professions," such as medicine, psychology, social work, even education. Politics and government (including the civil service), in the best sense, are also in view, as is the practice of law in helping people solve difficult problems and secure their interests in connection with such vital aspects of their lives as property, marriages, access to their children, and the protection of their most basic rights to physical security, personal freedom, and non-discrimination.

Even accounting for the limits of Aristotle's world, and the biases implicit in his thinking, we can understand how, for him, there are a great many kinds of work that, even today, are "the best" in terms of human happiness. The key take-aways for our time are two. Whether considering a career, or merely augmenting or focusing on the tasks within one's current job, consider taking Aristotle's learned advice and do: 1) work/tasks that either involve the creation or spread of new knowledge and new ideas, or 2) work/tasks that materially contribute to the happiness and well-being of others. These may motivate and satisfy you in ways other work cannot. Thus, work that is routine and does not involve genuine invention and creation, and/or work whose primary function is merely a personal financial one (e.g., making money and paying one's bills), is probably not going to offer much in terms of what Ben-Shahar labels "the ultimate currency": happiness.[218]

Money

Like pleasure, money is necessary but not sufficient for happiness. It is necessary because people *do* need enough money to meet their vital human needs: the lack of money and financial resources is a terrible drag on an individual's happiness, and any increase in money, allowing people to meet more of their vital needs, substantially increases their self-reported happiness (e.g., as research in the developing world has shown).[219] So it's not as though money can be dismissed entirely from the happiness equation, as many of today's thinkers seem inclined to suggest. Even good old Aristotle noted that, as an aspect of pure realism, one of the most important external goods conducive to human well-being is having enough resources to meet one's basic needs, and to enable one's fundamental progress and development as a person. We do, after all, need stuff on which to live; to that extent, the raw materials of life cannot be ignored or downplayed.[220]

Where exactly the line of vital need exists, in terms of money, depends on the society in which one lives and associated costs therein. Economist Richard Layard* cites data showing that the crucial line is about $20,000 USD in annual income per capita, at least in the developed world. For example, if one lives in America or Canada and makes below that threshold, then money becomes *both* a necessary and sufficient condition for happiness—any increase will also increase one's self-reported happiness, enabling the meeting of vital needs and staving off the worst kind of financial insecurity. But if one makes above

---

* Further studies since Layard contest the exact dollar figure of the income threshold, with many now pegging it at either $50K/year or even $75K/year in North America. But all the studies do confirm there is a threshold of income—not especially high—above which increases only marginally and temporarily boost happiness but below which every added increment boosts happiness.

that annual income threshold, increases in income bring—at best—only a temporary boost in happiness levels, which then gets frittered away as a result of hedonic adaptation, which we discussed in Chapter 1.[221] For instance, it's been widely reported that the CEOs of Fortune 500 companies report average levels of personal happiness that barely differ from those of their employees, even though the former make *over 300 times as much* on average. There's also research showing that luxury car drivers get no more pleasure out of driving their glamorous cars than the owners of compacts. And we saw previously how lottery winners revert to pre-winning levels of personal happiness somewhere between six months and 1.5 years after hearing their lucky numbers.[222]

There's more variability in the level of income throughout the developing world, as different countries can have widely differing average levels of personal income. But of special significance is what the United Nations (UN) has termed the line of worldwide "absolute poverty" (not poverty merely relative to people who have more money but, rather, poverty so severe that, without some kind of aid or help, one will eventually die). The line of worldwide absolute poverty is thought to be $2 USD/day, which comes out to an annual income of just $730 USD per person. It may surprise readers to know that there are, in fact, many countries—especially those in Sub-Saharan Africa—whose average annual income is at, or even below, that mark; and economists believe that at least one billion, and maybe as many as two billion, people endure life at or below that level. For those affected in this way, any increase in income is a guaranteed increase for their well-being and happiness.[223]

Quick comment should be made about how it's not just that one's income (or access to resources) needs to be above a threshold of raw human survival. It's not just about access to money and resources, and the ability to spend in such a way as to ensure one's ongoing existence. Research also shows that, assuming one *does* have access to money, *one should not substantially, chronically over-spend*: you need to avoid getting into severe financial problems wherein you have spent more than what you have saved, resulting in serious debt. Such a problem is routinely cited as one of the major factors behind divorce, for example, which we know is one of the most potent short-term hits to anyone's happiness.[224] Statistics also tell us that, in the developed world, financial struggles are blamed as one of the leading causes of suicide among men of working age (e.g., such suicides always increase substantially during periods of economic recession).[225] Finally, such concern—not merely with having enough but also not going overboard with spending—fits in with Charles Dickens' famously monetary equation in *David Copperfield*: "Annual income, twenty pounds; annual expenditure, nineteen six: result happiness. Annual income, twenty pounds; annual expenditure, twenty pound ought and six: result misery."[226]

Happier Spending

Providing we make above the minimal "happiness threshold" for income and are not drowning in debt, does the happiness literature have any further advice about using money to augment one's happiness? It does, and it can be listed here rather quickly:

- Since we are hardwired to receive pleasure from satisfying our basic physical needs, money well spent on adding and heightening the experiences of eating, drinking, sex, and a good night's sleep will definitely add to one's happiness.

- Shelter is another basic need, and often one's biggest expenditure. A comfortable, pleasant, and even beautiful living space clearly augments happiness.

- Money spent on one's health and fitness is worth every penny and then some. Some of this is covered by food/drink/sleep/ relaxing at home, but medicines and health devices/services are further positive expenditures, alongside anything needed for staying physically active.

- We'll talk more about the body and physical beauty in Chapter 7, but looking as good as one can—or at least not feeling bad about how one looks—is another component of well-being. Thus, some smart spending on flattering fashions and good grooming will augment happiness. (Two words: *cut*, in terms of clothing; and *retinol*, in terms of face lotion. And I once saw a Meg Ryan movie where an old man travels back in time from the future, informing the young people of today that the key to happiness, as one ages, boils down to one word: *floss!*)

- Since so much of happiness revolves around how we use our time, time-saving devices and services (from a dishwasher to a maid to many of today's apps) enable increased happiness.

- Anything needed for the pursuit of flow or micro-flow activities.

- The pursuit of "retail therapy" (i.e., happiness through shopping) is unlikely to succeed, as most consumer goods are subject to heavy hedonic adaptation. In general, spending *less on goods and more on experiences*—especially novel and adventuresome experiences—is the way to go.

- However, research has proven that buying objects that enable future experiences *does* heighten happiness—and also increases the pleasure of anticipation. An example would be buying a guitar, or new cookware.[227]

- The best experiences in which to invest, happiness-wise, are those that: a) reward and celebrate good news/achievements, b) draw you closer to other people, and c) have the potential to create stand-out positive memories worth savouring, now and in the future.

- It's worth emphasizing that expenditure deepening one's closest personal relationships is a superb happiness investment—like a romantic get-away, an awesome adventure with one's friends, or a neat tourist trip with the family.

- In general, any expenditure enabling a greater variety of experiences and the construction of a richly complex, multi-faceted self is likely the most joyous expenditure of all. As a wise financial planner once said: the single best investment isn't in real estate, or gold, or bitcoin, or stocks and bonds. *It's investing in yourself*: your future earning power, future opportunities; your own personal growth and life-long pursuit of happiness. Aristotle couldn't have said it better.[228]

Being Money-driven

With all that said, what should be the proper role of money in one's thoughts and behaviours? How "money-driven" should one be? All the research suggests that *money should not play a substantial role at all, if it's not connected to the above kinds of expenditure.* The main reason, or at least initial clue for this, is that people who define themselves as being the most money-driven—in terms of their personal goals and interests—also self-report levels of happiness among the lowest of those in the entire developed world. Let's consider this (perhaps counterintuitive) truth further.

People who define themselves as money-driven tend to have more money and a higher net worth than people who don't.

Which makes sense. So do the findings that money-driven people: are more highly motivated at work and over the course of their careers, tend to work harder and longer, and their higher earnings give them increased self-confidence in terms of their professional skill and identity (though not necessarily in other aspects of life, notably romantic relationships and family ties). However, research shows that such people: are significantly less charitable than non-money-driven people, tend to have impaired social skills (e.g., are more aggressive and less generous with their time, are worse listeners, and exhibit less empathy), and are reported as being less likeable by those close to them. Most tellingly, as stated above, money-driven people—when asked to rate their own levels of happiness—report, with brutal honesty, some of the lowest scores among the general population in the entire developed world. Why should that be when their "money-driven-ness" has given them all that money, financial security, material success, and career-related confidence?[229]

Researchers supply two main reasons for this. First, as just noted, is the hit taken to one's personal life when money-driven-ness becomes paramount. Given that—for almost everyone over the long term—close social connectedness is more powerfully productive of personal happiness, and given that being money-driven must come at some cost of time with others and attention to one's social connectedness, it's not surprising that those who are money-driven can be much less happy than people who do not have such material riches but who are more socially connected and invest in maintaining and nurturing their social connections. As we all know, without such time and effort, relationships tend to whither and die.[230] Second, being very money-driven tends to go hand-in-hand with jealous social comparisons to the wealth of others. Now, to an extent, most people are guilty of this. But when one places wealth at the centre of one's motivations, it's easy to see how this tendency actually becomes a recipe for stress and frustration: there's always more money to be made, and there's always someone else, quite close and visible, who has a lot more of it than you. As we'll see in Chapter 8, relentless and jealous social comparisons almost always generate deep unhappiness.[231]

It should be mentioned, as in Chapter 2, that *there's nothing essential* in the connection between being money-driven and being disproportionately interested in material social comparison. This finding just happens to be a strong correlation; of course, some people can resist this temptation. We saw, for example, how those who viewed their pursuit of wealth more from the intrinsic standpoint of securing personal freedom and/or proving their competence, do not succumb to the corrosive effects of jealous social comparison. And we must note the frank self-assessment of the group of money-driven people in general: in reporting their happiness levels, they are clearly not guilty of exaggeration or "impression management," and they don't seem to suffer from the notion that success in one field translates automatically into success in another.

Striving to view one's pursuit of wealth more in terms of an intrinsic achievement is one way or technique of inclining in the right direction. The residual problem, though, is that such continued pursuit of wealth is still going to run afoul of the things mentioned above. Another way is to consider the adoption of rival goals, which have been shown to be more productive for happiness than money. These are, indeed, the main subject matter of this whole book: pleasure, the other external goods, and the internal goods. This is consistent with what Ben-Shahar advises, which is to give up on making "mere currency" the focus of one's efforts and instead substitute "the ultimate currency"—happiness—as one's primary goal.[232] More narrowly, experiments have been run on ways to persuade money-driven people to be less so, and they've found that the most successful way—at least in the short term—is *to encourage money-driven people to swap out money for time.* The habit of thinking about value in quantitative terms is so deeply ingrained in money-driven people that most find it difficult to resist or give up. So, encourage them to continue their fondness for objective, quantitative measurement, but in terms of time spent on things rather than their monetary value. (They are, after all, inclined to view their own time, effort, and attention as valuable!) When such people are encouraged to spend wisely, viewing their life as The One Big Budget, they tend to take the point much more to heart. This leads them naturally down the path toward experiences (instead of material goods), spending quality time with family and friends (instead of always working), novelty and variety (instead of always cashing in on the one big skill), and, ultimately, the pursuit of meaning and happiness (instead of net worth).[233]

The case of Bill Gates is an instructive and inspiring one. The legendary founder of Microsoft and richest man in the world no doubt pursued his ambition with amazing skill and zeal, building Microsoft to the point where it was both: a) instrumental in the worldwide spread of everyday computing (both personal and professional), and b) the world's most valuable company. Yet, in the end, he stepped away from Microsoft and now spends his time very differently. In 2013, he said in an interview that "[m]oney has no utility for me beyond a certain point. Its utility is entirely in building an organization and getting the resources out to the poorest of the world."[234] This new organization, of course, is the Bill & Melinda Gates Foundation (BMGF), and it is (by assets under management) the largest philanthropic organization in the world, with a special focus on global public health measures (notably young children in the world's poorest nations).[235] Thus, he gave up the pursuit of wealth for helping others—and also persuaded his good friend Warren Buffett to donate his vast fortune over time to BMGF.[236]

These people exemplify how investing money in the well-being of others tends to bring much greater personal satisfaction than hoarding it and spending it all on oneself. (Research has found one important caveat: one needs to feel a deep association with the cause and/or people to whom one is giving money.) It's an interesting question to ask: *Which charitable causes and/or spending on others should you engage with and activate?* It happily taps into one's deepest values and interests, drawing one into broader engagement with others and the world. I speculate that this is especially valuable for the chronically afflicted, as a way to resist any tendencies to close in on oneself.[237]

Comparison, Class, and Control

We need to consider further the notion that most people find it hard to resist social comparisons, emphatically so when it comes to money and income. Perhaps a joke by way of introduction: apparently, there's an old Russian proverb about two poor peasants, Ivan and Yuri, who live on side-by-side farms. Ivan inherits a cow. Yuri becomes depressed and prays to God. God says: "What can I do?" Yuri replies: "Kill the cow!"[238]

There's evidence that, in the short term, one *can* become measurably (albeit temporarily) happier when earning more than one's immediate social peers. There's a study from Harvard in which a clear majority of respondents confirmed that they would much rather live in a world where they get only $50K a year with everyone else getting $25K, compared to a different world wherein they would get double their own amount—$100K—but everyone else made $250K.[239]

This income rivalry raises many questions: How much of these findings are truly about money and its import in our lives, and how much are about *relative social standing and status*? Many well-known studies report on the truth of the latter. One of the best known revolves around actors who win Academy Awards for either Best Actor/Actress or Best Supporting Actor/Actress. Researchers discovered that, to their surprise, *Oscar winners live on average four years longer than those merely nomi-nated.* Since many actors have similar backgrounds, similar work conditions, and most live in the Los Angeles area, researchers have suggested that what might be happening is that the raw fact of their superior standing and recognition among their peers gives Oscar winners an added biological boost—not only in terms of subjective happiness but also objective longevity! (It was also found that those who've won multiple Oscars enjoyed on average a further two years of life than those who had "merely" won once.)[240] And we saw previously evidence that, all things being equal, those who are higher up in an organization tend to be more satisfied with their work lives. One factor may be the added income and enhanced financial security; another, that those higher up are more likely to view their work as a calling. However, it may be just the raw fact that they are higher up on this social hierarchy, and take pride and pleasure out of their superior standing.

The converse is also true—those on the lower rungs of social hierarchies have been shown (on average and in general) to have both lower levels of self-reported happiness and satisfaction, and—objectively—noticeably higher rates of stress indicators, disease, and biological impairment. One of the more interest-ing studies has shown how monkeys and apes who are lower on their respective social hierarchies suffer both from enhanced displays of distressed behaviour (e.g., withdrawal, difficulties relating, awkwardness, aggression) and from objective factors like higher blood serum levels of the stress hormone cortisol, as well as more clogged arteries and other signs of heart disease. These findings have been replicated to an extent in humans, with one of the most systematic and influential of these studies being the Whitehall Studies on British civil servants, conducted by Sir Michael Marmot, among others.[241]

What the Whitehall Studies showed—among many other things—was that British government workers at the bottom-most ladder of the civil service hierarchy were three times more likely to die an early death (from all causes) than those at the top. The Whitehall Studies also showed, systematically, how a whole range of biological health indicators—heart disease, alcoholism, obesity, diabetes—are *statistically pegged* to the level one is at in the hierarchy. The reason why such studies are thought to be so telling, and vital for issues of inequality, status, and hierarchy, is that having *any* job in the British civil service is still pretty nice work. Even at the lowest rung, one has a decent salary, can afford to meet one's vital needs, enjoys reliable job security, has nice health benefits, and can look forward to their financial future with confidence. Indeed, this is precisely why this group of workers was chosen for the studies: to investigate how, even among objectively comfortable workers, issues of hierarchy, status, and control might come to affect people over time.[242]

Daniel Nettle details additional research from the UK showing that, while in general there's a weak association between one's annual income and level of self-reported happiness, there is, however, a much stronger relationship between one's socioeconomic *class* and their level of happiness. He's quick to note how one's class, while including income, also includes other large and important things such as level of education and professional attainment, recognized social status, and—above all—level of control over one's life (including the circumstances of one's working life). This is illustrated vividly in studies that went beyond the simple and traditional weighting of "annual income versus self-reported satisfaction." They created further categories, including some sensitive to the degree of control one has at work. Factoring in such things, the following result occurs: people who are relatively poor but report being in control of the circumstances of their work rate their happiness at 7.85 out of ten, whereas those who are relatively rich but whose work circumstances are largely out of their personal control on average rate their happiness at only a 5.82 out of ten. (First: note the degree of impact that one's *work* has on one's *life* satisfaction. Second: what's "rich but with low control"? Consider, e.g., a high-income job within a very large, competitive, hierarchical corporation—such as vice-president. Lawyers and finance people—investors, stockbrokers—are also mentioned in this category.)[243]

Nettle contends that two big truths can be inferred from these mammoth British studies:

- First is that the issue of autonomy and personal control comes up again and again as not only absolutely vital but actively productive of how happy we report ourselves in life. (Nettle's interpretation of the Whitehall Studies is precisely along these lines: what they show is not merely the effect of inequality and hierarchy per se but, moreover, *the effects of relative personal control over one's own life.* The crucial thing is that those at the top have more control, whereas those at the bottom have less. This is therefore empowering and liberating for those at the top, and frustrating and confining for those at the bottom. Nettle reports that personal control "accounts for more than twenty times of the variation" in happiness between people as compared to their relative levels of annual income. He observes that people "really don't like being told what to do, whatever the material inducements.")[244]

- Second, these studies reveal that one can actually take a rather large DECREASE in income *without* any significant negative impact on happiness levels so long as such a decrease comes with an INCREASE in the degree of control over one's work and life. He notes that people—especially in competitive contemporary corporate and professional environments—always tend to mock and laugh at those who declare (perhaps around mid-career) that they are going to "get out of the rat-race," quit their high-paying jobs, and go and do something like live a relaxed life by the beach, surfing and tanning all day long, eking out a bohemian living by selling custom-made surfboards online and giving lessons to tourists. Nettle comments that, while his peers may sneer with derision, it's almost certain that our beach bum in question will be happier so long as he can still pay for his needs, having greater control over his time, life, and circumstances of work.[245]

And Layard—to take us from the personal to the social—draws a third big conclusion from all these studies and concerns. He notes that, other things being equal, it will generally be true that *steps to make the distribution of income more equal throughout society will increase the average amount of happiness in said society.*[246] This ties into recent high-profile research by Thomas Piketty, highlighting concerns over substantially growing income inequality throughout most of the world—including in such developed nations as America. Among other things—the potential for alienation, class divisions, and even social conflict—we can, for our purposes, infer that *growing income inequality will probably make the majority of people in that society less happy.*[247]

Thus, it seems plausible to observe that a compelling social recipe for the happiness of most people in a given society will be one in which *there is not too much inequality, especially income inequality, but where people are allowed robust personal freedoms and opportunities for controlling the major aspects of their lives.* We shall turn to this crucial issue in greater detail as we move into the next chapter. We shall also witness, to a great degree, how those with chronic conditions confront serious obstacles in connection with these two vital factors: 1) freedom and control, and 2) equality.

Conclusion

There's a saying, often attributed to Coco Chanel: "Those who say money can't buy happiness don't know where to shop." That's funny, but there's little evidence backing it up. (Even funnier is Henny Youngman's quip: "What good is happiness? It can't buy you money!")[248] Money and income are necessary, but not sufficient for happiness—they constitute the first major external good we require for enjoyment and fulfilment in life. We each need enough to satisfy our vital needs, and in general to enable our pursuit of further personal development. But beyond that, gains in money and income translate only to small, relative, and temporary gains in happiness.

In terms of work, much research exists showing that Freud was right when he opined that work is an important part of happiness in the modern, developed world. We examined reliable methods for boosting happiness at work by: 1) pursuing work that is either a calling or can be interpreted in such a way; 2) pursuing work that allows one to experience flow; 3) using Ben-Shahar's MPS process for finding work (and/or work tasks) at the intersection of what one finds meaningful, pleasant, and expressive of one's strengths. We then explored concrete, detailed advice for those with chronic conditions, regarding how illnesses, injuries, and disabilities can and should be accommodated in the workplace.

In terms of income, we first considered advice on how to spend money so as to augment one's happiness. We learned that being too money-driven in life is strongly associated with self-reported unhappiness, and that it's better to view one's time as the most precious resource, and to spend both one's time and money on things that have been shown to augment happiness. It's important to avoid upward social comparison and jealousy when it comes to the income and wealth of others, though as we saw the research suggests this is less owing to raw quantities of money itself and has more to do with relative social standing and recognition. Hierarchy seems to matter more than money, and shows how the most important issues revolve around both freedom and equality. To be happy, people want to enjoy freedom and control over the most important facets of their lives, and they want to live in a society where there is not too much inequality. How happy societies have managed this balancing act between freedom and equality is our next subject, and it has special implications for those with chronic conditions.

CHAPTER 5

Social Institutions

While it's true that much of happiness rests in our own hands—the choices we make, how we habitually deal with events, our mindsets, etc.—it's also true that factors external to us have an important impact. Any theory of happiness that focuses entirely on personal psychology, ignoring the role of external goods, is incomplete. One of the most potent of these is a set of social institutions operative in our country (and, to an extent, globally); *social institutions create the context within which we live, choose, interpret, and behave.* The research literature is coming to an ever-firmer consensus that the depth of impact that this social context has on our quality of lives, and pursuit of happiness, is profound.

Social Animals

And how could it be otherwise? We don't live as atoms in a vacuum, or as Robinson Crusoe, isolated alone on an island.[249] Aristotle himself famously said that human beings are, by nature, *"zoon politikon"*—political animals. This is perhaps better translated as "social animals," as Aristotle's broader reference is to the *"polis"*—the community. We can only achieve true happiness, and fulfill our potential, as members of a social community. For Aristotle, the Robinson Crusoes of this world are destined to lead unnatural, incomplete, unhappy, and perhaps even stunted and twisted lives.[250] (Contemporary research has found a strong correlation between living alone and having very few or no friends, and being at much higher risk of various forms of mental illness, such as dementia.)[251] Broader ancient Greek civilization concurred with Aristotle: one of the ultimate punishments at the time was "ostracism" (i.e., getting kicked out of, and forbidden by, one's community.) The word derives from the Greek *ostraka*, which were literally the broken pieces of pottery on which were inscribed the name of the person being voted out of the polis.) Such isolation and alienation were thought to be not only sad and depressing, but also, perhaps, a vital threat to one's well-being and survival—hence one of the most severe punishments. As Aristotle said, no one person can literally meet all their needs on their own—nor can a family or even an extended tribe. It takes an entire well-functioning country or community to have that kind of self-reliant stability. To borrow and revise a recently used phrase: when it comes to happiness (and raising children), it truly "takes a village."[252]

As mentioned previously, one of Aristotle's favourite subjects—one to which he contributed immensely—was biology. He understood every creature, including human beings, through this biological lens of growth and development, and, more narrowly, through the implanted impulse toward the fullest possible realization of an innate natural potential (like a seed growing into a tree). The given potential and tendency toward growth are provided by nature; the uniqueness of this potential is what separates natural species from one another. For humans, Aristotle said, the *"differentia specifica"*—the exact difference from other species—is the possession of rationality. Though we have since come to doubt that we alone possess rationality (considering evidence of impressive intelligence in such animals as chimps, dolphins, elephants, and monkeys), this was an article of faith for Aristotle: we alone in the natural world possess reason, and this is nature's big clue to us, regarding how we should live our lives. We should strive to realize our rational potential to the fullest extent possible. And since reason itself is plural, this means developing ourselves in a range of ways. In particular, and as mentioned last chapter, there is *theoretical* rationality ("knowing that"—implying a kind of duty to, and impulse toward, the augmentation of knowledge and science) and there is *practical* rationality ("knowing how-to"—selecting and pursuing means and goals conducive to the one ultimate practical goal of living a happy and flourishing life).[253]

But for Aristotle, nothing could be more absurd than these complex processes of development taking place in a vacuum. The process would be doomed to fail. Proposing to leave the whole thing up to individuals ignores natural developmental processes and treats us as if we are all, always, full-grown, rational, and autonomous adults. But we don't come into the world that way—at birth, we are utterly helpless, irrational, and incapable of choosing and acting on our own. We don't achieve full-grown status for a very long time (compared to other species), and not without a great deal of help from others and from society in general. It's an evolving, multifaceted process. We can, crudely, diagram how Aristotle viewed the general process of our development toward the realization of our natural potential:

FIG 12 ARISTOTLE'S MOVEMENT FROM POTENTIAL TO ACTUAL

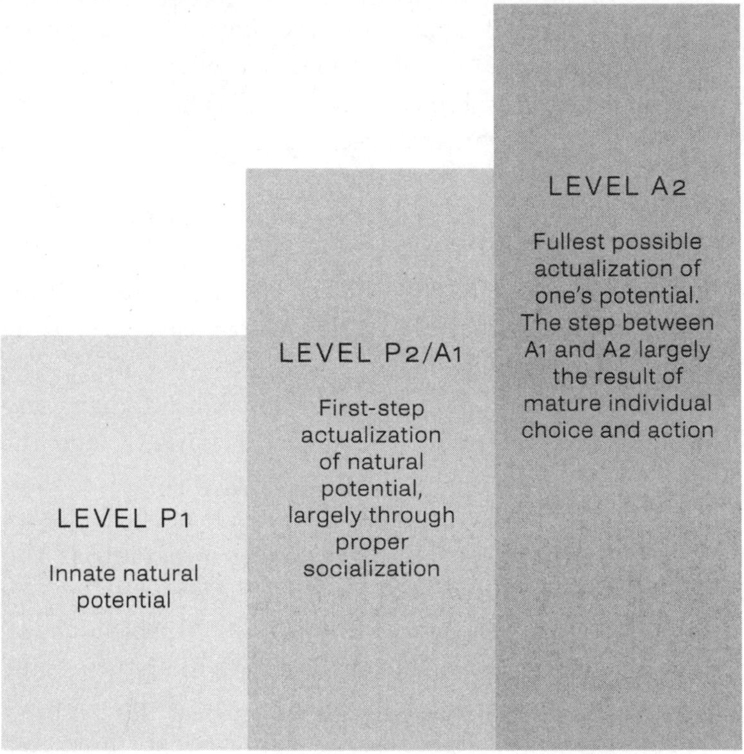

LEVEL A2

Fullest possible
actualization of
one's potential.
The step between
A1 and A2 largely
the result of
mature individual
choice and action

LEVEL P2/A1

First-step
actualization
of natural
potential,
largely through
proper
socialization

LEVEL P1

Innate natural
potential

P1 is what's given to us, individually, by nature: our biology and all its gifts and burdens. The question becomes: How shall this creature grow? How can it ever achieve happiness, or excellence? Aristotle's answer was that part of this is done through the help, aid, and intervention of other people and social institutions—particularly when we are young and still growing. Then, once a certain level of development has been achieved (A1/P2), our own individual choices and habitual actions become more prominent. Society has a vital role to play, for which there is no substitution—people without proper social context within which to grow and pursue happiness will be marked, scarred, and hampered by such early experiences, like a young one starved of crucial nutrients during growth. But vital, social help can only take us so far; in the end we must take over, as individuals, to finish the process, deliberating upon and choosing our fullest development and happiness (the move from A1 to A2). Importantly, the self-driven move from A1 to A2 means that not everyone will achieve their fullest development—something Aristotle thought completely obvious, owing to bad choices, ignorance, and a general lack of willpower and drive from which some people suffer. Thus, we see in Aristotle's account how different people come to lead such different lives and, in particular, experience such different levels of happiness and fulfillment. It has to do with: a) the society in which they live and were raised; and b) the individual choices they make, and habits they form, upon reaching adulthood. Our concern in this chapter is the first: What is the proper role of society in nurturing and encouraging people's happiness?[254]

Enduring Relevance

It needs to be stressed: *social context is always relevant,* and not merely when we are growing up. Were a civil war to break out, for instance, you better believe it would have an effect on all our lives and happiness, threatening certain interests and perhaps blocking some potentialities from being pursued and developed. Additionally, there exists much evidence that our social contexts have an impact on the status of our individual health, even as full-grown adults. The condition of our neighbourhoods (e.g., in terms of crime and pollution), the proximity of grocery stores and parks, the fitness levels and dietary habits of our friends and family, whether the government subsidizes health-promoting activities (e.g., gym memberships) and "punishes" health-damaging activities (e.g., taxing cigarettes and alcohol) have all been proven to shape the likelihood of full-grown adults making certain health choices over others.[255]

It's not just that social context is always relevant; it's that, even after becoming adults, we can nevertheless fall victim to illness, disease, and injury-causing damage that hampers our functioning, and perhaps becomes so serious that we can't plausibly be seen as full-grown, rational, autonomous adults anymore. Anyone with a parent, grandparent, or relative of advanced age can attest to this, and of course those with certain chronic conditions know this to be a background concern: not just the barriers posed to one's pursuit of happiness but the potential threat to being a self-sufficient, freely choosing adult. In all such cases, the reliance on others and social institutions skyrockets, and can become of the utmost importance. Hence, it's a subject of pressing import: a) for everyone, growing up and being constantly affected by such vital background needs as physical security; and b) for the chronically ill and challenged— more specifically as their own lack of capacity may become so severe that they need to rely more directly on other people and social institutions for their needs.

There are plenty of reasons and copious amounts of evidence agreeing with Aristotle's assertion that we need good social institutions *both* for our very survival *and* to further enable our pursuit of happiness. But how much do we need from society? What exactly should society give us? Our own answer today is probably something along the lines of, "it depends on the capacity of the individual in question," and thus needs to refer to the issues mentioned above regarding childhood development, infirm old age, and any disease or damage in-between that may hamper functioning and/or require social assistance. Aristotle's own answer—quite different from today's values, at least in North America—was that he suspected that most individuals need quite a lot of help from society. He favoured a rather robust form of what political philosophers now call "communitarianism": strong institutions with lots of influence over peoples' lives, but with the very best of intentions regarding enabling their full development and happiness. This is sometimes, less flatteringly, called a "paternalistic" view, presenting the government like a benevolent father who knows best and acts accordingly. Such old-school political thinking—while plausible during Aristotle's time—goes against the grain of perhaps the last 500 years of Western history, with its stress on individual rights, the Enlightenment, personal freedom, and democracy.[256] Plus, Aristotle's account of happiness—while helpful in many general ways—nevertheless *makes one big, specific omission*: having a large degree of control over one's own life. Autonomy and freedom, we now know, are vital ingredients for what makes people happy, alongside resistance to big, rigid hierarchies and sharp inequalities within society (e.g., what might be created within a paternalistic state wherein the government controls much of life). Thus, a prime task of this chapter is to consider: How do we balance Aristotle's generally correct observation that we need considerable social help to meet our needs and become happier with another general truth—that we need a large degree of personal freedom from social control in order to be as happy we can be?

The Basic Structure

Before tackling such a challenging question, it's worth considering what we mean by "a social institution." Acclaimed philosophers John Rawls and Thomas Pogge have coined and propagated the phrase "the basic structure." The social institutions that compose the basic structure are the most important, in terms of realizing our fundamental interests and enabling our personal pursuit of happiness. These institutions have an effect on people, which is, as Pogge said, "profound, pervasive, inescapable, and present from birth." The ruling idea is this: the most important social institutions shape the overall conditions within which we live our lives. These institutions do *not* literally determine us, of course, but they *do* exert profound influence over the social context in which we freely make our choices and forge our lives.[257] Which specific institutions count as part of the basic structure of society?

- The mode of *economic* organization: Do free markets exist, or does the government control the economy? How are goods and services produced and then distributed? What is the level of taxation (i.e., how much money do people get to keep for themselves), and how is the tax burden distributed? In short, how do people get access to material resources?

- The mode of *political* organization: How is government established and operated? Is it an accountable democracy or not? Into which fields of human endeavour does government intervene, and what scope remains for personal freedom? How are the interests of both majorities and minorities heard and protected?

- The mode of *legal* organization: Is there a written constitution or not? Is the judiciary separate and independent from other branches of government? What legal rights do citizens have? In general, do people observe the law or no? Is there an effective "rule of law," or is it the "rule of men"—privileged insiders with disproportionate power who create rules with little regard for consistency, predictability, and stability?

- The mode of deploying *armed force*: How are law and order secured? Is there law and order, or is it a society riddled by violent crime and/or armed conflict? How are police officers recruited and trained? When are people thrown, and kept, in jail? Do civilian authorities have ultimate control over the police and the military, and is corruption under control? What level of defence spending is present in the society, and how does that affect other public spending choices?

- The mode of delivering *basic social services* (e.g., food, water, shelter, education, and health care): Does everyone have access to what human beings vitally need? Are basic levels of education and health care guaranteed to everyone? What gets taught at school? Who gets into college or university, or into various professions? How are hospitals funded? How are drugs and medicines produced and distributed?

- The mode of *family* association permitted and encouraged: Is marriage encouraged? Is divorce allowed? What rights do parents have over their children? How are the special needs of growing children met and protected? What claims do spouses have on each other, in terms of resources and equality? Are same-sex unions permitted? How do the law, education, and the tax system treat family groupings?

- The mode for creating and spreading *culture*: In general, how does the society strike the balance between preserving and promoting majority culture (as a basis of unity) and tolerating and protecting minority cultures (as respecting difference)? How widespread are access to and use of both old-school cultural transmission (e.g., education, newspapers, TV/radio, groups, and clubs) and "new media" (smartphones, computers, apps, social media, and the internet)? Is freedom of expression, association, and information allowed and protected in the society?[258]

How a society answers these kinds of questions, and creates and runs the institutions under each of the above headings will indeed exert over time "a profound, pervasive, and inescapable influence" over its individual members from the very moment they are born. How a society shapes these seven kinds of institutions will come to have an enormous effect over the quality of life, and happiness status, of its people. *The basic structure, in this expansive sense, is probably the single most important external good factoring into anyone's pursuit of personal happiness.* Consider the following simple summary figure:

FIG 13 THE BASIC STRUCTURE OF SOCIAL INSTITUTIONS

Economy

Government

Law

THE BASIC STRUCTURE

Enabling Institutions

Armed Force

Culture

Family

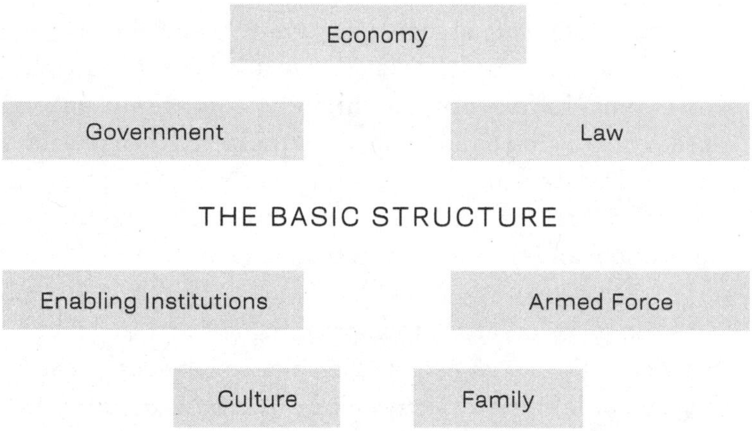

With this much sharper and stronger understanding of social institutions in mind, let's consider what's shared by the happiest societies in the world, particularly in terms of their basic structure. This will, presumably, provide our very best clue as to how a society ought to shape its most important institutions toward the fostering of happiness for all citizens, chronically afflicted or not.

The Happiest Societies

a) Rankings and Indexes

There are many studies and surveys out there regarding "the happiest countries in the world." These have existed for several years now, as interest in happiness research has grown worldwide. Over the years, some of the polling and methodologies have grown to impressive sophistication, and can reveal much of interest regarding the nature of happiness. Obviously, we can't consider all such contributions. Still, it's worth our while to consider three broad categories of happiness survey or ranking: 1) purely objective ones (which don't ask people how happy they are, or how they feel about things), 2) purely subjective ones (which only ask such things), and 3) ones that blend both objective and subjective measures. Though these are all worthwhile, it won't surprise you at this point to know that, in my opinion, the blended measures are probably worthiest of our attention (as happiness itself is a complex blend of such subjective experiences like pleasure, as well as more objective things like access to vitally needed material resources).

b) Objective Well-being

Perhaps the least persuasive surveys and national rankings are those offering happiness criteria that purport to be purely objective and don't consider the personal perspective at all. These are usually labelled measures of well-being, to make a clear distinction from happiness (which most people probably think *must* include some first-person perspective). Now, to be fair, such measures are vast improvements over older measures of quality of life, such as Gross Domestic Product (GDP) per capita. We saw in detail last chapter the limits of simply equating income with happiness. One of the most enduring and influential of these newer well-being indexes is the United Nations Development Programme (UNDP) *Human Development Report*, which first came out in 1990. It measures three major things: 1) access to material resources (in the form of GDP per capita), 2) life expectancy (in years from birth), and 3) educational attainment (years of completed formal schooling). Thus, the general three-fold conception of human well-being is: *wealth, health,* and *knowledge.* More recently, the UNDP has added a further criterion of inequality in a given society, measured purely in terms of the distribution of GDP per capita between rich and poor (e.g., how much of the total economy is owned by, say, the top 5 percent of income earners). The UNDP 2017 rankings (based on 2016 data) of the top ten countries, in order, are: Norway, Australia, Switzerland, Germany, Denmark, Singapore, Netherlands, Ireland, Iceland, and America and Canada tied for tenth. These rankings have remained quite stable over the past five years, as have those for the bottom ten, which are all in Africa: Central African Republic, Niger, Burundi, Guinea, South Sudan, Mozambique, Eritrea, Liberia, Congo, and Mali.[259]

c) Subjective Experience

Let's now go in the opposite direction and consider a decent, purely subjective survey. One of the very best is the Gallup Positive Experience Index. This is a huge and impressive survey, covering over 100,000 people spread out over 150 countries. It's a purely subjective report in that it's a compiled list of people's personal "yes/no" answers to the following five questions (Gallup always does this in time to have the results released by March 19th every year—World Happiness Day):

"Yesterday, did you feel well-rested?"
"Yesterday, were you treated with respect all day?"
"Yesterday, did you smile and laugh a lot?"
"Yesterday, did you learn or do something interesting?"
"Yesterday, did you experience a lot of enjoyment?"

Both the top ten and bottom ten lists look very different from the UNDP lists. The Gallup top ten were all Latin American countries for the year 2015, based on 2014 data (the most recent survey of its kind): Paraguay, Colombia, Ecuador, Guatemala, Honduras, Panama, Venezuela, Costa Rica, El Salvador, and Nicaragua. There's not one country that overlaps both the UNDP and Gallup top tens. The closest are: Singapore (twelfth in Gallup), Switzerland (thirteenth), and Canada (seventeenth). America here came in twenty-fifth. The bottom ten on the Gallup Positive Experiences rankings, from worst on down: Sudan, Tunisia, Turkey, Serbia, Bangladesh, Nepal, Lithuania, Georgia, Bosnia-Herzegovina, and Afghanistan. There is likewise no overlap between the two lists within these bottom ten countries.[260]

This lack of any overlap between the two lists, objective and subjective, suggests that something extreme may be going on with the methodologies, and indeed they do measure very different things. We shall see below, by contrast, that there is substantial overlap between the various blended accounts and measurements, which may suggest that there is something important and stable about the nature of happiness, and how most happy countries tend and need to be structured.

Before we tuck into those blended accounts, though, let's reflect on the Gallup Positive Experiences Index.

- First, the questions themselves are quite interesting, and refer to aspects of happiness we've discussed in some detail already, including: the importance of getting enough sleep, doing things that interest and engage you, and feeling like you've been treated with respect (which ties into both equality and autonomy). The importance of doing enjoyable things every day has also been repeatedly stressed: nothing is going to raise one's personal score more than consistent little "up-ticks" every single day.

- Second, the Gallup researchers used people's answers to quantify a score (out of 100) for the average person's self-reported happiness in their respective society. For the top country, Paraguay, it was eighty-nine; for the next three, it was a tie at eighty-four. (The average for the developed world was in the high seventies, with Switzerland at the top with eighty, followed by Canada at seventy-nine.) The happiest region in the world by this metric? Latin America. The least happy? The so-called MENA (i.e., Middle East and North Africa), with Sub-Saharan Africa and formerly communist European countries not far behind. Perhaps of most interest is the worldwide average at 71 percent, a number that, as Gallup researchers declare, "has remained remarkably consistent through the years." This ties in with previous remarks in Chapter 1, about evolutionary psychology and about how most people say that they are pretty happy in life, with an average score of just over seven out of ten. (Indeed, even in the very bottom country, Sudan, the score was a not-horrifying forty-seven.)[261]

- Third, the results underline the weak connection between objective wealth and subjective happiness, as was argued for last chapter and has been proven in countless studies. In terms of GDP per capita (in 2014, as measured by both the World Bank and the International Monetary Fund), Paraguay comes in ninety-ninth in the world, whereas in the Gallup it is at the very top! Second-happiest country* Colombia only comes in at thirty-first in GDP, with third-happiest Ecuador coming in at sixty-second. The same holds true the other way

---

* Country, as opposed to region or "economic unit." If the European Union is counted as one whole unit, then some economists view it as the largest economy in the world. See B. Orend, *Introduction to International Studies* (Oxford: Oxford University Press, 2nd ed., 2018), Chapters 5 and 6.

around. America has the highest GDP in the world, yet only scored twenty-fifth on the Gallup happiness index. China is second on the GDP index, yet comes forty-fifth in terms of happiness. Finally, third-wealthiest Japan comes in at a rather miserable eighty-third in terms of personal positive experiences.[262]

- Fourth, what explains the happiness of Latin Americans such that they have an almost unbelievable total lock on the Gallup top ten? Gallup researchers themselves argue that the region as a whole displays a "clear cultural disposition" toward *making an effort to be happy on a daily basis*, as well as searching for happy interpretations of, or expectations regarding, life events. This seems like it must be part, or even most of the answer—the region is neither wealthy nor well developed nor internationally powerful, and inequality is quite pronounced throughout. Gallup researchers further argue that the region now enjoys considerable stability relative to the turmoil of the 1970s–80s, when it was a proxy battleground between the superpowers (with both America and Russia supporting local rivals, with ensuing civil unrest). Some suggest that the troubles of the past have helped put cultural emphasis on enjoying life while it's there, leading Latin Americans to be more present-minded and focused on savouring than is typical of other cultures.[263]

The top ten Latin American countries are *all quite small, population-wise*, and perhaps that's relevant—and something to which we'll return in considering the blended approaches. Perhaps more relevant is proximity to nature, and often a beautiful natural backdrop combining beaches, oceans, lush forests, small mountains, deep greenery, and exotic wildlife. Other experts familiar with the region tend to put the biggest emphasis on time spent with family and friends, which is essential to life in Latin America.[264] We know this to be one of the biggest happiness boosters for most people. This fact provides eye-opening evidence as to how much adversity this kind of tight social connectedness can help people overcome.

Experts have noted the religiosity of the region as something that gives hope and comfort to people—we'll return to this in Chapter 8. Finally, others note how—owing to the mild climate—getting access to the basics of survival is quite easy in Latin America. Food is plentiful, clothing cheap, and the requirements for liveable shelter are pretty simple (owing to the warmth). Relatedly, one of the region's social policy hallmarks is the degree to which some form of basic preventative health care is viewed as an absolute right, to be provided to all.[265]

Combine it all and, in spite of the region's obvious limitations, you do indeed have some very potent happiness-boosters: basic human needs met, tons of time spent with family and friends, the savouring of experiences, a beautiful natural environment, a social context that has shown recent (and continued) improvement, and a cultural context emphasizing efforts at being happy. As Aristotle would say, there is much to be learned simply by asking good questions, listening to people, and paying attention to how they think, speak, and behave. Gallup's approach may be purely subjective, but when considering a thing like happiness—where the first-person perspective and lived experience are intrinsic components—the approach ends up shedding light on the facts of the matter.

d) Blended Measures

When we reflect on the nature of the basic structure and compare it to the results from Latin America, we see that much of the success there is limited only to two institutions: culture and family (and perhaps the enabling institutions as well, but more in terms of basic health care than, say, education). There's an overall sense that the success there is more personal, and about a shared "social psychology." One is almost tempted to say that the success there is *in spite of, rather than because of,* the deliberate institutional set-up of those societies. However, the best bet for most countries would be to create a set of social institutions *deliberately designed* to augment human well-being. Plus, we know from earlier chapters that, while it is essential to include subjective measures, we can't put all the weight on them, especially since people have been known to engage in deliberate "impression management," perhaps exaggerating their true levels of happiness.

As a result of these and other considerations, most attempts at measuring happiness levels over time—within and across national societies—employ methodologies that blend subjective surveys (i.e., "how happy are you?") with statistical data measuring objective standards thought indispensable for a pleasant, flourishing, and successful human life. For instance, there is such a thing called the World Happiness Report, put out by the United Nations Sustainable Development Solutions Network. Using tons of data at its disposal, it concludes that about 75 percent of the variation in happiness levels, across countries, is explained by a mere six variables (meaning that the remaining 25 percent is caused by various factors unique to particular countries). These are:

- GDP/capita
- life expectancy from birth

And in addition to such objective measures, the following subjective measures:

- the perception that one has personal freedom to make the most important life choices (such as which career to have, whether/whom to marry, whether to have children)

- the perception that one has "someone to count on" for help and companionship

- the perception that one's society has low levels of corruption

- the perception that people in one's society are more or less generous

Based on answers to these questions, the 2017 ranking of the top ten happiest societies (based on 2014–16 data) are, in order: Norway, Denmark, Iceland, Switzerland, Finland, Netherlands, Canada, New Zealand, Australia, and Sweden. (America came in nineteenth.) Note how very similar these rankings are to the previous UN Human Development rankings. Ditto for the ten unhappiest societies, which are, by the World Happiness Report: Central African Republic, Burundi, Tanzania, Syria, Rwanda, Togo, Guinea, Liberia, South Sudan, Yemen, and Haiti.[266]

One of the most impressive of the recent indexes, in my view, is the Social Progress Index. This ambitious index uses fifty-two indicators, and measures and ranks 133 countries containing 95 percent of the world's population (the remaining 5 percent is due to unreliable data, usually because the population in question either resides in a disputed territory or one lacking a minimally effective governing structure). The fifty-two indicators are grouped into three general themes or "super-categories." Note how these speak very deeply to each of the seven components of the basic structure, as discussed above.

The three super-categories, along with sub-components, are:

1 **Basic Human Needs**. The degree to which people in the given country have: sufficient food and drinkable water, shelter, personal security (in the form of social peace, low rates of violent crime, and low casualties from traffic accidents), basic medical care (e.g., vaccinations, opportunities for regular medical check-ups), and basic sanitation (e.g., for personal hygiene, basic sewers, systems that separate drinkable water from waste and garbage).

2 **Foundations of Well-being**. The degree to which people in the given country have: access to basic knowledge and elementary education; access to information and communication, both high (computers/internet) and low (books, radio, newspapers); "health and wellness" (e.g., all the usual health indicators are included here, such as life expectancy, rates of mortality—death—and morbidity—various illnesses—and injuries in the workplace); and even "ecosystem sustainability."

3 **Opportunity**. The extent to which people in the given society enjoy: basic personal rights and freedoms (i.e., life, liberty, pursuit of happiness, non-discrimination), degrees of personal choice (e.g., regarding marriage, freedom of speech, and lack of censorship in the society), tolerance and inclusion, and access to advanced education and enhanced professional training (for socioeconomic mobility).

Such criteria are not without controversy, of course, but the Index is an ambitious, comprehensive, and ingenious attempt to measure such things as vital aspects of human happiness in the contemporary world. Putting all the data together within the three super-categories, the top ten countries in 2017 according to the Social Progress Index are: Denmark, Finland, Iceland,

Norway, Switzerland, Canada, Netherlands, Sweden, Australia, and New Zealand. (America comes in eighteenth.) *A crystal-clear consensus amongst the blended accounts of happiness and well-being can now, truly, be seen.* And at the bottom, too: Central African Republic, Afghanistan, Chad, Angola, Niger, Guinea, Yemen, Ethiopia, Sierra Leone, and Madagascar.[267]

Drawing Insights from "The World's Happiest Societies"

We've already considered extensively what the Latin Americans can teach us regarding their high scores on mainly subjective surveys, and how they display such particular strengths in terms of culture (regarding resilience, positivity, and tight, active, supportive social bonds). But, as stated, this only speaks to maybe two or three of the seven social institutions of the basic structure that determines the overall context within which we must pursue happiness. So, let's turn now to consider what the countries that come out on top in the blended surveys have to teach us. Those countries, we've just seen, are mainly developed ones, with particular strengths throughout Scandinavia, Switzerland, and the ex-British colonies of Australia, Canada, and New Zealand. Perhaps the best way to do this is to consider each institution within the basic structure and note the characteristics displayed by the strong countries.

The Economy

Each of the countries that scored highly on the blended measures of happiness sport "mixed economies," which blend free-market capitalism[268] with strong welfare state "enabling institutions," notably public education and state-funded health care.[269] (The comparative lack of both of the latter may be one reason why the US under-performs on nearly every one of these lists. As one of my friends has opined: "In America, there's just too much DIY.")

The mixed economy blends two vital ingredients of any plausible conception of happiness. The first, via the welfare state and its enabling institutions, concerns material subsistence, or the meeting of such vital human needs as food, water, clothing, and shelter. All the strong countries do well in this regard, with very low rates of homelessness, and either the direct provision of food and water or at least the payment of a welfare income sufficient, for those who cannot provide for themselves, to purchase such things. There's no way to "adjust" to a lack of vital needs—you must have them met, or suffer grievous injury and/or death. *They need to be taken care of before we can speak meaningfully of any robust pursuit of happiness.* Luckily, most adults seem capable of meeting their subsistence needs on their own. For those who cannot, through no fault of their own, the strong countries listed have welfare state institutions—funded through taxation of those who have, with consequent redistribution to those who lack—to serve this function.[270]

But it's a *mixed* economy—the other happiness element it satisfies is wide space for human freedom in the economic realm. The strong countries in this regard allow their citizens the freedom to choose their own careers and jobs, to try to negotiate the terms of such, and to organize themselves in such a way as to advance their economic interests. Citizens in these countries are free to become entrepreneurs and open up their own businesses, and as consumers, have a wide degree of choice regarding the kinds of product they wish to buy, ranging from residences and automobiles to vacations and restaurant meals.

Libertarians, however, argue that the only kind of economy consistent with human freedom is a *"laissez-faire"* (i.e., "leave it alone") economy, wherein there is little or no government intervention. Whatever the theoretical appeal of such a view, history has shown the real-world limits of this scenario: when attempted, it has led to severe ups-and-downs in the business cycle (with the worst low being the Great Depression in the

1930s). Moreover, historical experience with the welfare state since then has shown that it's possible to have both: a great deal of personal freedom and a resilient social safety net that tries to catch everyone at risk of falling below the minimum of material subsistence and vital human need. Libertarians counter that such a safety net comes at a cost—paid for by taxpayers—and that taxation is a kind of theft and restraint on freedom. This is an extreme view, one at odds with the flow of history: everyone knows the ground rules on taxation *going into* participation in an economy, so it can hardly be considered theft. Plus, benefits are provided in exchange for taxation (another disanalogy to theft, wherein the crook only takes). We all want to make more money and pay fewer taxes—regardless of how well we are doing financially—but the fact of the matter remains that tax revenues are needed to rescue those who, through no fault of their own, cannot provide for their own genuine and vital needs. What the strong countries in this regard show is that healthy welfare states need not come at the cost of misery, so long as they allow for many freedoms. Robust welfare states, funded through taxation, can contribute very clearly to the happiness of society overall. It boils down to this: we *don't* just want one thing, such as freedom. As important as freedom is, we also want other things—notably security regarding our vital human needs, and living in a society that makes real efforts to provide and care for its members, especially its most vulnerable.[271]

Government

Government is in some ways involved in almost all the other social institutions, between which there are robust interconnections (e.g., economic resources are required by all seven institutions, people need to be educated and healthy enough to participate in any social practice, etc.). But for our purposes, it's important to note that the strong countries in the blended happiness surveys are all democracies, with governments chosen through regular, free, fair, transparent, and public elections. Moreover, there is a division of powers within government itself, usually into legislative (law-making), executive (law enforcing or realizing), and judicial (law-interpreting) branches. The point of this division of powers is to serve as a check and balance against any one branch becoming too powerful. In each of the strong countries, there is both a perception, and generally a reality, of there being very low amounts of corruption within government (defined as those using their power for personal, especially financial, gain). This enhances public trust in government, which is associated rather robustly with how happy and proud people are to live in their own society. The perception of widespread corruption, by contrast, produces anger and disappointment, and a deep sense of unfairness and lack of equality and equal opportunity; "the system" then feels rigged against the majority of people.[272]

It's worth noting that, in each of the strong countries, the practice of politics is itself very moderate, "boring," and focused on practical issues. Politics are "middle-of-the-road" and not extreme, and political parties representing extreme ideologies only occupy the fringes and do not enjoy widespread support. (Note: the strong countries on the blended happiness lists don't include either America or Britain, and very recently there's been evidence of a rise in both places of immoderate politics—the Brexit vote in 2016, divisive presidential candidates in America, increased race, gender and social tension, and ongoing controversies about cynical foreign meddling in democratic processes. Such potentially disturbing trends towards "tribalism" and a rise in "identity politics" only serve to highlight how the comparatively bland, moderate, and practical politics of places like Canada or Switzerland tend to serve average happiness much better.)[273] Finally, each of the strong countries is committed, as they say, to the rule of law, as opposed to the rule of men. This means that the democracy in question is governed by a set of public rules, administered by professional civil servants hired on the basis of merit—and not by a small cadre of ultra-privileged elites whose personal tastes, preferences, and interests go on to become laws (as sadly happens in dictatorships, and in many of the bottom ten countries listed above).[274]

The Law

Speaking of the rule of law, law in each of the strong countries listed is a series of public and transparent rules whose aim is to achieve a clear, stable, consistent, and predictable framework within which people can make meaningful plans (e.g., in terms of career, family, buying property, raising children, etc.). Many of the weakest countries on these blended lists have particular weaknesses in this regard. Each of the strong countries also has a legal system strongly committed to individual human rights, each featuring a bill (or code, or charter) of rights designed to secure every person's fundamental interests (e.g., in life, liberty, security, and the pursuit of happiness). Notably, each of these countries guarantees an extensive list of personal freedoms: freedom of speech and expression; of belief and peaceful association; to marry the person, and pursue the job, of one's choosing; to participate in politics; from slavery and torture; and of movement, and to emigrate if one chooses. Another vital set of rights, which connects to personal security, concerns all rights of due process—protections that exist in case one is brought under arrest and to trial, such as the right to be informed of the nature of any charges, to a fair trial based on evidence, the right not to be subjected to cruel and unusual punishment if found guilty, and so on. The final set of rights, and the function of the law more generally in each of the top-scoring happiness countries, concerns equality: the right not to be discriminated against, and entitlements to basic equality as a citizen and to fundamental fairness, including efforts at equality of opportunity.[275]

Armed Force

A prime function of government is to attend to the physical protection of its residents, in particular from criminals within and from any potential foreign invaders. It does this through the branches of police and military, respectively. The strong countries in this regard all have police services and military forces that are under the control of, and budgeted by, democratically elected civilian authorities. (This is in contrast to military dictatorships wherein the military is actually *part* of the government and makes public policy decisions on its own.) The strong countries have professionally trained police and military, and are staffed on the basis of merit. Low levels of corruption exist within such services, and they are subject to clear oversight authorities empowered to investigate and prosecute any alleged corruption, misuse of force, or illegal, rogue behaviour. In general, such forces exist for the sake of ensuring physical security—another obvious human need—and their role is to offer a measured, proportionate, and disciplined (but still effective) response to any malign violent threat. Most importantly, for each of the strong countries on the blended measures, there is social peace and the rule of law: the society is not war-torn (as in bottom-scoring countries like Afghanistan and Syria), there are low levels of violent crime (in contrast to many Sub-Saharan African countries on the bottom-most lists), and in general people feel confident counting on their bodily integrity and physical security being free from violent injury.[276]

Enabling Institutions

Regarding the welfare state protections afforded by the strong countries, the big institutions are education and health care. Health care is perhaps the more obvious connection to well-being, as we've seen throughout that injury, illness, and certainly death are major threats to human happiness. Each of the well-performing countries in the blended rankings has strong, publicly funded, and universally accessible health care systems—and each deliver strong "health outcomes" (i.e., positive results between entry into and exit from the system). All the bottom ten countries on each of the lists—by contrast—have thin to non-existent public health care systems.

Though health care has the more obvious and visceral connection to well-being, only a moment's thought is needed to see how basic education is likewise a vital enabling tool for the pursuit of happiness. By basic education, we notably mean literacy and numeracy. The strong countries on the blended lists sport over 97 percent basic literacy in their adult population (whereas the bottom ones can be as low as 20 percent, with none above 60 percent). Literacy is obviously a vital skill in the modern world, as a way to get information crucial to one's health, happiness, and well-being. If one cannot read, one is locked out of the online world, and blocked from even elementary education, to say nothing of high school, advanced education, and the opportunities therein. A very sad fact about illiteracy is that, disproportionately, it is young girls and women who suffer most. Often, this is because the right to an equal education is not present, much less enforced: some regions still see educating women as a waste of resources, as their perceived function is to get married and care for children. However, the strong countries show that, when equal investment is made in the education of girls and women, it correlates with strong results in other positive qualities for a community, such as average happiness, social peace, and low rates of crime.[277]

There's increasing evidence that basic numeracy is nearly as important as basic literacy, and moreover that there's a correlation between them. Rates of numeracy are not yet as well tracked and verified as literacy rates, but many researchers think that numeracy rates are probably a bit lower than literacy rates in general. And numeracy *is* vital to people's well-being and happiness—for instance, in connection with good personal finances and issues of work/income, as described last chapter. And there is interesting new research that poor numeracy can lead to serious health problems (e.g., making mistakes regarding medications—quantities and timings of pills). Freedom from such ignorance, and its harmful consequences, is vital for happiness in today's world.[278]

The strong countries on the blended surveys, in addition to having very high rates of literacy and numeracy, also have strong and universally accessible systems of public education, ensuring free, quality education at least until the end of high school. The strong communities also have some of the highest rates of post-secondary attendance and degree attainment in the world. The top ten list in this regard is nearly identical to the blended happiness lists, except that America, South Korea, and Japan now appear. Canada scores at the top, with Australia, New Zealand, and Scandinavia all present and accounted for. Education not only provides knowledge and training; it also provides upward social mobility, enhancing equality in a given society.[279]

It may go without saying, but the countries that score at the bottom of the blended happiness lists also have pronounced weaknesses with regard to the enabling institutions, with very low rates of literacy, numeracy, and educational attainment, very poor health care infrastructure, and high rates of preventable death and disease. Partially, this is because of the expense of having such institutions up and running—and many such countries at the bottom are extremely poor. But there are other reasons, too: armed conflict destroying existing infrastructure (e.g., Syria and Central Africa), and persistent discriminatory beliefs about gender equality for females (e.g., Afghanistan).[280]

Family

All the strong countries feature legal systems that respect the freedom to found a family and marry a person of one's choosing, as well as to divorce if things don't work out. There are robust systems for ensuring that, should children be produced within a marriage that goes on to fail, the children will still get the resources and support they need to grow into able and participating adults. As lawyers might say, in these countries there are strong and effective "family law regimes." These fundamental family and family planning rights and systems are almost completely lacking in the bottom ten countries on the various blended happiness accounts (often, it must be said, because of deep discrimination against women).[281]

Also relevant is the fact that each of the strong countries tends to invest heavily in supporting young parents and children—for instance, through tax breaks or subsidies, generous maternity and paternity leaves, and quality daycares to help ease the burden, especially on young mothers who may wish to return to the work force. Europe excels in this regard, with countries such as Sweden being inspiringly generous (in contrast, say, to both Canada and the United States, which have a long way to go to catch up).[282]

Almost all the strong countries allow for lesbian and gay marriages, and thus make tolerance for difference, non-discrimination, and concern for inclusion key values within their conception of the family and their family law systems.

Culture

We've spoken of culture in connection with the countries that seem to do the best in this regard—namely the Latin American ones. But in the strong countries within the blended rankings, we can see many things occurring in connection with culture which we know to augment the average person's happiness. First, the strong countries—as democracies with robust welfare states—all have clear commitments to some form of equality, non-discrimination, inclusion, and tolerance for difference. These ideals aren't always respected or perfectly realized, of course, and in many ways remain ongoing projects, but clearly they exist *as ideals*.

The strong countries additionally have very high rates of computer and internet access. Many experts have argued that, in today's world, having such is vital both for access to empowering information, as well as for making connections to others in ways that would've been impossible for previous generations.[283]

Other experts have argued that most of the strong blended countries are northern, with histories of mutual help and community efforts being necessary survival tools in the face of harsh environments. This has led to there being more social "caring" and mutual investment than what's present in other nations. Perhaps, though, the appearance of such southern countries as Australia and New Zealand in these lists challenges such speculations. Perhaps more relevant is the issue of population. As we've seen in connection with the subjective studies, none of the strong countries on the blended lists are very large in terms of population size. Canada is the biggest, with about 35 million people. Australia is smaller than Canada, at 21 million, and all the Scandinavian countries are much smaller still. *There seems to be a clear, interesting connection between average happiness and the population size of one's country.* No doubt it has something to do with both a feeling of togetherness and mutual regard, enhancing a sense of equality as well as perhaps a sense of freedom and control. One is not lost in the sea of humanity in a smaller country. And the very big countries—America, Brazil, China, India, Indonesia, and Russia—have, of course, much greater practical challenges at meeting the needs and wants of such massive populations. These connections are, perhaps, under-developed in happiness studies: small communities, or the feeling of being within a smaller community, might augment average happiness.[284]

The very strong blended countries sport two additional cultural features in this regard: they have high levels of "social trust" and high levels of "civil society" activity. Social trust refers to low rates of corruption (and perceived corruption) and high rates of trust in the well-meaningness both of public officials and, more broadly, the general populace. Excellent public surveys have been done in this regard, asking people to what degree they trust their neighbours. They are usually asked general "trust" or "faith in people" questions, as well as specific ones, such as: "If you dropped a ten-dollar bill in a public space, how likely is it do you think someone would return it to you, if they saw you drop it?" All the strong blended countries (especially the Scandinavian ones) scored very high on such surveys. The region reporting the lowest levels of social trust is Africa, followed by parts of Asia, Eastern Europe, South America, and the MENA.

"Civil society" refers to the sum total of all non-governmental associations, and broader social activity and participation. Civil society associations range from literal non-governmental organizations (NGOs) such as Greenpeace and Oxfam, to religious organizations and volunteer charities, cooking clubs and reading groups, sports leagues and fan clubs, and support groups for the chronically afflicted. Historically, in non-democratic societies, the government clamps down on all such activity, so as to keep its finger in every pie and not allow any organization to rival the power and prestige of the state. In democratic societies, by contrast, such activity flourishes. Robust civil society activity and participation increases happiness and pleasure by augmenting social connections and activity, by demonstrating a society's commitment to personal liberty and freedom of association, and by strengthening the means by which any individual can pursue those things that most interest and matter to them.[285]

Summarizing Insights from the World's Happiest Societies

There's perhaps no better conclusion than to summarize what the world's happiest societies do best, *the results of which are amazingly consistent across all tools of measurement.* The basic structures of those societies that score the highest on blended measures of subjective happiness and objective well-being tend to include, feature, or foster:

- a government that is democratically elected, with low levels of corruption, wherein most people believe their public officials are sincerely attempting to augment the common welfare

- a "mixed economy," which blends the freedom, wealth, and productivity of a free-market capitalist system with robust welfare state intervention, notably to ensure universal access to basic (yet high quality) education and health care

- high rates of literacy and numeracy, and ready access to the internet

- high levels of social trust and civil society activity (and they tend overall to be smaller in population)

- social peace, as the society is governed by clear, stable, and public laws (as opposed to the personal wishes of a small group of private elites)

- armed forces—police and military—which are under the control of civilian authorities, and have as their function the prevention of crime and/or the keeping of peace and rule of law

- strong "family law" regimes that place value on freedom of choice as well as on gender equality, and a clear commitment to investing in the well-being of young children

In these societies, there is a firm overall commitment to *three crucial elements*: 1) to substantial social help for everyone in general; 2) considerable space for personal freedom; and 3) equality, non-discrimination, tolerance, and inclusion. In practice, this three-fold commitment might sometimes involve complex trade-offs. But that's the way it goes; the strong countries tend to approach such trade-offs in a moderate, practical way as opposed to a rigid and ideological one. All the strong societies, in this regard, tend to have moderate political parties and practices aimed at improving people's lives as the litmus test of values, as opposed to fulfilling any extreme theory or radical orientation toward life.

Happiness and Human Rights

Well over a dozen years ago, I wrote a book on human rights. I argued that everyone should have the highest-priority entitlement to an abstract set of objects, which, in an attempt to make it stick in one's mind, I labelled "The Foundational Five":

1 Physical Security

2 Material Subsistence

3 Personal Freedom

4 Elemental Equality (by which I meant a combination of non-discrimination and an equal distribution of rights)

5 Social Recognition (as a person and rights holder)

I then argued that any given, specific human right we plausibly wish to claim boils down to one, or some combination, of these Foundational Five. These five things are truly "the all-purpose means" we each need to pursue anything we may find valuable and enjoyable: they denote what it means to have, and lead, a minimally good life.[286]

The more I reflect on these values, and of what the happiest societies share in common, the more I come to believe the enormous overlap *cannot* be a coincidence. When I think about happiness, and especially what social institutions can do to advance human happiness, I become convinced that what *social institutions are best designed to do is to secure our human rights*, and, once that has been achieved, to then leave people to be free to pursue further happiness as they see fit.[287] I see the pursuit of happiness and the pursuit of human rights as forming a fundamental partnership: a society that cares about happiness is one that does whatever it can to realize the human rights claims of all its citizens, not merely the majority. It's of special relevance to those with chronic conditions that their unique needs be taken into account by caring and rights-respecting societies, and not to get lost in the shuffle of accommodating only the majority.[288]

Concluding Thoughts for the Chronically Afflicted

Of course, all the preceding values and institutions—described in connection with the strong group of happy and rights-respecting countries—help the chronically afflicted in some capacity. We might even say that this institutional alignment provides such people with the best odds for having their basic needs met and their fundamental interests satisfied, allowing them to pursue personal happiness. The strong focus on individual rights, democracy, freedom of speech, and political and civil society participation allows all people to advocate for their interests and/ or for new accommodations. Society has progressed enormously during our lifetimes in terms of accommodating those with special educational needs, as well as those with physical mobility problems and other unusual health challenges. Of course, *every society still has work to do*, even if only to better realize the good abstract commitments already on display. But the chronically afflicted have special interests in the following areas:

- **material subsistence**, for those who, for provable medical reasons, genuinely cannot work or provide for themselves

- **the quality and affordability of health care**, with new technologies and treatments offered in a timely way

- **the quality of affordable education**, both as a way to ensure their own best odds at good employment and opportunity, and educating the general public about different chronic conditions so as to diminish prejudice and to augment accommodation

- good and affordable **access to the internet**, to connect with others of like-condition, and to find out about their rights and the development of helpful new treatments and technologies

- **robust civil society activity and encouragement**, perhaps including government funding, so that people can organize groups for themselves, along with fundraisers, activism, and awareness-raising

- measures regarding equality and, especially, **non-discrimination and an ever-growing tolerance for difference**, with prime emphasis placed on the inclusion and welcoming of those who are different and vulnerable.

One time-honoured, well-meaning, and persuasive way to measure both the justice and caring of a given society is how well it treats its most vulnerable members—and how hard it strives to protect those who are ill, injured, weak, and malfunctioning. Societies that historically have not made serious efforts in this regard—or, worse, have gone out of their way to target such people with cruelty, discrimination, exploitation, and/or violence—are societies that we now judge to have been brutally inhumane and dreadfully unhappy. As we pause here, mid-way through our investigations, and reflect on what it means to pursue happiness in a concrete way—to nurture it productively in everyone—we cannot forget the manifest importance of structuring our societies in as helpful and as decent a way as we can.

CHAPTER 6

Interpersonal Relationships

Studies by Martin Seligman and Ed Diener show that the difference between (merely) happy people and the very happiest of people is precisely the degree to which they each experience love and close personal relationships.[289] Other studies by Harry Reis and Shelly Gable conclude that good relationships are the single most important source of life satisfaction and emotional well-being for people *across all cultures*.[290] Systematic studies have shown that the reason most often mentioned for people entering into psychological therapy is the breakdown of an important relationship. Indeed, when people are asked to reflect on bad events in their lives, and/or about "where things went wrong," the overwhelming majority will reply by mentioning a relationship breakdown—be it with a parent, a sibling, an authority figure, a close friend, a romantic partner, or a child.[291] We've already spoken about the importance of relationships, and about us being "social animals" by nature. But the above research findings go well beyond anything captured in those straightforward propositions: good relationships aren't merely important; *they may be the single most important thing, after vital needs, to the pursuit of happiness*.[292]

The need for proper social institutions is still there, and irreplaceable. But once they've achieved their job of securing a decent basic structure (last chapter), we as individuals turn elsewhere for fulfillment and happiness. This "looking elsewhere" can be through work (Chapter 4), through pursuing pleasure and flow (Chapter 3), or—as is the case for many of us—through personal relationships. The point of this chapter is to consider such things while adding the unique perspectives and pressing concerns of those with chronic conditions.

We've seen throughout this book that those with chronic conditions have multiple and potent constraints on their pursuit of happiness. Unfortunately, the issue of interpersonal relationships is no exception—and this is especially important, given the impact of such relationships on one's level of happiness and life satisfaction. As I write this, I'm reading the poignant and gripping graphic novel *Epileptic*, by French author and artist David B. It's a fictionalized memoir, detailing how a family dealt with the epilepsy suffered by their eldest son, Jean-Francois. The artist is depicted as the youngest son, and describes his family's struggles with brutal yet touching honesty. The epilepsy and its sudden seizure attacks call forth genuine empathy, care, help, and love, and bring the family closer in a range of ways as they close ranks to deal with the challenges of having an afflicted child/sibling. Simultaneously, David B. is frank about how the disease also creates distance, loneliness, puzzlement (as no one can fully understand what the eldest brother experiences), inconvenience, frustration, struggle, and—because of those things—at times a total *lack* of empathy, and even a kind of impatience, anger, and contempt. The eldest brother, Jean-Francois, in many ways traps the other family members by his disease and the frequency of his seizures. David B. writes about sometimes actually punching and kicking Jean-Francois, in the midst of his seizures, as an aggressive expression of frustration with this entrapment. The author/artist imaginatively diagrams the epilepsy as being an enormous, hideous, inescapable, contorting snake/crocodile/dragon, which has the whole family in its menacing clutches as it lashes out with destructive unpredictability. Unfortunately for the family, it's not a story with a happy ending.[293] Similar accounts, I'm sure, could be offered by many of the chronically afflicted, as to how their illness or injury has had enormous impact on their interpersonal relationships, both positive and negative. We shall consider these in detail throughout this chapter. There are, after all, a zillion books about love and friendship in general. But there aren't very many about how those with chronic conditions can try to navigate their challenges, and still be successful and loving in cultivating close interpersonal relationships. The connection between relationships and happiness is vital, and demands extended and enthusiastic treatment.

Two Theories: Head vs. Heart

In contemporary psychology, there exist two prevailing and rival theories about the nature of love and why people seek it out. These are: 1) the *benefit* theory, which is highly cognitive and thus appeals to the head; and 2) the *attachment* theory, which is more affective, and thus expresses (as it were) the desires of the heart. Let's consider the content of these theories.

1) Benefit Theory

The basic insight here is that humans get involved in relationships—including ones of deep friendship and romantic love—because of the benefits (both real and perceived) of doing so. These benefits are robust, both in quantity and quality. Friends and loved ones provide us with:

- companionship, and warm, non-task-focused personal interaction where we can be ourselves

- goods (e.g., gifts)

- services (e.g., emotional support when we are down)

- information and feedback (e.g., advice)

- money or an equivalent (particularly with close friends and partners)

- physical affection, including (with romantic partners) sexual contact and release

- social status (e.g., basic belonging or enhanced standing)

- help, perhaps combining many of the above, with the achievement of our individual goals, which we know are conducive to happiness

Finally, friends and loved ones provide our most immediate and effective rescue from the opposite—loneliness, isolation, and alienation—and all the negative consequences associated therein. (Interestingly, in January 2018, the British government created the world's first national minister tasked with decreasing loneliness and its bad results.) Research has shown there's a strong correlation between self-reported, long-term loneliness and such negative health consequences as higher rates of depression, addiction, and even disease and death. Having a robust social life, by contrast, has been linked to both longevity and good health during life.[294]

In terms of predicting the success or failure of a close relationship, benefit theory proposes the following: there must be a perceived proportionate benefit of the relationship to all parties involved, relative to the costs of being so involved. (The "costs" of being in a relationship include: time and effort involved, any outlay of resources, any negative emotions and experiences felt alongside positive ones, and opportunities foregone by investing in one relationship as opposed to another or a different activity.) So long as everyone in the relationship feels they are getting about as much out of it as they are putting into it, the relationship will thrive and continue. If, by contrast, one or both parties feel either "overpaid" or "underpaid," it will probably become unstable and end. Those who feel overpaid by the other person come to feel guilty and unworthy, and their discomfort can lead them to draw away. Whereas those who feel underpaid come to feel resentful and superior, believing that they can get a better deal with someone else, and hence move to end the relationship on that basis.[295]

As Chris Peterson notes, the proportionate equality of benefits to costs doesn't have to be exactly literal, and it doesn't have to refer to *every* dimension within a relationship. (Though, it often does: people tend to be with others of very similar levels of physical attractiveness, for example, and marry those of the same ethnic and religious group, or of the same socioeconomic class.) It is at least possible for inequalities in one dimension of a relationship to be "made up for" in another, as in the clichéd case of a highly attractive younger woman marrying an older and less attractive man who nevertheless has many financial assets.[296]

Influential relationship researcher Elaine Hatfield has noted that, in addition to the roughly proportionate perceived equality of overall benefits to costs, benefit theory (some label it "equity theory") further predicts that long-term romantic relationships (such as marriages) will tend to endure in so far as: 1) both partners remain satisfied, and perceive an *ongoing* equity of benefits and costs between them; 2) there are no compelling alternatives for either person to pursue; and 3) each participant has already invested a lot of time and effort into the relationship.[297]

As common-sensical as benefit theory is, and as true as it *must* be on some level, there are nevertheless serious limits to it as an overall account of why we get into close, interpersonal relationships, and why we stay in them and invest so much of our time, effort, and energy into their maintenance and success. These limits notably include:

- Benefit theory struggles to account for altruism or self-sacrificing behaviour in general. It must re-cast such behaviour as being motivated by giving pleasure, or by being done in expectation of future self-sacrifice on the part of the other. That may well be true, but many people find it an inadequate account of many acts of self-sacrifice in a relationship, as when one partner makes a big career sacrifice for the sake of the other, or in many cases of how much parents willingly give up for the sake of the success and flourishing of their children, with no realistic expectation of any kind of proportionate "pay-back."[298]

- Relatedly, benefit theory struggles to account for the fact that most people will say that, other things being equal, they find it more pleasant to give than to receive. We saw this in chapters 3 and 4: experiments have established that spending for the benefit of others almost always brings more happiness and pride than spending the same amount of money on oneself.[299]

- As Peterson says, no one really wants to think of close relationships in this kind of bloodless, purely cognitive, and strategically self-interested kind of way. It seems like a mode of thought better suited to a business deal than to any kind of close, happy, personal relationship.[300]

- Finally, even if researchers can demonstrate how, in the background, some kind of calculation might be going on, we don't *experience* friendship and love relationships in this kind of way. The subjective experience—certainly of romantic love—is simply different than what objective benefit theory views as going on. According to Peterson, we don't have friends and significant others because we think they'll benefit us; *we have them because we like them*. We have sincere affection for them, which goes above and beyond calculations of perceived long-term selfish net benefit.[301]

2) Attachment Theory

And so, this is where the alternative account begins: precisely with a conviction that an interpersonal relationship is more about affectionate and positive attachment than it is about an expectation of receiving enough benefits from a person to make it worth one's while.[302]

Two sets of psychological experiments have been foundational in the attachment theory of relationships. One was by Harry Harlow, the other by John Bowlby.

Harlow's experiment involved taking baby monkeys away from their mothers and families, and raising them in a controlled environment. In particular, the monkeys were raised in a cage with two kinds of surrogate mother. Both surrogates were crude, inanimate objects made to look roughly like a monkey. The first was made of wood and wire, but had fake breasts and nipples out of which real, nourishing milk could be drawn. The second surrogate also had a wood structure, but was covered in warm, comfortable material that would be pleasing for the baby monkeys to cling to and touch. This second surrogate had no fake breasts and no real milk. Harlow was testing the truth and limits of benefit theory. If benefit theory is true, and higher mammals such as humans get involved in relationships mainly for the real and perceived benefits, then the baby mon-keys should've only cared about the first, wire surrogate. What the experiments showed, however, is that while the monkeys would indeed negotiate the wire to get at the milk as hunger demanded, they otherwise overwhelmingly preferred the com-pany of the soft, felt-covered second surrogate. In particular, whenever the baby monkeys were presented with a frightening situation, they would go to the second surrogate, and climb all over and cling to "her." They sought no such companionship, support, and comfort from the wire/milk mother. Harlow con-cluded that it's false to suppose that the ruthless calculation of selfish benefit is all that's going on; he posited a natural need for a warm, soothing, affectionate bond.[303]

Subsequent experiments have confirmed this. Longer-term studies showed that monkeys raised in individual isolation—with all their vital physical needs satisfied—developed and displayed pathological behaviours for their species, including: repeatedly banging their heads against an inanimate object or wall; displaying excessive (even morbid) amounts of fear; and/or more troublingly, biting themselves repeatedly.[304] John Bowlby's studies focused on raising orphans in Europe in the immediate aftermath of WWII. Bowlby arrived at similar find-ings with human children: even when their physical needs were completely met, if they did not feel a close and caring attach-ment to other humans, they went on to display pathological behaviour. Interestingly, this included repeated head banging, but ranged all the way up to more multifaceted conditions like a lack of empathy and even clinical depression. Bowlby inferred the existence of a natural need for affectionate attachment and declared that, should such be thwarted (especially during child-hood development), pathology and twisted psychological growth would occur. Bowlby's reports changed how orphanages were run at the time, adding to the duties of those running them seri-ous efforts at forging close, affectionate bonds between orphan and caregiver, and with lots of opportunities for positive, affectionate interactions with their peers.[305]

Contemporary biochemical studies have shown fascinating further evidence of natural need in this regard. Remember our discussion in Chapter 3 of the "happiness chemicals" oxytocin and dopamine? Researchers have determined that, during social interaction—and emphatically during skin-to-skin contact with another human—oxytocin is released throughout the blood stream. During pregnancy, birth, and after-birth, oxytocin is produced in large quantities within mothers and, interestingly, even within fathers (albeit to a lesser degree). Some researchers have thus labelled oxytocin "the cuddle hormone," or even "the love drug." (Indeed, there's evidence of connection between the action of oxytocin and the release of dopamine, a proven producer of pleasure, reinforcement, and relaxation, with the potential for some addictive effects.)[306] Many of us can attest to, at some point in our lives, having been involved in an intense relationship that seemed to produce drug-like effects of pleasure, heightened involvement and excitement, obsession and withdrawal-like symptoms, and of course the desire for more and more (and more!) contact and shared company. Neuroimaging studies have shown that brain activity differs in people when shown a picture of someone they love versus photos of strangers or even photos of people they know and like but who remain just friends. The same studies have revealed that, when shown photos of their own children, almost all mothers experience a deactivation in the brain regions responsible for such "relationship saboteurs" as social comparison and negative judgment. As Peterson summarizes, the contemporary micro-level biochemical research experiments seem to show that "our biological bodies are designed to draw us to one another . . . [o]ur biology teaches us that relationships in and of themselves matter."[307] We mentioned in previous chapters what must be the ultimate evolutionary underpinnings behind such powerful, unconscious, and objective responses, as our earliest ancestors of course needed to band together in order to survive and thrive. Evolutionary theorists and anthropologists have concluded that the earliest humans probably lived together, and travelled together, in small family-like bands of twenty-five to thirty people—large enough to have an effective division of labour but also small enough for people to know each other well and to cement their togetherness with genuine liking, affection, and even love.[308]

Clearly, attachment theory has a lot going for it. It can explain how we are willing to engage in self-sacrificing behaviour and even get gratification out of doing so, and it can account for a lot of seemingly odd and/or extreme behaviour in interpersonal relationships, such as the heightened attention and excitement—and withdrawal effects—associated with the strongest romantic attractions. Yet it, too, has its limits.

The biggest and most obvious is that following the dictates of attachment theory—or, more precisely, acting as if attachment theory provides a complete explanation of, and motivation for, close interpersonal relationships—can produce bad results or lead to trouble. In particular, encouraging people to believe that attachment is all there is might lead some to keep up with relationships that have become destructive, or that are not in their long-term self-interest. There's evidence that victims in abusive relationships do indeed think of them much more in terms of attachment than in terms of a reciprocal exchange of benefits, and that it can take such victimized people great and strenuous—and very costly—efforts to end such relationships, and strive for something healthier and better. Some studies have found that women in abusive relationships, where substance abuse is a factor, on average try to leave their partner six times (!) before successfully moving on.[309]

The other limit is that, whether in the background or foreground, most adults at least consider the relative distribution of costs and benefits involved in creating and maintaining any given relationship. There's no point in downplaying that we do this, or suggesting that this is a purely mercenary perspective on the part of heartless bastards. While it might involve such an unfortunate perspective in some, for most people it simply involves the application of practical intelligence into a consideration of how best to spend one's finite time, resources, and emotional energy.

We conclude with Peterson then, on how the divide between benefit theory and attachment theory is indeed a false dichotomy, and that *robust aspects of both* are required in any comprehensive account of how we get into interpersonal relationships, what we get out of them, and how we most like to think and talk about them. We form affectionate attachments naturally, and there's evidence that such connections are deeply rooted in our historical experience as a species, and even in the very structure of our bodies. However, there's no doubt that attachments can sometimes be irrationally held and result in harmful relationships. Benefit theory provides a nice outside limit, or "rationality check," on the degree to which we should allow such attachments to dictate our decisions about interconnection. Similarly, we can freely admit that we *do* usually have some kind of (at least rough) consideration of comparative costs and benefits when it comes to many of our relationships. While doing so can be smart, practical, and in some ways unavoidable, it does not capture the full range of human experience, or the profound value of close, personal connection. Our comprehensive account can be depicted thusly:

FIG 14 A BLENDED ACCOUNT, INTEGRATING BOTH ATTACHMENT AND BENEFIT

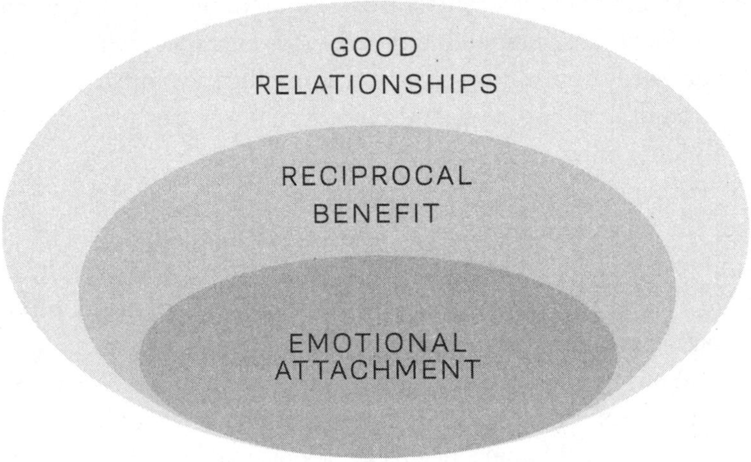

GOOD
RELATIONSHIPS

RECIPROCAL
BENEFIT

EMOTIONAL
ATTACHMENT

Chronic Conditions, and Their Impact on Cognitive Benefit and Affectionate Attachment

In his bestselling book *The Five Love Languages*, Gary Chapman describes different types of approach to close, interpersonal relationships and how, to be successful, participants in such relationships need to understand each other's approach and make efforts at "translating" each other's style and "love language" into one that allows for effective two-way communication and mutual understanding. I like the metaphor in general, and it certainly seems apt for discussing potential roadblocks that a chronic condition, injury, or disability might put in the way of relationships.[310]

Using the tools given to us by the benefit and attachment theories, we can detail how the onset of a chronic condition might affect afflicted persons as well as any significant others in their lives. If not careful, this could easily lead to a "lost in translation" situation, which damages or even destroys their relationships.* It's my view that using these theories allows us to speak more clearly and insightfully to each other regarding exactly what is going on, in the context of a relationship challenged by a chronic condition.

It seems fair to say that a person's having of a chronic condition cannot logically *decrease* the costs of a relationship and *probably will increase them*, perhaps substantially. It may require more effort both on the part of the afflicted and of the other, and the condition may—nasty as it sounds—call into the other's mind alternative, non-afflicted partners who might seem more attractive. The crucial thing on the cost side is how much said costs are allowed to increase before they impact not only relationship satisfaction but also the affectionate attachment residing at the core of the relationship. Whether this happens will be a mixture of both objective circumstances outside one's control as well as the subjective effort one is willing to put into the absolutely vital task of *keeping your costs under control*. What are some of the added relationship costs that we can predict alongside many (or most) chronic conditions?

---

* See the thoughtful 2003 movie *Lost in Translation*. Becoming sick is somewhat like getting lost in a foreign culture, and looking for familiar, reliable ways to navigate such. Another effective movie depicting how couples can often speak "different languages" within their relationships, leading to problems, is the 1986 movie *Children of a Lesser God*. The female lead, played by Marlee Matlin (who won an Oscar for her portrayal), compounds the gender difference with a disability—deafness.

- The afflicted person has *less time to devote to relationships*, as they've got to devote time trying to manage this new and pervasive thing: the condition itself.

- The condition and/or its treatment may cause *fatigue and/ or pain*. This renders the afflicted less physically capable of producing the energy and good spirits needed to nurture a relationship.

- In the case of romantic relationships, such fatigue/pain/affliction might *negatively affect the giving of physical affection and sexual intimacy*.

- The condition may cause *uncertainty and/or fear*. This in turn causes stress, certainly to the afflicted but also to their close relationships. It's well documented that such stress negatively impacts intimacy, the ability to relax, even a willingness to pay attention to the needs of others.[311]

- The condition and/or its treatment may increase *the moodiness and grumpiness* of the afflicted, which can in turn challenge the peace and satisfaction of interpersonal relationships. In this regard, others are targeted precisely because they're available, and come to bear the burden of any inability of the afflicted to contain their frustration.

- Trying to manage the condition effectively may render the afflicted *too controlled and rigid* in their personality, and in how they manage their time and tasks.

- Depending on the kind of chronic condition, it *can increase the "time toll" and financial costs of the relationship*. This is especially true if the condition changes the employment status of the afflicted, brings substantial new charges related to medications and/or treatment, and/or affects things like the afflicted's ability to drive.

- Most seriously, we know that chronic conditions tend to drive the afflicted into themselves. They tend to become *more socially withdrawn, more introverted, and—it needs to be said—more self-centred.*

In spite of its reputation for dispassionate "accounting," we can see how benefit theory actually provides a vocabulary for articulating concerns and frustrations potentially experienced by those with chronic conditions, as well as their partners and/or intimate connections (e.g., close friends, family members). It thus enables both better communication and a more targeted problem-solving approach, as people move beyond raw emotions (like frustration and anger) into brainstorming solutions to these potential issues.

Note how, in spite of some of these increased costs, *none of the previously mentioned relationship benefits disappear upon the advent of a chronic condition.* Even those who are ill or injured can still provide many or all of those items. So, it's not as though the advent of such a condition spells immediate disaster for close relationships. And, clearly, one can be (or become) deeply attached to someone with a chronic condition, and such a person can feel profound attachment in return. Even the added costs mentioned above don't *always* happen, or at least not to a damaging degree. To go through them more systematically:

- Realistically, there's only so much time in the day. Thus, added time for managing a new condition means less time for other things. But it doesn't have to mean less time for relationships: one can find ways to save time elsewhere (e.g., time spent watching TV or being online). Usually, there's a period of adjustment with a chronic condition, beyond which things can normalize. Some patience may be required, along with a long-term perspective and a commitment to mutual support.

- Gaining as much knowledge about, and control over, one's condition as possible can mitigate uncertainty and fear. Knowledge needs to be shared so that all parties understand each other: what the afflicted is going through, and why they might be behaving in a sub-optimal way from time to time.

- Information sharing should cut down on outbursts of frustration and anger. The main thing is always to be mindful of the fact that *those closest to you are the least deserving of any kind of angry outburst* on your part. Love and affection, not frustration and anger, are the things most likely to make you happiest over the long term.

- Next chapter contains an overview of, as well as many tips and resources for, *making one's body as healthy and strong as it can be, consistent with one's condition.* Such things—especially exercise and good sleep hygiene—directly counteract fatigue, and even aid with pain and mood control. They also enhance sexual desire. In any event, there are a zillion ways to share soothing, enjoyable physical affection with people apart from sexual contact. (See the note for further practical sources, notably David Linden's on touch.[312])

- In terms of straightforward financial costs, the reader is directed to Chapter 4, on work and income. Clearly, *more income and better medical benefits would be of great service.* Yet, there may be substantial constraints in this regard. The loss of a driver's licence, for example, can be a significant challenge.

- As for the most serious challenge—introversion and social withdrawal—I direct the reader to the forthcoming chapters (8 and 9) on mental and emotional hygiene.

In summary, the realities of chronic conditions may well increase the costs to one's relationships. But they don't have to; or, they don't have to on a ruinous basis. One can resist this by using the many pieces of advice given throughout this book. One is also logically free, and encouraged, to focus on "upping the benefits" as an effective way to counteract the increase in costs. Each of the below sections is designed to offer concrete tips on precisely how to do that.

One of my favourite tips in this regard draws directly on benefit theory, and comes from Sonja Lyubomirsky. It's a nice way to end this section, and pave the way for further thoughts. She notes that, when most people use the cost/benefit approach in considering their relationships, they do so from their own first-person perspective (i.e., "What are the costs and benefits *to me?*" "Is this worth *my* while?" and so on). This is natural, yet not always helpful—and certainly not the whole story. It also ties in nicely with the language/translation metaphor: we're all committed, in the first instance, to talking about relationships from the perspective of our own costs and benefits, resulting in these little personal "bubbles" of interpretation and potential misunderstanding. Lyubomirsky urges us to do two things to help us "pop the bubbles," to see and communicate more clearly with each other. Instead of always coming at things from the first-person perspective, consider as well the other person's perspective: *What are the costs and benefits to that other person?* As she suggests, two things might follow:

As stated, you might consider whether *you are doing enough to provide enough benefits to that other person to make it worth their while*, especially if you are the one imposing increased costs.

As an interesting and quite fun exercise, take some time to consider, write down, and appreciate how *you* might be the one currently getting "the better deal."[313]

Aristotle on Love and Friendship

Let's now turn to this book's theoretical roots for inspiration. Aristotle helpfully adds new things to our reflections; he actually thought very highly of love and friendship. This may come as something of a surprise, given his stressing what might seem like the selfish pursuit of personal excellence (or *eudaimonia*) and his recommendation to pursue *either* a life of advancing knowledge *or* one of sociopolitical engagement: demanding careers often seen at odds with a robust personal life. But this should be no surprise at all. Aristotle is, after all, the man who declared that human beings are, by nature, social and political animals, and thus *we can only find true fulfillment in ongoing association with others.* He actually favoured a much tighter and more communal social structure than what any contemporary "egoist" or "individualist"[314] would feel comfortable with. Aristotle was keenly interested in love and friendship, and wrote several extended chapters specifically devoted to the subject.[315] This is rather unique among history's top philosophers, who generally shy away from such "touchy-feely" subjects. Of course, Aristotle realized how important love and friendship are to most people. But his main theoretical interest in the subject was how he was convinced that, for a person to secure their fullest individual potential they need not only support from their parents while growing up, and not merely decent background social institutions to secure the ongoing context of their lives; they also require more intense and involved mature social relationships, like we see in the very best friendships and close, love-based relationships.

There are three basic kinds of friendship, according to Aristotle (he uses "friendship" in a very broad way). These correspond to what he saw as the three basic reasons why someone might like someone else, and view them as an associate or friend. First is pleasure, of the sort detailed in Chapter 3. If you provide someone with pleasure, you have a *pleasure friendship*. Or perhaps you like someone because they provide you with some benefit or other (seen by Aristotle as moving beyond sensory pleasure to include a useful good or service). Shared mutual benefits are the basis of *utility friendship*. Finally, you might like someone because you think they are a genuinely good person, and you admire that goodness and are attracted to it. Aristotle was especially interested in the kind of goodness associated with his own theory about human excellence—intellectual and moral goodness, in particular. This was Aristotle's most preferred kind of friendship, where those involved help each other to become better and happier people. This is probably his most unique contribution to this subject, as it doesn't appear straightforwardly in either of the previously discussed contemporary theories of benefit and attachment. Aristotle labelled this sort of friendship—wherein there is mutual support, and aid of each other's development toward excellence—as *"true friendship,"* even *"perfect friendship."* [316]

Perfect friendship, for Aristotle, has a dozen elements, ordered hierarchically as in the diagram below. (He thought the best romantic love relationships are forms of true or perfect friendship.) Such friends/partners need (1) to like each other, and there needs (2) to be a mutual exchange of the thing that is the basis of the friendship, be it pleasure or utility or virtue/excellence. You need (3) to spend time together—no long-distance relationships—and you need (4) to display sincere goodwill and empathy toward each other. Aristotle further believed that the most successful friendships involve (5) rather robust forms of equality between friends. He is skeptical that people quite different in their personal attributes can sustain genuine friendship. While we might resist such a claim today, Aristotle believed it as simple fact, noting how good friends tend to be (6) of similar age, levels of education, (kind of) occupation, and socioeconomic background. Too much difference and distance are fatal to a friendship: opposites might (merely) physically attract for a while, or for the sake of novelty, but in the end such inequalities are likely to spell doom for the maintenance of the relationship.[317] Relatedly, Aristotle argued that the best friends tend (7) to share the same general outlook on life, and similar sets of values and beliefs. Here as well, too much difference provides too many grounds for disagreements, conflict, and dissolution. Adding it all up, it's natural to come to the conclusion that: a very good friend (8) is actually "another oneself."[318] You share time together, the same outlook and values, and similar attributes and personal qualities. This sameness and equality provides a rock-solid foundation for the successful continuance of the friendship, and in many ways explains further things that Aristotle wanted to say (and/or which we commonly assert) about good friendships and love relationships: you (9) enjoy spending time together; (10) there's trust, honesty, openness, respect, and loyalty; and you feel (11) comfortable and secure with each other. Above all, you (12) help each other toward personal excellence—to complete happiness—and to being the best you can be. *You both push, and pull, and lean on each other as you journey onwards and upwards in life.* And all the latter things (9–12) are true because, of course, that's how you treat yourself, that's what you want for yourself, and that's how you think of your ideal for your own life moving forward.[319]

This is to say that the ultimate basis of love and friendship, for Aristotle, is a kind of self-love, as if to say, *if you care for your own happiness and fullest development, you should invest in love and friendship.*[320] Why? Because everyone needs that kind of close, intense support, companionship, and caring. When you're a child, it comes from your parents, but then you grow and things change—and, eventually (in the natural course), you lose your parents and need the support of others. And yes, there's fellow-membership in a good society, but it's distant, detached, objective, and impersonal. Aristotle made an analogy to both orphans and property in this regard. He said that orphans who were not cared for, singled out for special attention, or shown loving support tended not to grow up as happy and well adjusted as those children with parents to offer such support. Likewise, Aristotle continued, when property or an asset is held in common (public ownership), it tends to decay, but when held by a specific individual, one who doesn't want the asset to lose value, it is maintained with greater care.[321] Similarly, *human beings require feeling special*; they need all the particular time, care, and help of love and friendship if they are to become the best they can possibly be.[322]

Moreover, when we discuss the two kinds of excellence that Aristotle was most interested in—intellectual and moral—we see that both are intrinsically social traits. And not just social, *intensely* social. Your intellect, for example, thrives with close, caring, and critical but also nurturing support and attention. Teachers who simply gave you an A-minus on an assignment, with a banal "good job," did absolutely nothing to further your intellectual growth, and you know it. Likewise the pitiless "ball-breakers," who only find fault and never once offer praise or encouragement. In terms of morality, Aristotle argued that our closest friends provide us with the most "moral practice," as it were, because these are the people with whom we spend the most time. Our relations with them are living proof of how we treat people. It's easy, say, to be honest or decent to a total stranger you'll never see again, or to simply pay one's taxes and obey the laws like a good citizen. It's quite another thing to have patience with a child who's making you angry, or to forgive a close friend who has betrayed you, or to tell a loved one a difficult truth.

In summary, if you love yourself, and want the best kind of life for yourself, you need to invest in close interpersonal relationships of the sort where the dozen previously listed items are present and vibrant:

FIG 15 ARISTOTLE'S TWELVE INGREDIENTS OF GREAT FRIENDSHIPS
(read from bottom up)

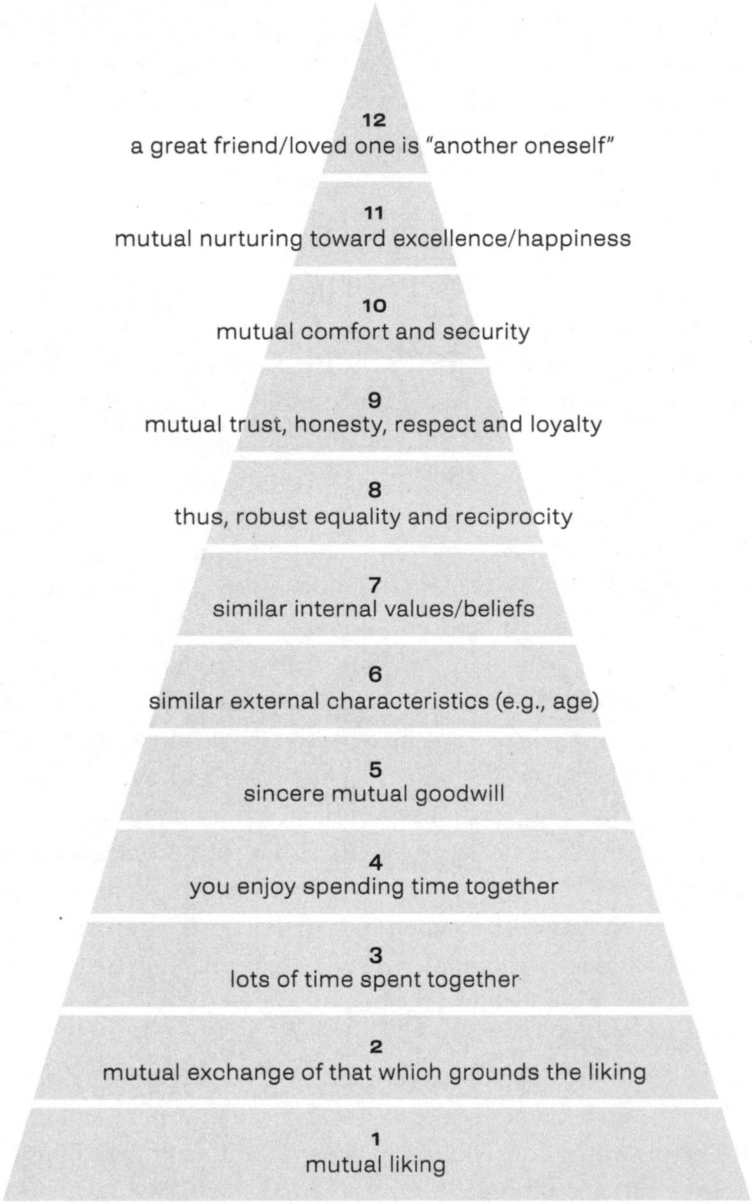

12
a great friend/loved one is "another oneself"

11
mutual nurturing toward excellence/happiness

10
mutual comfort and security

9
mutual trust, honesty, respect and loyalty

8
thus, robust equality and reciprocity

7
similar internal values/beliefs

6
similar external characteristics (e.g., age)

5
sincere mutual goodwill

4
you enjoy spending time together

3
lots of time spent together

2
mutual exchange of that which grounds the liking

1
mutual liking

Of course, that all takes an enormous amount of effort and, as a result, Aristotle said that we'd probably have only a handful of such friendships in our lives, if at all. Interestingly, contemporary research tends to bear out such speculations: *at any given time, people tend to report only about a half dozen (or fewer) "close friends."* The age for having the largest group of friends is immediately after getting married. Researchers have suggested this is because of the "coming together" of two social circles. Otherwise, the number is remarkably consistent, and quite small, from childhood through teenage and college/university years (where most friendships revolve around school), through adulthood (work), and finally into old age (nostalgia, raw companionship, and mutual help). We tend to keep the same friends through the years if we can, and resist strongly any move toward those relationships decaying and falling apart—though they can, of course, through physical distance, less time spent together, failure of effort, substantial change in someone's personality, a substantial wrong-doing, or, ultimately, death.[323]

Application of Aristotle to Chronic Conditions

Aristotle's thoughts about love and friendship provide wonderful inspiration but also clear challenge for those with chronic conditions. Let's consider the challenges first. *The main one focuses on Aristotle's insistence regarding equality, similarity, and reciprocity.* Obviously, when one falls ill or injured or disabled, this can introduce a substantial inequality and difference into a relationship. Not everyone can handle such changes, and this goes for both sides. But, by Aristotle's own terms, such an experience can also be viewed as an opportunity for moral growth and the improvement of one's character. Dealing well with such conditions requires courage, patience, and growth in terms of achieving an *objective understanding of the condition* and its likely impact, as well as *subjective affection and willingness to care*. Previously, when considering the costs and benefits of coming down with a chronic condition, we paid a lot of attention to the notion that the condition will probably increase costs—thus one needs to be vigilant about keeping costs down. However, it's not impossible that one's condition might actually—surprisingly—come with certain benefits, depending on one's choices and the reactions of those in the relationship. Seeing, or being, someone newly confronted with such challenges *can actually open one's heart*, allowing them to arrive at a more mature and loving state. Being, or being with, such a person *can encourage the development of new skills and aptitudes*, including organizational skills, or learning to relate to those who are substantially different. This is (unfortunately) the rarest outcome, but as I've actually seen it in my own life I know that it's at least possible. But perhaps the main thing that Aristotle wanted to urge is for us to pursue a path in life that promises the greatest potential for becoming a better, happier, more fully developed person.

Aristotle's insistence on reciprocity is valuable because it calls on those with chronic conditions to not forget that they, too, are being challenged to deal with the relationship changes brought about by their conditions. It's too easy to let the condition do damage or—worse—to use the excuse of one's condition as a reason for trying to turn a formerly reciprocal relationship into a one-way friendship wherein other people are treated as resources to be used for the sake of better dealing with one's condition. I have tried to make this ugly but important point in several ways throughout this book: *one ought never to use the excuse of one's condition to become worse as a person, and thus ultimately unhappier*. It needs to be admitted that this is a very real and frequent tendency (e.g., I quoted the disturbingly high rates of substance abuse among the chronically afflicted in Chapter 3).

Aristotle's strict and demanding account of love and friendship is especially valuable for its realism and sage advice in this regard. While we might correctly view those with chronic conditions with some degree of empathy and pity, we cannot make the mistake of saying, "well, because they suffer from X, the standard for their behaviour is now lower and we should indulge them or look the other way." Aristotle's call for reciprocity is not merely for individuals who must deal with those saddled by chronic conditions; it's a call to strength and courage on the part of those afflicted to resist the corrosive tendencies of the disease/disability, and to never forget that loving friendships are, indeed, two-way streets. Further, Aristotle provided a rock-solid reason never to forget this: if you love yourself and care about your future happiness, you need to do some extra work to ensure that the condition's effects don't wind up ruining what research shows is your very best chance at lasting happiness: close, loving, nurturing relationships.*

The upshot of all of Aristotle's reflections is this: Are your closest relationships not merely benefitting you, or expressing your emotional attachments, but actually helping you become a better and happier person? This is to say: Do you truly have *good* friends? And *are you yourself* truly a good friend—making

---

* I know first-hand how this is easier said than done, and how difficult such a commitment to growth and interpersonal relationships can be, especially in the immediate aftermath of illness or injury. Yet, the stark alternative is real, and much worse. If all else fails, don't forget to consider the option of animal companionship. Taking care of a pet, especially a cat or dog, has been proven to have substantial positive effects on most people's happiness—and, lord knows, such relationships are much easier to navigate than those with humans. See J. Klum's bestselling *You Had Me at Woof: How Dogs Taught Me the Secrets of Happiness* (New York: Riverhead, 2011). (Epileptics may be interested to know that there are dogs that can apparently sense seizures before they happen. See: http://www. epilepsy.com/information/professionals/hallway-conversations/can-dogs-detect-seizures)

it worthwhile for those closest to you, and doing what you can to help your friends and loved ones become better and happier people? Too often, I think, we only view the love between parent and child in this way: the parent is there, ultimately, to help the child grow and become better. But why should we limit this idea to that one kind of relationship? Why shouldn't we, throughout our lives, continue helping each other become better, as opposed to being mere sources of pleasure, "mutual benefiters," or—more dubiously—expressions of attachments formed in the past? This approach is uniquely helpful for the chronically ill, as they require added help, attention, and care from those around them. But Aristotle's high standards point out that the proper price for this is one's own commitment to growth in the face of such a challenge, and to being as good and as true a friend and loved one as possible in light of changed circumstances.

In moral philosophy, Aristotle's approach has inspired a whole new line of thought known as "the ethics of care." It captures the essence of this understanding: the best relationships, and the ones we most need for happiness and flourishing, are ones where *we care for each other's growth and excellence.* And not just "care" in some abstract theoretical sense (as in "wanting" or "being interested in"); care in the very active sense of *taking* care, *being involved in* the giving of care, *nurturing each other* toward betterment and greater fulfillment. Contemporary research actually bears this out: Gary Lewandowski points out that those who define themselves as happiest in their marriages, for example, see their life as overlapping with the life of their partner. They can't, or don't, keep track of where one ends and the other begins (recall Aristotle's remark about "another oneself"). Such is the depth, involvement, and investment in mutual caring between them.[324]

Marriage or Equivalent: Learning from the Best . . . and the Worst

Many happiness experts refer to the research of John Gottman regarding what makes for the happiest and most successful long-term love relationships, specifically marriages. He's one of the most experienced marital researchers, and claims a 91 percent successful prediction rate regarding whether a marriage will stay together or break apart. He can claim such a rate based on the thousands of marriages he's seen and experimented on, with many couples agreeing to come "live" in his experimental apartment for a few weeks, wherein all interactions between them are recorded and/or observed, and then dissected and analyzed. His primary interest, though, is the general relationship patterns he's seen in the most successful loving couples, and in those who've gone on to bitter break-ups. Since over 90 percent of adults worldwide will at least try some form of stable cohabiting relationship, such as marriage, at some point in their lives, such advice is well worth considering.[325] Doubly so if what David Meyers has discovered is true: that "there are few stronger predictions of happiness than a close, nurturing, equitable, intimate, life-long companionship with one's best friend."[326]

Research confirms many things that lead to relationship breakdown and divorce. Interestingly, unhappiness is but one factor. Others such as career moves, financial difficulties, sexual problems, and/or disagreements over children can be as large factors as outright dissatisfaction, anger, or disappointment in the other.[327] Gottman doesn't do research on those sorts of things: he excels at discerning, from how a couple interacts, the likelihood of whether they will break up over the next couple of years. He notes that it's not the fact that a couple fights that ruins their marriage—one of the major findings of his research, which surprised him, was precisely this: happy and successful couples seem to disagree and fight just as much as unhappy couples who go on to split. The crucial difference between them is *how* the two groups disagree or fight. In particular, couples that go on to break up almost always experience the same sorts of phenomena when they fight:

- a rapid escalation in the argument when there is some kind of touchy disagreement

- a disproportionate resort to personal attacks on the other's character, as opposed to a more neutral approach focused on solving the problem at hand

- hair-trigger defensiveness, resorted to by one or both individuals (e.g., protecting the self by putting the blame and responsibility on the other person)

- negative body language displayed in abundance during the disagreement: arms and/or legs are crossed, lips are pursed, head tilted at an unusual angle, evasive eye contact

- a lack of validation of the other, which can manifest itself in a range of ways: from rolling one's eyes, to constantly interrupting the other, to withdrawing from the conversation

If such things are regular features of disagreements in your relationship, Gottman predicts it will end unless you take remedial action and learn from how successful couples handle disagreements.[328] We can, in general, invert the above to predict much greater success and happiness at handling differences when:

- arguments are kept in perspective and proportion—resist the urge to escalate an argument beyond what it is

- you do not engage in personal attacks on the other person's character; try to focus instead on understanding the nature of the dispute (including self-reflection on the reasons behind one's own disagreement) and ways to solve the problem that are mutually satisfying

- though it might be hard, you try not to display negative body language

- you do not deprive the other of validation, and certainly do not show contempt for them

- you try to understand the other person's perspective, and consider how you might be wrong, or at least approaching things from a rash or only partially correct point of view. Don't forget the wisdom of military science: there *is* such a thing as a "Pyrrhic victory," wherein you "win the battle"— perhaps with the nasty tactics described above—but in the end you "lose the war," as your relationship falls apart due to the cumulative effects of all these negative experiences.

One of the most important and effective things to do *during* an argument, not afterwards, is to explicitly reach out to your partner in a way that deflates tension and validates them. The most common strategies employed in this regard include a sudden resort to humour (especially self-deprecating humour) and the use of gentle physical contact (like softly touching the other's arm or hand). To motivate such a gesture, force yourself to remember a particularly sweet/touching/loving/impressive action from the other person. It's hard for anger to stay sharp when recalling them at their loving best.[329]

This is all just about good behaviour and strategies during arguments. What about good strategies for maintaining one's relationship in general? What do those in the best relationships do *on a regular basis* that can be of use to the rest of us? Gottman and his research partners recommended the following:

- The most successful couples devote at least five hours per week, every week, to having quality time just between the two of them. This might seem like not a lot—five hours spread over seven days. However, it's about truly relating, and being active and mindful in that relating (e.g., sitting together on the sofa and watching TV passively does not count).

- Successful couples make efforts at having nice daily "starts and finishes." Happy couples say "good morning" to each other, and don't just pounce out of bed to get ready for work. Before leaving in the morning, they find out at least one thing the other is planning on doing that day. Then, at the end of the day, upon seeing each other again, they have a low-stress "reunion conversation" about their day, lasting at least twenty minutes.[330]

- The happiest couples go on at least one "date" a week, wherein the time is just for the two of them (even if they have kids).[331]

- The happiest couples display tons of physical affection. They touch each other a lot; they hug, kiss, and have sex. But it's more about the raw contact and display of affection, and the feeling of being close and in love, which is sought after (as opposed to pure sexual release).

- Every day some genuine verbal affection and appreciation is exchanged between the couple. We'll see, in chapters 8 and 10, the surprisingly powerful effects that sincere displays of gratitude have on people: both giver and receiver.[332]

Two further things of crucial note: Researchers have studied in detail the raw ratio of positive to negative experiences and communication between couples. There is disagreement on the exact ratio, though the number most often reported is that, for every one negative experience/saying there needs to be five positive experiences/sayings. More recent research tends to put the number closer to 1:3, but all researchers agree that *negative experiences and communication must be made up for,* and *on a more than one-to-one basis.* One of the most proven truths of psychology, as we've seen, is that negative information/experiences stick much more in the mind than positive ones.[333] Evolutionary psychologists think that this is because, for our earliest ancestors, avoiding serious mistakes was much more important than enjoying some extra smiles and laughs. (Those flowers over there might look pretty, but if there's any indication that a hungry bear is lurking on the other side of them . . .) Thus, we are hardwired to pay more attention to anything negative or potentially threatening, whether it's criticism from our peers or something more serious, such as a deep hurt caused by our partner. We'll return to this more generally in Chapter 8, when considering things like optimism versus pessimism. For now, we note how the aforementioned ratios are evidence in favour of the notion that—emotional attachment notwithstanding—consciously or unconsciously, the calculation of benefit to cost is a profound and ongoing feature of most people's understanding of the quality of their relationships.[334] Here are three fun, helpful, and interesting tidbits of advice related to this issue of positive versus negative communication/experience:

- Researchers (and bestselling authors) Harville Hendrix and Helen LaKelly Hunt urge us to take the "zero negativity challenge" and see how far we can get: keep track of how many days you can go without doing or saying a single negative, hurtful thing to your partner. When you break the streak, start again, and try for a longer record. To keep a streak alive, they suggest the following: *instead of complaining or criticizing, make a polite request for the future.* For example, instead of criticizing your partner's lack of organizational skill, be more specific and constructive, saying, "well, maybe next week we can try booking things a few days in advance, so that things don't fall through at the last minute?"[335]

- While keeping track of costs and benefits is to some extent unavoidable and even rational, some people can get carried away and become poisonously disproportionate in this regard. *Men's Health* magazine recently urged its male readers to consider this as an antidote to obsessive and destructive "score-keeping" within a relationship: consider the things you do for your significant other *not* as "his/her debt" to you but, rather, as "YOUR GIFT" to them.[336]

- In a nice twist (or take) on the "three happy things" advice mentioned earlier in this book, marriage expert Harriet Lerner urges us all, when having trouble in our relationships or even when just wanting to make efforts to improve them, to do so by figuring out *three concrete things that we can do over the next week, which we know our partner will appreciate.* Then do them, and reap the rewards.[337]

Of further relevance to the ongoing success of a loving relationship is how couples habitually react to news. Not just bad news, wherein many of the strategies listed above (regarding arguments) would be compelling. But even good news, especially when it comes to how one partner reacts when the other receives good news. In such cases, *only one form of interaction is seen as good for the long-term health of a relationship:* "active constructive responding." Say, for example, that Beth has just received great news, like a promotion and pay raise. Her husband,

Bill, might respond one of four ways:

1 **Passive destructive.** A response that conveys disinterest, such as if Bill were to ignore this great news and respond instead, "It was so hot and humid today."

2 **Passive constructive.** A positive response that lets the speaker know you've heard them, but is muted and not proportionate to the magnitude of the good news. Like if Bill were to reply, "That's nice, honey. Congratulations. What's for dinner?"

3 **Active destructive.** A response that on the surface might seem positive, but is actually negative in that it hastens to point out the downside to the good news. Like if Bill were to follow his congratulations with, "That means less time for us now, though, won't it?"

4 **Active constructive.** A sincerely enthusiastic and congratulatory response, with full engagement and interest, and no mention of any potential negatives. Like if Bill said, "Great news, honey! It's what you deserve—and I hope it's the first of many more." First, note how this mode confirms Aristotle's comments about sincere goodwill toward the other. Second, and unsurprisingly, researchers have shown that the most successful marriages *routinely feature both partners using this response mode when hearing good news from the other.* (All other modes constitute "raining on the parade" of the other person, lowering expectations for how you might handle future bad news and creating general insecurity in the relationship).[338]

Speaking of attempts at manipulation and control, autonomy is important to many people's experience of happiness. This was found to be especially crucial at work (Chapter 4), and also in connection with the basic structuring of society (last chapter). We haven't yet said enough about this, and recall from previous chapters that personal freedom was never one of Aristotle's main values. But autonomy is vitally important in happy relationships, which can seem somewhat odd since relationships tend be viewed as being about togetherness and not autonomous individuality. Relationships are, of course, about togetherness, but contemporary research shows that there still needs to be healthy respect for the independent achievements, personal space, and self-determination of the other. In particular, *strategies of domination and control must be avoided*. Instead of just raw closeness and attachment, researchers urge us to think more of *the ideal of mutual loving support and nurturing*, which involves things like respect, mutual growth, and support for each other's goals and achievements.[339] I've tried to offer, above, a modern gloss on Aristotle that can accommodate our needs for individuality even in the midst of committed and terrific love and friend relationships. It's no doubt a balancing act, requiring effort and open communication. Today's psychology researchers, instead of using terms like "reciprocity" or "mutual care that still respects individuality," prefer to use more scientific-sounding terms like "relational efficacy" to describe the overall state-of-being of the best kinds of close relationships. The following is generally true of those experiencing relational efficacy:

- they can handle problems and arguments constructively

- they communicate openly and well

- they know each other intimately, and sincerely care for each other (in Aristotle's robust sense)

- they have more positive than negative experiences and communication

- they exhibit basic kindness, decency, friendliness, and sincere goodwill toward each other

- there is a great deal of physical affection, and expression of genuine appreciation

- there is a clear and substantial mutual investment of time, effort, and attention to each other and to the health of the overall relationship

- there is mutual loving support for each other's own individual goals, involving a commitment to growth and betterment on the part of everyone.[340]

Speaking of the Best: Clinging to Ideals?

Martin Seligman has crafted an interesting, controversial theory about some of the best relationships, and a tool said to be used often by both partners within them. He has, to some extent, backed this up with experiments, and received endorsements from such prominent happiness researchers as Tal Ben-Shahar and Sonja Lyubomirsky. Here's the set-up: there's powerful evidence of some hedonic adaptation (Chapter 1) to the happiness generated by long-term relationships, and moreover marriage. There is a huge, authoritative, longitudinal German study most often cited in this regard. While good marriages can provide a steady stream of some happiness over decades, *for most couples the happiness boost from marriage lasts for only a handful of years* before there is some adaptation toward the pre-marital baseline of self-reported happiness—for both people. Importantly, note the word "some": many studies have shown time and again how, even if there is some "climb-down" from the initial high, most married couples continue to report themselves as measurably happier than single people, and (notably) as measurably happier than their formerly single selves. Daniel Nettle reports, using British sociological data, that marital status has a statistically proven more powerful impact on one's happiness than socio-economic status, which, as we've seen, plays a not-small role in its own right.[341]

In essence, we are talking about how to resist some of the tendencies toward hedonic adaptation when it comes to close love relationships. Everything said in Chapter 1—about mindfulness, complexity, variety of experiences, pacing out the timing, taking on challenges, being open to growth—applies here.* But another strategy not previously discussed, and which Seligman developed, has to do with *how each partner should perceive the other over time*. Seligman, in researching the psychology of optimism, has carried over some of that research into the realm of relationships, purportedly discovering the following: *the happiest couples each report having individually idealistic conceptions of their partner*. They idealize the other, and view them through rose-coloured glasses (compared, say, to how other people—even close family members—view that person, or even how that person describes themselves). The lover minimizes

---

* Related relationship advice often includes travelling together, as that expands each other's sense of the other, and of the relationship. It also includes doing new things together, even if not travelling (such as taking dance or cooking lessons together), doing things with other couples, exercising together, buying novel items together that can then serve as sources of positive reminiscence. Psychologist Arthur Aron has documented the powerful effects of novel experiences for couples: those who deliberately pursue such a strategy report themselves as much happier with their relationships than couples who merely do routine (yet pleasant) things together. Aron says—echoing Aristotle—"you're happiest when your mate expands your sense of who you are." From L. R. Stains, "25 Ways to Save Your Marriage," *Men's Health* (Sept. 2015), 103–9.

or ignores the flaws of the loved one, and pays more attention to, and even exaggerates, the loved one's strengths. Seligman goes beyond this reportage and argues that, to an extent, we should actually *cultivate* such idealized views of our significant other. Not only to make ourselves happier, but because viewing them as better than what they really are actually *exerts social pressure on them* to live up to that idealized view (as they don't want to disappoint what is probably their closest relationship). The result will lead to greater happiness: the lover is happier by viewing the loved one optimistically; the loved one then strives to improve him/herself to live up to the other's optimism. The result is a stronger relationship made even happier—and thus buffered against the corrosive acids of hedonic adaptation.[342]

It's an interesting theory, but controversial as mentioned. The controversy revolves around three things. The first is what some may interpret as *the manipulation behind* the "exerting of pressure" upon the partner, as if viewing them as a "fixer-upper," and/or viewing oneself as something of a white knight riding along to their rescue.[343] The second controversy concerns *the rationality* of this kind of loving optimism. You should know your partner for who they truly are, Aristotle would say—and probably most contemporary relationship experts would concur. Loving and caring for one's partner, "warts and all," is surely the ultimate ideal, no? Making it work in the real world, as opposed to some romantic fantasyland? Other critics have further mentioned how indulging in such blissful ignorance about a partner *may leave oneself vulnerable* to bad and exploitative behaviour on the part of that other, whether that includes infidelity, abuse, or just everyday "taking advantage" of the other's goodwill and optimism (e.g., in terms of imbalance in the share of housework or child care).[344]

That said—and I lean toward this critical stance—Seligman *does* have some experimental evidence showing that this is, in fact, how the happiest and most successful love partners view each other. Plus, it's obviously part of how our culture views love—romantic love especially. All the great couples of romantic fiction, like Romeo and Juliet, view each other with absolutely breathless and passionate enthusiasm. We might even say that romantic love is, essentially, an idealistic and optimistic enterprise. We get involved in these kinds of relationships, and make all the effort and put up with all the bother, *precisely on the hope* that they will work out in the very best way. So why not go along with Seligman's advice and make it work for you? Consider as well how the phenomenon he describes almost certainly details how a great many (all?) loving parents tend to view their children. What parent does not, to some extent, downplay or even ignore some of their children's flaws and pay heightened attention to, or even exaggerate, their strengths? Some evolutionary psychologists, maybe with tongue-in-cheek, have opined that perhaps such idealization and optimism is needed to inspire us and strengthen us psychologically for the substantial difficulties involved in keeping a healthy relationship alive and strong for so long—so that everyone's needs (especially the next generation's) can be met, and the whole human enterprise can continue. Thus, why not *for strategic reasons* go along with Seligman? Douglas LaBier says we should: "Look above the things you find annoying or unpleasant [about your partner]. . . . Respond [only] to the best qualities in [them] . . . which will always make [their] best side stronger."[345]

You no doubt have your own views about Seligman's provocative theory, and I'll leave you to them, with these parting thoughts:

- Lyubomirsky endorses a more cautious version of Seligman's thesis, noting that there *is* some genuine scientific evidence backing up his claims that the happiest couples do tend to report idealized visions of the other, with one feeling at least some social pressure to live up to such ideals and not disappoint their beloved. She then offers an excellent concrete relationship tactic, connected with Gottman's work on marriage and managing conflict: when the other person does something that disappoints you, or makes you angry, *force yourself to consider first the most positive interpretation you can of their motives and actions*—as opposed to jumping the gun and fixing on the worst possible interpretation. More targeted, "in-the-moment optimism" may save you from a fight you need not have at all, and from the mental strain of dwelling on the worst-case scenario before knowing the truth.[346]

- Ben-Shahar also endorses Seligman's account, perhaps more robustly, noting that some "groundless" optimism about one's beloved may be a very small price to pay for all the demonstrated benefits (listed above) of a successful, ongoing love relationship. The very best benefit, according to Ben-Shahar, is that close love creates a kind of empowering circle within which people feel more secure, are more creative and resilient, are more generous and open, display willingness to take more and greater risks, and thus grow as humans in the kind of progressive, developmental way that Aristotle described. Harkening back to Ben-Shahar's theory regarding happiness in the workplace (Chapter 4), he argues that, as in one's personal life, having an excellent social circle of close loving relationships allows one to exercise their signature strengths more fully.[347] Indeed, if ever there was a good definition of a strong relationship, it's that. Within it one finds: 1) meaning; 2) pleasure; and 3) opportunities to show off, and further develop, one's signature strengths. There's an MPS Process, and test, for which kinds of relationships one should nurture and develop, and how one should behave within such, in order to advance them. Truly, for most people, family and friends (and the love shared with them) not only provide happiness, they also provide purpose to one's life, give it extra meaning, pleasure, and help finding and further developing one's strengths. We've seen in previous chapters how each of these things is a happiness generator in its own right.[348] All great—but the greatest of Ben-Shahar's reflections is how much he stresses how successful and happy love relationships, and family and friend relationships, *have absolutely nothing to do with the prevalent, passive mythology of finding or discovering something* ("Have you found The One?"); rather, they are all about *deliberately, actively cultivating and creating*—putting one's best efforts into—the relationships one has, and wishes to have.[349] We've mentioned previously how passivity is almost never in the best interests of the chronically afflicted; and note how active, effortful development is totally in line with everything Aristotle recommended.

Conclusion

Research shows that, of any one thing, it is our interpersonal relationships that, over time, compose the largest chunk of our happiness status. We reviewed the most influential theories behind relationships in positive psychology today: the benefit and attachment theories. Both add something vital, yet each contains drawbacks that need to be transcended by a more blended account. Seeking ancient wisdom, we saw how much emphasis Aristotle placed upon good love and friend relationships, and we updated his account and discovered a dozen principles for enjoying wonderful relationships filled with active, mutual care. This account was noted as having special relevance for the chronically afflicted, as they are in heightened need of care from others—yet ought never to take such care for granted, offering what reciprocity they can. We saw that the chronically afflicted probably increase the costs within their relationships and have a harder time offering expected benefits.

Useful, concrete strategies were offered for handling this important task. *Such heightened efforts are, no doubt, worth it—owing to the centrality and efficacy of the quality of one's relationships to one's overall happiness in life.* Finally, we turned to contemporary theories regarding what those in the best relationships do, and how we can make sustained and creative use of those many tools to fashion for ourselves the kind of friendships and close love relationships we all need.

CHAPTER 7

The Body

This is the last chapter on the external goods; it marks a transition into the book's final section, the internal goods. This chapter also highlights the artificiality of the conceptual division between external and internal. Recall that, here, the crude external/internal division is between "internal," meaning anything directly *within* our states of mind and consciousness—beliefs, emotions, and values—whereas "external" refers to anything *outside* of that (which nevertheless impacts our happiness substantially). We've explored how the worlds of work and income, social institutions, and interpersonal relationships affect our pursuit of happiness, whether well or chronically afflicted. But what about the body? It's external in our technical sense (of not itself being a state of mind/consciousness), but, obviously, the body can have a colossal impact on our experience and level of happiness and well-being.[350]

Now, I've said a great deal about the body already. It might be said that—whether directly or indirectly—this whole book is about the relationship between the health of one's body and one's experience of happiness. And we've dealt with the body in more explicit and targeted ways. For example, straight off the bat in Chapter 1, we considered DNA and the biological role of genetics in the pursuit of happiness. And in Chapter 3, we explored gathering and enjoying pleasure from the five bodily senses, as well as sleep hygiene and deep breathing exercises that are directly relevant to the proper functioning of vital bodily systems. We also warned of the dangers of poisoning one's body, and ruining one's happiness, through substance abuse. In Chapter 5, as part of the basic structure of social institutions, we noted and discussed the role that a decent health care system plays in both the subjective happiness and objective well-being of the people within its domain.

This is then the first thing that ought to be said in this chapter, especially for the chronically afflicted: *one needs to acquire the best and most appropriate medical care for one's body, and for the treatment of its malfunctioning.* One cannot and should not "go it alone" in terms of trying to understand and manage one's condition. Now, this does *not* mean that you should blindly trust what medical authorities say: as someone victimized by medical negligence, I can hardly endorse such a view. It's about acquiring as much objective evidence, and as much critically informed advice, as you can—and then doing what's possible to improve your bodily functioning and, subsequently, your happiness.[351]

Thus, *do not avoid medical practitioners: just try to find good ones, and always question why they say what they say.* There is disturbing evidence that a significant chunk of those who suspect they may have a serious diagnosis (such as cancer) either deliberately avoid or substantially delay seeking medical help, either out of fear or denial. Men form the largest part of this chunk, for whatever reason. Obviously, it's a huge mistake—wishing it away doesn't make it so, and in many cases delay worsens a condition and renders successful treatment less likely. This fact makes us mindful once more of the prominent role courage plays in this regard.[352]

Also, *do not try to diagnose yourself*; and do not think that your quick Google searching constitutes "medical research" on the same level as a licensed doctor or a professional university medical researcher. Social science evidence has long shown that people seek out information that confirms their pre-existing beliefs and biases: they tend only to confront genuine counter-evidence *if forced to* by an external process, such as formal education or a court procedure. Clearly, what we all should want is the truth, and not soothing validation of our current inclinations.[353]

While being mindful of the structure of one's health care system is important, and that there may be some things outside of one's control, in general one needs to:

- *Get a good diagnosis, and a map of options for treatment and management.* This should involve a blend of expert advice and one's own diligent, self-critical research (used to question experts and come to a fuller understanding before making any choices).

- *Keep all your doctor and specialist appointments,* and make sure you see them regularly (at least once a year). Be honest and offer full disclosure so as to receive the best advice. Don't neglect your general practitioner/family doctor, as they may be best positioned to see how a specific ailment, and its treatment, fit into one's overall health.

- *Don't make the mistake of thinking that, because you have a chronic condition, this somehow exempts you from ageing,* or from other things going wrong with your body. Life's not like that, even if you'd like to believe that you've already "paid your dues" with your main affliction. In fact, having one thing wrong with your body makes it *more likely for additional things to go wrong,* so extra vigilance is needed overall.[354]

- If you live in a jurisdiction where your medical treatment involves out-of-pocket costs, do three things:

1 Seek lower-cost options of equal, or acceptably equivalent, proven effectiveness (e.g., generic over brand-name prescription medications). Press your doctor for information about such alternatives.

2 Do not forego necessary drugs or procedures merely for the sake of costs. (Studies have shown that as many as 30 percent of American men have admitted to not taking prescribed medications for this reason.)[355]

3 Do what one can to lobby and vote for the creation of a well-functioning and decent health care system that is: universal and accessible; competent and efficient; public, transparent, and accountable; focused on prevention and humane treatment; and effective at achieving good "health outcomes," such as low rates of morbidity, high rates of longevity, and enjoyable physical quality of life.[356]

Now, since this book is targeted at the chronically afflicted, it goes without saying that—while there usually *are* common experiences and reactions to such afflictions—each disease, injury, or disorder imposes its own unique physical challenges upon the person in question. (Readers are strongly urged to research phrases like "health and X" and "living well with X," where "X" represents their own affliction.[357] Seek out government, university, or university press sources for the best available information.) The bottom-line is this: dealing with any chronic condition is *rendered easier by having as healthy a body as possible* given the circumstances. And a healthy body is both relevant and enabling to anyone's pursuit of happiness and well-being.

Physical Health and Happiness in General

Let's consider first the overall relationship between physical health and happiness. We considered this in Chapter 2, when canvassing reasons to pursue happiness as a goal—indeed, as *the* goal of life. Among other things, we saw strong evidence from multiple sources that those who report themselves as being happy or very happy tend—objectively—to have better health, less disorder and disease, and greater longevity. And vice-versa: there are clear connections between low happiness and clinical depression, as well as a whole host of physical disorders. Daniel Nettle has noted that, in rigorous surveys, there tends to be a direct correlation between people's self-reported levels of happiness and their self-reported levels of physical health and well-being.[358] Recall from Chapter 5 how, in the Gallup surveys about happiness in different countries, one of the major categories defined as being co-constitutive of happiness was precisely physical well-being: people were asked about whether they felt they had "enough energy to get their daily tasks done," which turned out to be positively correlated with their overall life satisfaction. In light of these powerful, proven associations, it's tempting to agree with Sonja Lyubomirsky's assessment that physical health and happiness are in a deeply interconnected, powerful, bi-directional relationship with each other, such that—in general—when one goes up, so does the other; and when one goes down, it drags the other down as well.[359]

FIG 16 COMMON UNDERSTANDING OF THE HEALTH/HAPPINESS RELATIONSHIP

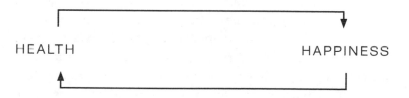

HEALTH   HAPPINESS

I think this claim is generally true, and very important to note for everyone, including those with chronic conditions. Since, by definition, the latter suffer from impairment of their bodies, it follows that overall their happiness conditions will probably be lower than those of unafflicted people. And we saw in previous chapters (from Nettle's research) that this is indeed the case: most people who define themselves as chronically afflicted routinely report their average subjective happiness scores as *10 percent lower* than the average person (in the sixes out of ten, as opposed to the usual sevens).[360] This was certainly the case for me, at least at the onset of my epilepsy: it was clearly the cause of the major bout of unhappiness that began my journey into investigating happiness, its causes, and ways to augment it in one's life.

That said, I think there are real limits to this observation regarding "bidirectional causation," and a powerfully positive interrelationship between physical health and happiness. We've seen evidence of substantial hedonic adaptation, even to quite severe chronic conditions and afflictions. People get used to the challenges they impose; there's evidence that happiness levels rise after an initial adjustment period, even while their afflicted physical bodies remain about the same. Additionally, while we might quip that "the healthier you are, the happier you are," it turns out that there's a clear limit and absolutely no evidence that ultra-healthy people—such as professional athletes, yoga instructors, Olympic competitors, nutritionists, or marathon runners—are substantially happier (or even happier at all) than the average person.[361]

So, it may turn out that physical health is actually more like money and income in its relation to happiness: necessary, but not itself sufficient for happiness. The worst kinds of sickness and injury can indeed pull down one's happiness, even factoring in hedonic adaptation. (And, of course—as Nettle notes—there's no adaptation at all to the very worst kinds of injury/illness wherein one's vital needs, or life itself, are threatened.)[362] Thus, some baseline level of physical functioning and health is truly necessary for happiness: as Martin Seligman says, some amount of physical functioning and vigour is *the most fundamental resource one has* for the pursuit of any kind of happiness at all.[363] But, after one has achieved that level, further incremental increases in health may lead to further incremental increases in happiness (again, insofar as they provide increased energy for the pursuit of other happiness-inducing things like relationships or career success). However, it needs to be understood that, eventually, there will be an upper limit reached where further health gains will make no difference to one's overall level of happiness. This is particularly important to note for anyone out there who is a "fitness fanatic"—someone so obsessively dedicated to their physical fitness regimen that they let it eat away at the time and resources they have to devote to proven happiness boosters without perceived upper limits, notably interpersonal relationships.

The assumption of this chapter, though, is that most of us inhabit the zone wherein some gains in health *are* going to translate into gains in happiness, or better enable such, and we can leave behind worry about hitting any upper limit or ceiling on our health/happiness correlation. Generally, *the healthier one is, the more physical resources and energy one has to do, pursue, and enjoy all the other activities which clearly bump one's happiness.* Dare I say, for many or even most of the chronically afflicted, one of the biggest daily challenges is either chronic pain and/or simply not having enough physical energy. In either case, their ability to perform activities that make them happier is hampered. It would be great if such roadblocks could be overcome, or at least mitigated, by attention to things that generally improve people's health and functioning.

Such things are the focus of this chapter, and are very close to my heart. Why? Because my biggest and clearest initial gains— in terms of bringing the seizures under control, even during the period of misdiagnosis and non-treatment—were brought about precisely by a rigorous commitment to physical exercise, consistent nutrition, and overall trying to bring my out-of-control body into as much healthful, disciplined control as I possibly could. *Improving my physical health was one of the first and most powerful tools in my anti-illness, pro-happiness toolbox,* and one that I still rely on and remain committed to. I can't imagine my life without it, and dread to consider what my condition might look like if I dropped these tools and let my physical health slide. I'll now share some of the things I've learned in the hopes that you might experience similar stabilizing, energizing results.

Big Picture: "Blue-Zone" Longevity

Much recent attention has been paid to "Blue Zones," and the connection between health and happiness displayed therein. Blue Zones refer to a handful of areas around the world where the highest average levels of longevity have been documented. Now, we can't make the mistake of confusing mere quantity of life with *quality*, but—as stated—these zones have gotten much attention, and there's no denying that average life expectancy is a major factor in considering the objective well-being of citizens around the world. But, as we'll see, there's more going on in these Blue Zones than mere length of life.

Demographers and other experts (e.g., Dan Buettner, who wrote *The Blue Zones: Lessons for Living Longer from the People Who've Lived the Longest*) have discovered five small regions around the world that qualify as Blue Zones.[364] They are:

- Sardinia, Italy
- Okinawa, Japan
- Loma Linda, California (especially a large group of Seventh-day Adventists who live there)
- Nicoya region, Costa Rica
- Icaria, Greece

The first three regions have the highest concentration of those living over 100 in the whole world. The last has the highest concentration of those living over ninety (one in three!). In all five regions, they suffer from diseases and disorders at rates only a fraction of what's commonly seen around the world. Thus, it's not merely the length of their lives that's extended; it's *the length of healthy, vital years* extended well over the norm. (For example, in Icaria, the population gets cancer at 20 percent the rate of the developed world's average, and only 50 percent the rate of heart disease. Moreover, there are statistically zero rates of dementia.) As said: there's something important going on in these communities. A longer, healthier life is like the ultimate resource input for the pursuit, and maximization, of personal happiness over time.[365] What do these Blue Zones share in common that we might learn from them?

Researchers like Buettner have come up with the following list of crucial commonalities among Blue Zones:

1 **They tend to be quite small communities.** Indeed, three of the five are islands (Sardinia, Okinawa, and Icaria), and Nicoya is a peninsula; Loma Linda is a small city (population under 22,000) disproportionately composed of members of one religious group, Seventh-day Adventists.

2 Not only are these communities small, they tend to be very tight-knit. **Family togetherness and robust social lives** are hallmark features of these communities. (E.g., in Okinawa, there exists something called "moais," which are tight-knit, informal, extended social networks that parents plug their kids into while still very young. They function as extended families, meeting regularly for social events, and supporting and advising one another. Many people are members of these moais for eighty-plus years!)[366]

3 Most in these communities have **purposeful lives,** and a robust sense of focus and purpose that comes from: tending to the family and nurturing one's social connections; the sense of tight-knit togetherness that comes from being such a small community; and/or above-average levels of spirituality and/or religious practice (be it Catholicism in Sardinia, Ryukyuan in Okinawa, or Seventh-day Adventism in Loma Linda).[367]

4 All these communities enjoy **abundant sunshine.**

5 In each of these communities, which are considered walkable, **near-constant physical activity is built into the structure of people's lives.** Walking and gardening, and similar low-to-moderate impact physical motions, are near-universal daily activities. People in these communities also have **above-average sex lives** (e.g., averaging sex twice a week even after fifty years of age). The crucial thing, according to Buettner, is that all this physical activity is almost "unconscious," in the sense that it's built into the fabric of their lives—as opposed to being part of a formal, forced "fitness regimen" separate from one's daily activities.[368]

6 **There exists serious, successful, built-in stress reduction and stress management in these communities** (unlike in big city centres, with tons of people and all the problems such numbers generate—crime, traffic, noise, garbage, and pollution—as well as impersonal, or non-existent, social connections).[369]

7 There is either **very little or no smoking.**

8 There is either **no alcohol consumption, or else moderate alcohol consumption that is almost entirely composed of (local) wine.**

9 Such communities share many commonalities in terms of diet. (Indeed, there is now a Blue Zone Diet.)[370] **Moderate calorie intake** is the social norm (i.e., portion control). Moreover, diets in these communities are **heavily based on plants and/or fish**—only very modest amounts of meat are consumed.) Of the plants, legumes tend to be featured quite substantially (fava beans in Sardinia, nuts in Loma Linda, soybeans in Okinawa, black-eyed peas in Icaria). The food consumed is **overwhelmingly locally grown, fresh, whole or raw, and very high in antioxidants**, which help to rid the body of things that can accumulate and cause ill health. Examples of healthful foods that the oldest Blue Zone residents report eating on a near-daily basis are:

- In Nicoya, it's the trinity of beans, corn, and squash (often supplemented by eggs), alongside such sweeter fare as papayas, yams, and bananas.

- In Okinawa, it's tofu, brown rice, and shiitake mushrooms, supplemented with garlic and melons, and washed down with lots of green tea.

- In Loma Linda, it's salmon and avocados, with lots of nuts and beans. Oatmeal and whole wheat bread are staples, as is soy milk.

- There are similarities in the two Mediterranean locations: in both Icaria and Sardinia, they drink goat's milk and eat lots of feta cheese, chickpeas, fish, and locally grown wild greens; in Icaria, they eat black-eyed peas as well, and lots of potatoes. Honey is ubiquitous, as are lemons. In Sardinia, they eat tons of tomatoes and drink red wine on a near-daily basis, but only sip it in small amounts, balanced by tea made from milk thistle, which has long been thought to aid liver function (and thus help process alcohol).[371]

We'll talk more about nutrition later in this chapter. For now, we leave off our examination of Blue Zones by noting one further thing: *personal freedom and autonomy.* We've seen throughout this book that, for most people, these are vital ingredients in happiness and personal well-being. In addition to all those things mentioned above, people in Blue Zones have a robust sense of personal freedom. At first glance this might seem odd, given what's been said about how tight-knit, together, and social these communities are. But don't forget that many people experience such social support as being empowering and pleasant, cutting down on the "bad side" of personal freedom: loneliness and alienation. But the main points here, I think, deal with: the small scale of these communities; that most people walk everywhere; and that, on a daily basis, they are engaging in effective stress-management techniques. This no doubt gives them a sense of liveable scale— of individual empowerment—and a hassle-free way of being.

The thrust of all Blue Zones research has been confirmed independently by psychological research into "successful ageing." Many studies have confirmed that the following general behaviours tend to empower people to become "successful agers" (i.e., to live as long, as happily, and as relatively disease-free as possible). Thus, all of us—whether chronically afflicted or not—can profit from understanding (and implementing!) successful ageing, which is generally foreshadowed by:

- not being a smoker (or having quit permanently by the age of forty-five)

- not having a history of alcohol or drug abuse

- being of healthful weight for one's age, height, and gender*

- getting near-daily regular exercise

---

* The Body Mass Index is the most common tool for determining norms for body weight, though it's not without controversy. See, e.g.: http://www.nhlbi.nih.gov/health/educational/lose_wt/BMI/bmicalc.htm

And then a couple further things, which we've discussed in other chapters:

- years of formal education are positively correlated with successful ageing (Chapter 5, education section)

- being in a stable, satisfying, cohabiting relationship, such as a marriage (last chapter)

- having mature defence mechanisms and successful ways of resolving interpersonal conflict (last chapter, though we'll return to the idea of "maturity," and its connection to happiness, in the forthcoming chapters on mental and emotional hygiene).

Small Picture: "Fake It Until You Make It"

We can learn from those living in Blue Zones and what they do to live longer, and more healthfully, than the vast majority of the world's population. But let's go now to the other end of the spectrum, and focus on one solitary person and the physical and/or bodily things they can do, generally, to augment pleasure and happiness. Something not mentioned in Chapter 3, around the discussion of pleasure, and for which there is plenty of (slightly weird) evidence, is to do with the branch of psychology known as "behaviourism." All the rage in the 1950s, behaviourism focuses not so much on how people subjectively report and experience states of mind and consciousness, but on their objective behaviour and physical manifestations within their bodies (e.g., pulse, rate of breathing and blinking, flushing of skin, etc.). The more external and objective the physical behaviours, the better. It was an attempt to make psychology much more rigorous and genuinely scientific.

A number of behaviourism's propositions have been demon-strated in rigorous experiments. One of them is that *if you force your body to do things that happy people do, you will feel a boost in mood*, and report feeling happier. The effect is not enormous, but is still measurable, and even endures for a while immedi-ately after the behaviour has ceased. Which physical things? These, in particular:

- forcing yourself to smile, and hold the smile

- forcing your shoulders back and stretching / "puffing out" your chest

- standing as straight and tall as possible (without stretching or going up on your toes)

- forcing yourself to laugh

- when in social situations, force yourself to hug people (assum-ing they are receptive) as part of the "hello/goodbye" ritual[372]

Each of the above has been proven to have an immediate, and surprisingly enduring, boost in mood. Two interesting experi-ments in this regard:

1 Research subjects were asked to evaluate whether some *Far Side* cartoons were funny. As they did, they had to hold a marker with their mouths. One group was forced to put the marker between their teeth, with the consequence that their mouth was opened similar to a smile. The other group had to hold the marker between their closed, pursed mouth and the base of their nose, which made their face crinkle as if they were frown-ing. The result? The "fake smilers" always rated the cartoons as being substantially funnier than the "fake frowners."[373]

2 At the other end of the spectrum, recent experiments have shown how, when Botox was given to women diagnosed with clinical depression, restricting (for a few months) the use of their muscles to frown, they all reported substantially better moods. Indeed, there's a condition known as "Moebius Syndrome," and those who suffer from it have a kind of facial muscle paralysis, such that they cannot move the muscles in their face to express emotion. They have "frozen," neutral facial expressions. Those afflicted by this sad disorder very frequently report being unable to feel happiness, but more than that, they're unable to experience *any* emotions at all.[374]

If this all seems too weird or implausible, contemporary science has since shed light on why such things are perceived as true. The key is that the old model for understanding these things turns out to be false: causation is not a one-way street from the psychological state of feeling happy to the movement of one's muscles (e.g., in a smile). It turns out that the causal mechanisms go both ways. When one's muscles or movements are cued up a certain way, they send signals back to the brain. This is quite similar to how one's stomach sends signals to the brain when either hungry or full, prompting a matching state of mind. These mechanisms are what enable us to engage in deliberate physical manipulation of our bodies and muscles, to "prime the pump" of our state of mind—moderately, at least, and for a time.

Of course, it's not just that there's a change in individual physiology and brain response. Studies have shown that when you smile, the world smiles back at you. When you act confident, people find you active and fun, and pay more attention to you. When you hug people, they hug you back. When you're watching a show, and lots of people are laughing at something, you tend to laugh along as well. All these things improve your level of happiness.[375]

There's substantial reason to agree with Lyubomirsky upon her referencing a famous slogan from Alcoholics Anonymous (AA): "Fake it until you make it." In the context of AA, it means that all that matters is that you don't engage in the behaviour of drinking: it doesn't matter whether, internally, you are actually wrestling with a massive alcoholic craving. All that matters is that you don't actually drink. Over time the mind will follow, and your internal state will not be as afflicted by such ravenous cravings—you'll have replaced the mental space formerly devoted to the addiction with other, more empowering things. Similarly, *the more you engage in happy-like behaviours, the more you'll drag your brain and consciousness along for the ride*—and then, hopefully, one day your brain will just wake up that way on its own, or even prompt your body to perk up when it might be tired or hungry or what have you. If all else fails, fake being happy; or, more exactly, regularly condition the physical movements of your body to behave like a happier person—until, over time, you actually become one. Lyubomirsky concludes:

> So go for it. Smile, laugh, stand tall, act lively, and give hugs. Act as if you were confident, optimistic, and outgoing. You'll manage adversity, rise to the occasion, create instant connections, make friends and influence people, and become a happier person.[376]

Aristotle (and Others) on Body, Beauty, and Happiness

Every chapter, we've paused to consider what the fount of our philosophical inspiration—Aristotle—has to say about the subject at hand. It may not surprise you to know that he wasn't "into" modern behaviourism. It may, however, surprise you to know that he didn't seem to dwell excessively, or much at all, on the role of health and physical well-being. This is quite counterintuitive, since it's so obvious that a basic level of physical functioning is absolutely essential for any pursuit of happiness. It's also unexpected, as ancient Greek culture placed strong emphasis on physical well-being: it's the land where the Olympics were born, after all![377] Further, we can't forget that there were many wars fought among the various Greek city-states (e.g., Athens, Sparta), and then between the Greeks, banded together, against such bitter foreign foes as the Persians, and later the Romans. All such armed conflicts required a great deal of physical fitness, as most of the fighting was gruesome, high stakes, hand-to-hand combat. Ancient Greek culture practically glorified the warrior, and many of its most prized values and practices can be interpreted as having come from success and prowess on the battlefield. (Aristotle's own obsession with courage may have arisen from this context.)[378] Finally, one of the most time-honoured sayings and principles of ancient Greece, which was handed down to the Romans, was "sound body, sound mind." (One hears the reverse just as often.) This principle expresses, of course, an ideal for a good and happy life, and conveys how the two elements are deeply interrelated—a healthy body is the physical basis for a clear, creative mind, and a sound mind will make every effort to get information on what the body needs and enforce a healthful discipline that will lead to overall flourishing. (Some contemporary experts now use one integrated phrase, "bodymind" or "mindbody," to capture this mutuality.)[379]

In light of all that, one might have expected Aristotle to dwell at length on the role of physical health in the pursuit of happiness. But he didn't. There are but a few fragmented comments, and broader things that it seems fair to infer, but he never developed a robust account of the role of physical well-being as a crucial component of happiness the way that people do today. Now, this isn't to say he was dismissive. He *did* define humanity as a natural creature with three general parts: one shared in common with plants, one shared in common with animals, and one unique to humanity itself. The part shared in common with plants is that of "nutrition and growth," and so we have an explicit acknowledgment of the necessity of tending to one's basic bodily needs and impulses. The human part shared in common with animals, Aristotle continued, is both "motion" and "sense perception." These are clear references to the body, and possibly exercise. There's just no denying, though, that Aristotle was mainly interested in the third part of the human animal—the rational part—and the role it plays in guiding us toward our fullest development and the happiness experienced therein.[380] We can't forget that he occupied a very privileged position in his society, and thus probably never had to do manual labour. His life's work was about "the life of the mind." Overall, I think it's safe to say that Aristotle endorsed care of body as a necessary component of, and resource for, the pursuit of excellence and happiness, at one point even directly endorsing a famous inscription at Delos: "The most just is the most noble, but *health is the best* [emphasis added], and to win what one loves is the pleasantest."[381]

We might be tempted to go further, and suggest that Aristotle's entire picture of happiness and full development is analogous to the process of physical growth and care of the body. Aristotle was insistent that we move from our natural potential toward our fullest development and perfection. Implicit throughout, however, is the analogy of the flowering of a plant from a tiny, immature seed, and/or to the complete growth and life cycle of an animal from mere embryo to a fully grown and flourishing specimen. There's clearly a sense in which, for Aristotle, the successful pursuit of happiness marked the complete process of human growth and what it meant to have enjoyed a successful life. Most Aristotle experts have even translated his phrase for complete happiness, *eudaimonia*, as "flourishing." While this involves much more than mere physical well-being, flourishing is nevertheless a notion with clear and powerful suggestions of, and undertones regarding, robust physical health—being, as they say, "in the prime of one's life." Additionally, thinking back (chapters 1 and 3) on Aristotle's definition of pleasure and virtue, he made so much of "the doctrine of the mean." In terms of pleasure, Aristotle argued that we should always aim, in our actions, toward the mean between the extremes: neither total (stoic) denial of pleasure nor complete hedonistic self-indulgence. Why? Because adhering to the moderate, middle path is precisely what will lead to the best development of the organism in question. [382] When he spoke of virtues (which we'll return to in Chapter 10), Aristotle used the example of courage as the mean between the extremes of cowardice and rashness. Such extremes are seen as bad not merely because they are extremes, but because they are risky, dangerous, and worse for the well-being of the person or organism. In other words, it can be said that *following the mean is the healthiest option amongst our choices.* Thus, the entirety of Aristotle's vision might be interpreted as being based on a kind of "health model" regarding what most strengthens and nourishes an individual, leading to their very best odds at excellence and happiness.

One specific and perhaps surprising thing about the body that Aristotle *did* explicitly say concerns physical beauty: ". . . a man who is very ugly in appearance . . . cannot be considered altogether happy."[383] This may strike the modern reader as harsh and unkind. Aristotle would, no doubt, reply that such is merely truth, and explain further that: a) if the lack of beauty is owing to being unhealthy, and the latter refers to a necessary condition for happiness, then this *must* be true; and/or b) people have been known not to be as social and friendly with people lacking stereotypical beauty, and thus such lack (or snubbing) will cost those people in one of the most important happiness domains—having robust social lives. Again, that may strike today's reader as abrasive. But it's worth our while to explore this subject, as it actually does have a research literature around it, and I think it's fair to say—and can say from my own experience—that a number of chronic conditions can make one feel less attractive. And it's not just chronic pain, or fatigue, which is very often present (at least relative to one's pre-afflicted self). One can also feel less alert—not "on" in a social way—and just not as mindful or as caring about one's physical appearance. I think it's fair to say, though, especially after the initial adjustment and as the ongoing nature of the affliction sinks in, demanding to be managed, that the chronically afflicted *do* think about this issue. The above things concern them, and they do eventually think about their appearance again, as much as the next person. So, what is the truth about the connection between beauty and happiness?

The relationship may require firmer evidence, but the findings that do exist probably overturn ordinary understandings. The rigorous scientific experiments that have been performed *find no strong relationship between physical attractiveness and self-reported happiness.* In one high-quality study, a group of subjects—S—were recruited, as were a group of judges—J. The S group was intensively interviewed and tested, and then ranked individually according to their levels of happiness (mainly self-reported, but also as reported by close associates and revealed through exterior signs like frequent, sincere smiling). The S group was then paraded one by one in front of the J group, who took their time to evaluate the attractiveness of the S group. The S group were totally un-adorned in terms of makeup, flashy clothing, and so on—in fact, they were put in bulky white coats, hair nets, and/or made to stick their faces into cut-out holes to minimize any extraneous influences except raw, physical, facial beauty. The results of the experiment found no significant linkage at all between the happiness levels of S and the attractiveness levels of S as judged by the people in J. (There was one interesting correlation to which we shall return: the people in S who were higher in happiness status *thought of themselves as being more attractive* than how they were ranked by the [perhaps more objective] people in J.)[384] Another excellent study examined the happiness levels of some of the world's most beautiful people: professional models in Paris and New York. It actually found them to be quite an unhappy lot, complaining frequently about: being valued only for their beauty; feeling little autonomy in their work; feeling enormous pressure to maintain their levels of beauty, often at great discomfort and sacrifice (e.g., not being able to eat food they enjoy); and citing how constant travel left them with next-to-no time to develop meaningful interpersonal relationships. The models' self-reported happiness levels were *well below* those of random others within the same age range. (Commentators have emphasized the irony of this: for example, young girls of high school and college/university age often fantasize about being glamorous runway models in Paris and New York, yet the reality is not at all what's desired.)[385]

As a result of these and other findings, Michael Argyll claims there is a "poor" association between beauty and happiness. Chris Peterson goes even further, declaring that there is "zero to small" connection between looks and well-being.[386] Sonja Lyubomirsky summarizes the views of all these psychologists, saying that beauty "does not correlate with happiness," observing that "good-looking people aren't any happier." She explains this, saying that, in general, *when people reflect on their happiness levels, they do not lean too heavily on any one category, such as physical beauty.*[387] Indeed, her thoughts are borne out by the replies of the models just mentioned: when asked about their happiness, they mentioned a whole range of things—autonomy at work, being able to manage their diet how they wanted, relationships, etc.—as opposed to focusing on the one factor of physical attractiveness. It seems compelling to say that such a factor, if present at all, doesn't hit anywhere near as high on "the happiness metre" as others. Ask yourself how happy you are. The things that go through your head are probably not going to rush immediately over to how pleased you are with your looks. Moreover, one's physical appearance is, no doubt, something powerfully subject to hedonic adaptation—you get very used to how you look, for good or bad—and so, over a long period of time (like a lifetime), your physical assets probably dissolve into "background noise," and your attention focuses on other things, such as goals, career, and friends and family.

Yet doubts naturally linger, and one asks: Can this zero-to-small association really be true? Especially when we know—and as these psychologists themselves point out—there's extensive, proven evidence of links between physical attractiveness and the following benefits:

- the initial inclination/disposition of others to like you (and/or to want to get to know you in the first place)

- favourable first impression on job interviews

- heightened likelihood of being elected (if running for public office)

- favourable treatment by the legal system (especially with jury-based trials)

- garnering more attention from parents, caregivers, teachers

- a heightened likelihood of being helped by strangers, either in case of emergency or merely upon request

Plus, in Chapter 1 we discovered research suggesting that, *provided* that people were happy with the results, cosmetic surgery procedures (notably breast augmentation) were actually quite *resistant* to hedonic adaptation, and provided a clear and lasting boost to levels of self-reported happiness. Further, gender studies experts have long noted that, especially for women, society puts much emphasis on their physical attractiveness, and commonly attaches quite real benefits for beauty, and lack of benefits for those deemed lacking. Most men in countless studies and opinion polls, for example, will say that when looking for a female mate, youth and attractiveness are the two most important attributes. (Whereas women tend to say it's the relative industriousness of the male, and his ability and willingness to provide and share resources.)[388]

How can all this NOT add up to a happier life for more conventionally beautiful people? Several thoughts occur:

- The link is under-studied. No doubt this is because researchers have not viewed it as serious or as pressing as other happiness issues, such as clinical depression or the connection between ill health and life satisfaction.

- The research that does exist looks at *direct*, proven links between beauty and happiness, and has found them lacking—or, at least, lacking in clear evidence. But many of the benefits of beauty mentioned above may provide an *indirect*, yet still real, boost to happiness, which research subjects don't separate out from their looks because they are used to them. But they would notice them if they were gone and people started paying less attention to them, stopped complimenting them, or stopped asking them out on dates, and so on. Some of the chronically afflicted may have experienced this first-hand, as a disease, injury, or disorder affected their looks for the worse and through no fault of their own. There are a number of conditions (and/or their treatments) that do this. This negatively affects happiness levels, at least initially, because an expectation regarding how these individuals are used to being treated has now disappeared.

- None of the above research really deals with the connection between beauty and happiness in the way in which Aristotle mentioned it. The research focuses on happiness levels at the top-most strata of beauty, and has found no robust association. But Aristotle's claim, we saw, was actually the reverse: that people at the bottom-most levels of physical attractiveness must have less happiness (presumably for reasons noted above). Aristotle saw such people—no matter how happy they might appear—as still nevertheless wanting to be more attractive. (Indeed, we might ask ourselves: Wouldn't we all choose to be more attractive in some way? Doesn't that itself reveal some kind of positive association?)

As a result, the truth about beauty's connection to happiness may actually be a lot like most of the other external goods we've discussed, such as money and health. This is to say: there's a vital threshold, and it might be a mixture of objective characteristics (e.g., symmetry of features) and subjective phenomena (e.g., how pleased you are with your physical appearance). If you fall below this threshold, your overall happiness *is* negatively affected; however, if you are above this threshold, beauty probably does *not* have a robust association with your life satisfaction. I speculate, too, that direction matters—especially to the downside: if you were previously pleased with your appearance, and it has since fallen below the threshold, your happiness will (likely) be negatively impacted. Many people on popular weight-loss reality shows describe their motivation in these terms: they became very displeased with how they looked, which made them angry, and motivated them toward change. But note that, in such circumstances, beauty gains to the upside likely mean gains in overall happiness.

It's important to note that, if you suffer from a chronic condition that has negatively impacted your physical appearance it might positively affect your happiness if you make an increased effort to look after your appearance. Now, of course, you likely have bigger fish to fry. But then again, *every little bit helps*, especially when it comes to boosting happiness. Luckily, many things that affect or boost one's looks also boost one's health in general: sufficient sleep, good nutrition, and regular exercise in particular. But perhaps easier gains can be made via a new hairstyle, some fresh fashions, or just in general *making an effort to not surrender.* Doing any of the above will also enhance one's feeling of control—a vital component of people's happiness, and of special relevance for the chronically afflicted. In any event, of course your main focus in this regard should be in terms of what you yourself find attractive and beautiful and not to place undue pressure on oneself in light of social standards of conventional beauty.

One final thing to recall about the link between beauty and happiness: in Chapter 3, we noted how research associated beautiful surroundings with increased pleasure. Another happiness booster is thus *to surround oneself with beautiful things*—a special work of art, a particular colour scheme, some new interior decoration or furniture, people you like and love, or simply being out in the everyday grandeur of nature.

Motion and Exeroise

There exist all kinds of evidence that physical activity, on a daily basis, is one of the best things for one's overall health and happiness. We evolved as beings-in-motion, and our mammal bodies still crave physical activity, rewarding us with physical fitness, mental alertness, and emotional boosters. As many experts have noted, however, these Stone Age cravings have, in the past few decades, run up against the structure of our advanced Information Age economies, which demand that we put in time sitting in front of a computer, or stuck in traffic, and otherwise being sedentary in ways that our bodies were not evolved to handle. The consequences of this can be: obesity, lack of energy, disruption of sleep patterns, and higher risk of all kinds of chronic conditions—particularly diabetes and cardiovascular disorders like heart disease.[389]

There's irrefutable scientific evidence that physical exercise is one of the most *immediate* mood boosters (e.g., its impact on one's heartbeat, hormones, overall energy, and brain focus), and one of the best *long-lasting* mood boosters over time. The evidence is so compelling that doctors throughout North America are increasingly—literally—writing out *prescriptions for exercise* as a way to persuade people to become more physically active.[390] I myself have such a medical prescription—in my case, it's for strength/resistance training, as my anti-seizure meds are known to contribute to long-term bone loss. Working out with weights counteracts that. Upon being misdiagnosed with a heart condition, I took it upon myself to exercise aggressively, every day. At the time, I focused on cardiovascular training, to strengthen the heart. This was the only thing that seemed to work as I began my pro-happiness program. It provided more stability with the seizures, helped me sleep better at night, enhanced my mood and interest in social events, and I regained a sense of control and mastery when things were spiralling into chaos. I now have a more diverse kind of exercise program, and would evangelize such activity to anyone willing to listen—including those whose chronic affliction renders them physically limited or unable in some ways. At its core, exercise is about physical motion—moving the body around—and, for very nearly everyone, *some kind of motion is possible.* Let's quickly look at the basic forms of exercise, and then return to the evidence connecting physical motion to health and happiness.[391]

There are three basic kinds of exercise. They are:

1 **Strength training**. Also known as resistance training, or weight-based training. This is intended to prevent muscle loss and atrophy, and to help grow one's muscles by subjecting them to challenge/resistance/tension. ("Time under tension" is a favourite phrase of some weight trainers.) Now, there are many so-called "body weight" strength exercises, such as doing leg squats without weights. Many of these can be excellent, especially classics such as push-ups. Anything designed to create and build stronger muscles counts as strength or resistance training.[392] Commonly, though, we think of people picking up barbells or dumbbells or kettle bells and lifting them, either with one's legs or one's arms. See the note for various exercises using such.[393]

2 **Cardiovascular training**. This is exercise that targets the heart and lungs. It's focused on strengthening the power and endurance of the body's most important muscle—the heart—as well as on increasing the health and vigour of the lungs and their ability to absorb and deliver oxygen, and to eliminate carbon dioxide. The classic exercise here, of course, is running, but cycling is also great and can be less of a strain on the joints.[394] Swimming is also excellent and, in fact, is one of a handful of truly superb "total body" workouts where everything is employed—strength, cardio, and stretching. Swimming is also probably the lowest "impact" exercise in terms of long-term effects on one's joints.[395] Other great cardio workouts include two you might not think of: rowing and shadow boxing (i.e., practice boxing without an actual opponent). The constant motion and push/pull of the upper-body muscles blasts one's heart rate and gets the sweat flying, and your breathing is intensified.[396] One of my favourite cardio exercises is something called a "burpee." It's

a body weight exercise and requires no equipment. Start at a standing position then quickly squat down on all fours. Put all your weight on your arms and hands, and kick back both feet until the legs are fully extended, toes touching the ground. Then reverse the motion by quickly bringing your legs up and tucking them into your torso, and then re-extending your whole body to the standing upright position. That's one burpee. To add challenge, do a push-up at the bottom and a jump at the top. It may interest readers to know that the latest research suggests that cardio training, or sustained aerobic exercise, is the single best exercise for the long-term overall health of the brain.[397]

3 **Flexibility training**. Also called stretching. It's more than that, though; it involves a controlled stretching out of one's muscles that both strengthens them and relieves tension. But the control requires deliberation and balance, which is why it's more commonly called "flexibility training." The classic example here is yoga, one of the world's best, cheapest, and most accessible forms of exercise. *Men's Health* magazine surveyed owners of some of the best gyms across America a few years ago and asked them the following question: "If you were restricted to only one form of exercise, which would it be?" Fully 100 percent answered yoga. It's easy on the joints and thus can be practiced for a lifetime; very cheap (you just need a small space and comfy clothes—mat optional); eases tension and leads to deeper sleep; reduces chronic pain and lowers blood pressure; strengthens and tones all muscles; augments immune response; even touches on cardio in the sense that it conditions deep breathing techniques.[398]

Only you know what kinds of exercise you like. *The point is to do something, and to integrate it into your daily life.* Cardio is, generally, the most demanding for those new to exercise programs, and thus should be entered into slowly and cautiously, especially if one has a chronic condition. Start with walking, or light cycling on a stationary bike. There's plenty of emerging evidence that *any kind* of weight training, even with fairly light weights, is crucial, and seniors taking weight training for the first time in their sixties, seventies, and beyond have experienced a range of clear and substantial positive health benefits much greater than what was previously thought.[399] But yoga, I think, is probably overall the best single recommendation, especially for those with chronic conditions who may also have a physical disability, injury, or limited range of movement.

The key with exercise, as many have noted, is to gain knowledge about it—to know yourself, your preferences, and capabilities:

- **Pace yourself**. Evidence shows that people who begin exercise programs most commonly fail because they try to do too much, too soon. They can end up finding it too straining/unpleasant, and either injure themselves or give up. Start small. If you are patient, you'll be shocked at how much your body will respond, and how quickly you'll be able to do more and challenge yourself. The body—even a sick one—can be an incredibly impressive instrument if you give it what it needs and treat it with respect.[400]

- **Make it a habit**. Build exercise into the structure of your daily life. I have a formal workout routine that I do every morning after breakfast for an hour and a half, six days out of seven. It's a total-body workout, which is to say it blends all three kinds: strength, cardio, and flexibility. It has aspects of high intensity, to get the heart pounding and sweat flying, as well as low intensity, with slow and deliberate stretching. It's the very last thing I'd ever give up, in terms of both my treatment and my happiness program. People tell me that they "admire my commitment" in this regard, and I appreciate their kindness. But it's so much a part of me, and how I manage my life and my disease, that I don't even think of it in those terms. And the workout is its own thing: I don't skimp on other physical activities because I've done it. If my son wants to play tennis in the afternoon in the summer, or if I feel like doing some physical activity in the evening, I do it. It's all just "fitness gravy."

Numerous studies have established the amazing effects on health and happiness created by regular physical activity. Let's focus first, and quickly, on health. Consider how the residents of Blue Zones are quite active (albeit in a low-impact way) and have both striking longevity as well as impressively low rates of disease and disorder. According to Lyubomirsky:

> Physical activity reduces anxiety and stress; protects us from dying in general (and from dying of heart disease and cancer, in particular); reduces the risk of numerous diseases (diabetes, colon cancer, hypertension); builds bones, muscles and joints; increases quality of life; improves sleep; protects against cognitive impairments as we age; and helps control weight.[401]

Physical activity also improves one's sexual desire and performance, and we've seen previously that a good sex life contributes to self-reported happiness. Many people conduct physical activity with others—whether group exercise or team sports—and thus enjoy both exercise and a deeper social life. There's really nothing in life that being physically active doesn't help. It is, simply and commandingly, *one of the most proven overall happiness boosters*, both directly and indirectly.[402]

Many recent studies have taken to comparing the effects of exercise on people with taking direct happiness boosters like strong anti-depressant medications (e.g., Prozac and Zoloft). Time and again, these high-quality studies have shown that making physical activity a part of your daily life has *at least as much* positive effect—and often more—as taking a course of anti-depressants. Additionally, exercise is: much cheaper, can be combined with augmenting one's social life, and benefits one's entire body—brain, heart, lungs, muscles, blood flow, immune response.[403]

Pain is one of the top reasons why people go to see a doctor at all, and it's estimated that 50 million Americans suffer from chronic pain of some kind (i.e., one in six or seven).[404] As the legendary Garrison Keillor once noted in an essay on ageing: "You learn that many medications promise vague benefits but make you feel lousy. You learn that pain is hard to ignore and talking about it makes it worse, and that a cheerful heart is a good strategy."[405] Other good strategies may include acupressure, acupuncture, massage, and (gentle) electrical stimulation of some nerves, alongside getting good sleep, meditating, positive visualization, yoga, and, in general, considering very seriously what motion and exercise—in any form—can do for you. An emerging trend in health research shows that traditional advice to "let it rest" generally does *not* help with pain management, and that *motion is better*. Further recent findings illustrate how, in almost every jurisdiction in North America, veterinarians get more, and better, formal training in pain management techniques than general practitioners. Yet most people still consult their family doctors for pain-management advice. Do so certainly, but also request a referral to a specialist board-certified in pain management. Pain is the opposite of pleasure and can be a severe drag on one's quality of life. When long lasting, it's thought to double one's risk of attempting suicide.[406] Chronic pain is itself a chronic condition, and a formidable foe of human well-being.

Nutrition and Hydration

In their book *The Happiness Diet*, Tyler Graham and Drew Ramsey make several sharp remarks. First, they note how strange it is that, in the recent proliferation of happiness literature, so much of the message is about inspirational motivation and deploying various techniques discovered by positive psychology. It is either personal psychology or (increasingly) recommendations for socioeconomic policy of the sort we saw in chapters 4 and 5. Almost none of it deals directly with what we eat and drink, and how it can have an enormous impact on one's mood, and on the biological resources needed to be happy and to pursue other techniques—goal selection and fulfillment, robust social life, autonomy at work, flow, etc.—known to make most people happier. This is bizarre and unfortunate, of course, as those further things (regarding career, relationships, physical exercise, and so on) presuppose and require sufficient nutrition and hydration. Truly, if ever there was a necessary condition and external good required for the pursuit of happiness, it's having enough quality inputs of food and water to power the very machine with which one pursues happiness and flourishing. This subject is of further relevance for those with chronic conditions, as of course having such high-quality inputs is required to provide one with the best odds at having the biological resources needed to heal, or at least cope as best as one can, with the burdens of affliction. Summarizing these thoughts, Graham and Ramsey quote Hippocrates—one of the Western world's earliest doctors, whose life (460–370 BCE) briefly overlapped with that of Aristotle. Hippocrates suggested: "Let food be thy medicine, and let thy medicine be thy food." Hippocrates is today considered one of the all-time greats in the history of medicine and, indeed, is the namesake of the very oath upon which doctors swear, fulfilling the requirements they need to practice medicine. We'd be foolish to ignore the advice of so distinguished and influential a person.[407]

Yet we often do. Rates of obesity and diabetes are rapidly growing throughout the developed world, and it's thought that at least the majority of adults in America count as either obese or overweight for their age, gender, and/or height. Diabetes and insulin sensitivity (or "pre-diabetes") are among the fastest-growing chronic diseases in North America, and can have serious long-term negative consequences on one's life. Many such cases have been associated with poor dietary habits, as well as with a sedentary lifestyle lacking regular physical activity. However, our focus here is not weight loss but the kind of basic nutritional habits needed to enable and promote the pursuit of happiness. We can thus agree with Graham and Ramsey that it would be profoundly wrong-headed to focus all one's efforts on techniques of psychology—gratitude, meditation, socialization, etc.—while filling up one's body with sub-optimal nutrition, which sabotages mood, saps energy, kills mental focus, and offers only third-rate resources for powering bodily systems, healing damaged tissue, and helping one handle everything life throws at them—including, perhaps, a chronic condition.[408]

Graham and Ramsey cleverly note how so much of the modern American diet (which they labelled "MAD") is composed of eating a series of "Unhappy Meals." These are fast foods dripping with unhealthy fats, processed foods with natural nutrients removed and replaced by chemical preservatives, diets sky-high in sugars and related simple carbohydrates (not to mention salt), nowhere near enough fresh fruits and vegetables, liquid calories (usually fizzy, sweet sodas) instead of pure water, and portion sizes completely out of control. All add up to a range of health problems (e.g., obesity, diabetes, high blood pressure and heart disease, certain cancers, and non-alcoholic fatty liver disease), and a range of inputs completely inconsistent with the effective pursuit of happiness and flourishing. As Graham and Ramsey view it, the ultimate seat of the experience of happiness within the body is the brain. The brain is the body's master controller and computer, and—as seen in Chapter 3—is in charge of the release of chemicals associated with both comfort, pleasure, and relaxation (like serotonin), and those associated with anxiety, anger, and discomfort (like cortisol). The very structure of one's brain, as well as the effectiveness of its functions (like electro-chemical release), has been built—and maintained—using the raw materials from food and drink ingested on a daily basis. (Even though the average brain amounts to only 2 percent of one's body weight, it needs approximately 20 percent of the total calories one consumes every day.) Tyler and Graham thus concur with the famous phrase "you are what you eat." If you truly care about your happiness, you have to do what you can to take care with what you eat and drink, and to find what works best for your particular body's needs.[409]

Specifically, Graham and Ramsey cite numerous studies showing the very negative impact that the typical MAD diet has on three areas of brain function crucial to most people's experience of happiness: cognitive functioning, emotional control, and the management of anxiety and worry. Diets high in the things mentioned above, and low in such things as fresh fruits and vegetables, whole grains, high-quality proteins (e.g., fish, meat, eggs, nuts, and legumes), and water, have been proven to affect people's reasoning power and attention span, their irritability and ability to remain calm and composed under strain, and their capacity to put a lid on their worries (especially social anxieties) and get on with their daily tasks. They offer their "formula for brain happiness":

Clear thinking and focused attention = a greater ability to plan and execute

Steady and content moods = a greater ability to absorb the frustrations of life and regulate your emotions

Freedom from worry = turning your wheels, not spinning them

PLUS

Energy to engage = a vibrant pursuit of all life's possibilities

They conclude, "Achieving these ideals is possible only through a well-fed, well-nourished brain."[410]

Of course, there's more to your body than your brain; yet, when broken down in this way, the connection between nutrition, hydration, and happiness is irrefutable. Some further facts:

- Losing as little as 1 percent of your body weight in fluid leads to measurable decreases in mood, concentration, and energy. Further, there is substantial evidence that, systematically, we mistake thirst for hunger. Water, of course, is the supreme thirst quencher, and is that which our bodies most require. *Sufficient hydration with water thus meets a vital need, cuts down on over-eating, and enables happiness.* Experts differ on the exact amount needed per day—it depends on your activity levels and sweating—but it should be substantial, and enough to make you urinate at least five times daily.[411]

- *There's evidence of a vicious cycle between bad dietary decisions and a bad mood.* We've seen how filling your body with bad ingredients is going to hamper its ability to function, and thus your ability to be happy over the long term. But the opposite is also true: when in a bad mood, one is more likely to make poor dietary decisions, both in terms of eating too many calories (quantity) and in terms of those calories being "empty," biased toward short-term taste (seeking a mood boost) rather than enduring, helpful nutrition.[412]

- More narrowly, researchers have discovered *a robust link between clinical depression and the consumption of either fast food or junk food.* Regularly eating these types of foods raises one's risk of being diagnosed with clinical depression by between 40 and 60 percent.[413]

- At the other end of the spectrum, researchers have discovered *a connection between the consumption of fresh produce and self-reported levels of subjective happiness.* Those who eat at least two to three servings of fresh fruit and vegetables every day have measurably higher happiness scores than those who eat less. The happiest? Those who report consuming seven to eight servings daily.[414]

I urge people to read some good books/magazines on general nutrition, and keep up with reliable nutrition columnists online. In terms of magazines, I recommend the nutrition columns in *Men's Health* and *Women's Health* magazines, and also *Prevention* magazine. Rodale Publishing puts out many nice, relevant books in this regard. Avoid "niche" books, especially by celebrities, which focus in on one eccentric food factor in particular, be it wheat, bacon, dairy, or what have you. Knowledgeable experts insist on two things: 1) it's about your diet as a whole, and no one thing is a magic bullet, either for weight loss or general nutrition; and 2) the best diet is one you're actually going to follow, thus extreme diets that call for the utter elimination of something, or only eating one thing, are highly implausible. Many of the major newspapers now have nutrition columns and, in terms of books, I'd recommend in particular Dr. Andrew Weil's *New York Times* bestseller, *Eating Well for Optimum Health*.[415] More recently, Mike Roussell's *The Six Pillars of Nutrition* offers "six pillars of healthy eating":

- it's better to eat more frequent and smaller meals throughout the day

- reduce the amount of processed food in your diet

- eat plenty of fresh fruit and vegetables

- eat lots of lean protein

- drink water, as opposed to any other kind of liquid

- be highly limited and strategic when it comes to eating sugars and carbohydrates. As a general rule, avoid anything that is coloured white except as a rare treat.[416]

These are all great pieces of advice, to which I'd add the following:

- Strive to eat local and/or organic food wherever possible, especially in connection with fruits and vegetables, to cut down on pesticides in your diet. Organic fruits and vegetables have also been shown to have more antioxidants.

- When going to the grocery store, stick to the perimeter of the store for your food purchases: all the processed, packaged foods are in the middle.

- You want to eat as many raw and natural whole foods as possible (i.e., foods with only one ingredient: the thing itself). In terms of carbs, whole grains, as opposed to any kind of processed white grain, are the order of the day. You should not eat white bread every day, much less with every meal. Train your palate to enjoy whole grains.

- When it comes to fruits and vegetables, eat many and a wide variety. Experts recommend you "spread your colours around," so that you eat fruits and vegetables adding up to a rainbow of diverse colours (as each colour is usually associated with its own unique health-giving benefit).

- Be aware that sometimes, yes, you should eat for taste (Chapter 3, on pleasure), but other times you should eat purely for health reasons ("let food be thy medicine . . ."). As you get into the groove of advanced nutrition, you'll find that, over time, you can make those two categories almost completely overlap, such that what you *want* to eat and what you *should* eat are the same.

- Beware of empty liquid calories, especially with sweetened drinks of any kind. In general, it's best to get all your calories from food and drink mainly water (which is calorie-free and one of your body's most-needed substances). Other good, water-heavy, nearly calorie-free drinks include tea and coffee (without sweetener—green tea and black coffee especially). Milk is neither the amazing elixir nor the terrible villain it's often made out to be: if you can digest lactose, exercise regularly, and have potential issues with loss of bone density, it can sometimes be a good choice.[417]

- Also beware of any advice that obsesses about "micronutrients" at the expense of the big picture "macronutrients." Macronutrients form the vast majority of your diet, and consist of protein, fat, and carbohydrates. Micronutrients, by contrast, are so called because only tiny amounts are needed, and they notably include various vitamins and minerals. Many a quack and charlatan focus on their favourite pet vitamin/mineral and promote it relentlessly. The key is this: if you get your macronutrients right, and follow the above advice, the micronutrients will take care of themselves. The latest research suggests that, at any given meal, if what's on your plate totals 100 percent, then fresh fruit and vegetables should be about half that; the remaining 50 percent should consist of about 30 percent lean protein and 20 percent carbohydrates in the form of whole grains (keep in mind that fruit supplies simple carbohydrates or sugars). It should all be washed down with water, or tea/coffee, possibly even milk. Any other kind of liquid should be considered a treat—wine, even if consumed regularly, should only be imbibed in small amounts (and with lots of water).[418]

- Experts are fond of the phrase "nutrient-dense foods." In general, these refer to foods that give you the most, and most-diverse, nutrient content for your hard-earned grocery dollar. *They are the best building blocks for a healthful and happy body and mind.* Notably, they include foods that are: high in protein, like eggs and lean meat; high in fibre, and natural vitamins and minerals, such as fruits and vegetables; and high in "good fats," like nuts, legumes, and some dairy (especially unsweetened yogurt). Eating a diet heavy in nutrient-rich foods provides excellent nutrition and is both filling and satisfying.

Relatedly, nutritionists have arrived at a general consensus on so-called "super foods"—those that are nutrient-dense in both macro and micro senses. The following list, though decent, is not exhaustive or definitive:

Proteins: eggs, salmon, tuna, sardines, lean chicken breast, grass-fed organic beef

Beans/Legumes: edamame, navy beans, kidney beans, chickpeas/garbonzo beans, lentils

Nuts: almonds, peanuts, walnuts, pine nuts, pistachios (note: pure "nut butters," with only crushed and churned nuts, count as well)

Fruits: apples, oranges, bananas, watermelon, figs/prunes, pineapple, bing cherries, grapes, tomatoes, and all berries

Vegetables: avocados, carrots, sweet potatoes, artichoke, Brussels sprouts, broccoli, spinach, kale, bok choy, beets, seaweed, peppers (especially red and yellow), mushrooms, garlic, onions, leeks

Grains: whole grains, quinoa, oatmeal, flaxseed

Dairy: unsweetened yogurt (especially with probiotics), butter

Condiments: olive oil, curry (turmeric), cinnamon, ginger

Sweets: honey, dark chocolate, pure maple syrup, molasses

Liquids: pure water, green and unsweetened tea, black and unsweetened coffee, wine or pure grape juice, milk or chocolate milk[419]

Finally, there are many high-quality online resources and food guides, broken down into specific subjects, which also have mobile apps to help keep track of what you eat and drink, calorie expenditure, and so on.[420]

FIG 17 CORE ELEMENTS OF BODY HAPPINESS

Knowledge (about health, a.k.a. "health literacy")

No pollution (no smoking, substance abuse, excessive alcohol, or any behaviour carrying substantial risk of bodily harm)

Good sleep hygiene (and hygiene in general)

Proper breathing

Good hydration

Nourishing nutrition

Proper weight range (and monitoring)

Lots of (daily) physical motion and exercise

Sufficient sexual release (preferably a mutually enjoyable sex life with other, consenting human beings)

Taking care of one's appearance

Decent institutional support (notably, effective use of a good health care system) and **qualified medical advice**

Short-term behavioural manipulation

Long-term mimicking of the blue-zones' lifestyle

Conclusion: Aristotle's Warnings About Weakness of Will

We'll return to this subject at the very end of this book, but for now it's worth wrapping up this chapter (and section) by mentioning one of Aristotle's deepest and most relevant thoughts. It focuses on the relationship between *knowing* something to be true/good/right and actually *doing* that thing, and truly making it part of your life. Aristotle wisely noted the potential gap between these two things—knowing and doing—and observed that it allowed space for "weakness of will" to occur. Weakness of will is a common human failing that happens when you know what you should do but still fail to do it. This can be due to short-term things, like fatigue or excessive emotion (e.g., fear, anger, greed, lust), or long-term things, such as procrastination, a lack of discipline, risk-prone tendencies, or—in the moral case—even a bad or corrupt character. In any event, one's will fails to execute what one's mind knows is best.[421] We'll come back to the moral question, wherein weakness of will can lead to ethical mistakes (e.g., lying, infidelity, cruelty), usually doing harm to one's interpersonal relationships. In this chapter, however, we note that it's not enough merely to know what makes for a well-functioning and happy body: *one must use willpower to make it happen*. This holds true for exercise, nutrition, weight control, not hurting one's body, and so on. In most cases, it boils down to habitual actions and daily practical routines. We'll discuss in the next section (on the internal goods) effective strategies for taking all the knowledge—the "well-being wisdom" and "happiness literacy"—we've learned in this book and sewing it into the fabric, and daily habits, of one's life.

The Internal Goods

CHAPTER 8

Mental Hygiene

This book's final section is on the internal goods: the third pillar of happiness. Internal goods are: states of mind, states of feeling, and states of valuing. There are three sizable subjects in the happiness literature that concern us here:

1 processes of thought and cognition (*belief* in general)

2 processes of feeling and affectivity (*emotion* in general)

3 processes of making judgments about ethics and morality, and motivating oneself to act decently—or not (*values* in general)

By this point, it goes without saying that these distinctions— like others previously encountered—are artificial, and purely for the purposes of conceptual analysis and an organized layout. *There's strong interconnectedness amongst all three factors of belief, emotion, and valuing.*[422] The first subject in this chapter, to illustrate this interconnectedness, is how the life of the mind figures into our pursuit of happiness. We've encountered substantial thoughts on this topic already:

- In Chapter 1, we discussed goal selection, the weighting and prioritizing of goals, and the resolution to pursue them.

- In Chapter 2, we considered a life of happiness as the most rational and fulfilling goal, and pondered what some say is a rival form of life—that of meaning. We also saw that happiness and meaning need *not* be mutually exclusive.

- In Chapter 3 we encountered pleasure, which is more about sensory stimulation and gratification than cognition; however, we also discussed flow, savouring, and mindfulness—states that involve the mind and, it might be said, are the very essence of *thinking in a happy way about the present moment.*

- Chapters 4 and 5 described the world of work as well as the full set of social institutions more broadly. These manifestly involve intelligence, brain power, and effort—though perhaps the only subject there of present concern is the role of formal education in a happy life. So perhaps the first thing that needs to be asserted in this chapter on mental hygiene is the general proposition that *the more you know, the greater your chances at happiness.*

Aristotle would, no doubt, strongly agree—knowledge about reality is empowering and provides one with further tools with which to pursue fulfillment. It was an article of faith for Aristotle that the fullest development of one's rational potential is the most distinctive and special part of human nature. Indeed, his whole conception of happiness was based on the idea that reason—assisted by willpower and guiding our emotions, bodies, and actions—*understands* that happiness should be our main goal in life, and *is in charge of locating* the best ways and tools to lead us from here to there.[423]

For any lingering suspicions that "ignorance is bliss": such perhaps gets its "hook" from memories of happy childhood innocence corroded by worldly adult experience. But there's no denying that, over the long term, it is to the impersonal benefit of everyone that humanity advance its knowledge and skill as much as possible. No doubt we've all discovered that the achievements, experiences, and pleasures of adulthood vastly outweigh the simple joys of childhood. This book has made much of the idea, stressed last chapter, that *an absolutely vital pro-happiness tool for the chronically afflicted is knowledge about one's condition—* its nature, treatment, and management options—as opposed to ignorance, continued debilitation, and perpetual victimization.

So, having already discussed such things in detail, we're not going to repeat them here. But, beyond this firm general linkage between knowledge and happiness, there are a number of additional topics to which we've yet to pay sufficient attention. These are:

- positive thinking and "optimism versus pessimism"

- the role of social connections and comparisons in positive thinking

- the avoidance of rumination about self, others, and the past

- spirituality and religious belief

- meditation and related forms of absorbed mindfulness

One thing we've already discussed (e.g., in chapters 1 and 2) but will need to return to here is evolutionary psychology. Recall: this is the idea that the inescapable process of natural selection must have had—over the millennia—a huge impact upon how we humans typically think, feel, and what we value.

According to Daniel Nettle, when it comes to our pursuit of happiness in life—whether we are ill or well—we have no choice but to rely on the very psychological programming (and tendencies of thought and feeling) that are, in many ways, designed to limit our happiness. *Evolution wants us to be mostly—but never entirely—happy.*[424]

Why the chapter title "Mental Hygiene"? Hygiene, of course, refers to health, and to rules and practices that promote health. I like this metaphor, about states of thinking and feeling that are healthful and invigorating. Not perfect or excessively "sunny," as some of the positive thinking material can come across as promoting. Just healthy thinking habits, which are conducive to happiness. Also—perhaps more importantly?—I like the hygienic implications of getting rid of (or minimizing) bad habits, unhelpful thoughts, and things that induce sickness, malfunctioning, and unhappiness. Scrub those tendencies with some conceptual toothpaste, so to speak! Finally, it's important and persuasive to note the daily implications of hygiene. To have good teeth, you need to brush them every day; to get in good physical shape, you need to exercise regularly; likewise, to be in good mental and emotional shape, certain things need to become part of one's daily life, while certain others need to be firmly and consistently avoided.

Positive Thinking

One of the major topics in the happiness literature—indeed, prior to the popularity of such—is whether we can condition our style of thinking into one that's positive, and thus pleasant and a contributing factor toward our well-being. Much of this book, of course, is broadly about positive thinking; what I mean, here in this chapter, is the narrower sense in which our processes of thinking either contribute to or detract from our fulfilment. Looming largest in the literature on this topic is the clash between optimism and pessimism.

There's dispute about how best to define these terms. Some define optimism as a disposition to believe that, in the future, things one finds good and pleasant will be more plentiful than things one finds bad and unpleasant. This is then combined with a disposition to act in accordance with such beliefs (i.e., to pursue said good and positive things). Pessimism then would be a disposition of thought that, in the future, more negative than positive things will happen in one's life. Thus defined, optimism has been at least moderately linked in rigorous scientific experiments to actual positive outcomes in life, *most notably in terms of effective coping with negative events* (including illness or injury). Conversely, pessimism thus defined has been moderately linked with negative events, and researchers have argued—quite plausibly—that this is because such beliefs induce behaviour that effectively counts as "giving up" and surrendering to the negative event.[425]

We should canvass other definitions before delving more fully into the causal connections. Many researchers contrast "big and small" optimism and pessimism. Big optimism is the belief that this brighter future concerns large-scale events, whether in the world or in one's own life. In the world, this would concern things like peace, prosperity, and progress; in one's life it may concern a successful career, a happy marriage, great kids, and overall good health. Big pessimism, by contrast, is the notion that, writ large, the world is not on such a broad-based upward trend but, rather, on a rougher ride toward conflict, economic struggle, and cultural decline. Small optimism would then concern tiny, trivial events in one's life: believing that one will catch their flight in time, or be pleased with their haircut, or give a "bang-on" presentation at work. And small pessimism would be that similarly scaled events will not turn out so well: the person you want to ask out will say no, or you'll actually hate your new haircut, or that a struggle you're having at work won't be resolved in a pleasant way.[426]

Relatedly, some define the core difference between optimism and pessimism as the difference in one's "explanatory style," particularly with regard to negative events in one's life. The notion is this: consider a substantially negative event in your life, whether a major illness or injury, a failed marriage, unemployment, legal trouble, and so on. How do you talk about it or explain it, to others, and especially to yourself? Pessimism has been defined by researchers as talking about the causes of these negative events in ways that are: internal, stable, and global. By contrast, optimists are defined as those who discuss the causes of negative events in their lives as being external, unstable, and specific. For instance, those who would view job troubles as being caused by a downturn in the nation's economy, and/or by their current boss' poor management style, or by their own temporary loss of temper, would be considered more optimistic than those who think, by contrast, that it's *always* their fault; that they can't ever really find the proper fit and have given up on the idea of career satisfaction.[427]

We don't need to agree on perfect definitions of optimism and pessimism to agree that we are now substantially inside the ballpark of important issues we need to discuss. Using the definitions above, psychological researchers have proven the following associations between the two tendencies of thought:

Optimism has been associated with:

- positive short-term mood

- longer-term upbeat morale or attitude toward life and others

- resilience and more resourceful and focused problem solving

- real-world success and achievement in academic, athletic, professional, and political life

- popularity and a robust social life

- good health

- enhanced longevity

By contrast, pessimism has been linked to:

- negative short-term mood, especially in terms of sadness or anger

- long-term clinical depression

- passivity and fatalism in the face of challenges and/or obstacles

- consequent failure, or lack of success, across a range of dimensions: professionally, romantically, athletically, and politically

- social estrangement, alienation, and loneliness

- higher rates of sickness (or morbidity)

- a shorter life span[428]

It may be of special interest to learn of a detailed, long-term, and rigorous study undertaken at Harvard on the association between optimism and health. Research subjects—as undergrads in their early twenties—underwent painstaking interviews, surveys, and related interviews with their friends and family members, and were then ranked according to their relative optimism or pessimism. They were kept track of—not just for years but decades—and had to report in regularly, both on their attitudes as well as their health status. It turned out that *being an optimist was a strong predictor of good health and well-being for over thirty-five years* following the original set of tests![429]

Many of these associations can be traced to the attitudes of resilience and perseverance (in the case of optimism), and tendencies toward giving up and surrendering (in the case of pessimism). To this extent, *both attitudes are clearly associated with coping patterns*, and in particular (in the case of health status) either healthful or unhealthy behaviours. If one believes that things are going to get better, and there's a lot to look forward to in the future, they have a strong added incentive to engage in the kinds of healthful behaviours that will facilitate energy and vitality. We discussed such healthy behaviours last chapter, in connection with exercise, nutrition, sleep hygiene, and so on. Conversely—as seen in Chapter 3—if one is convinced that things are going to get worse, they might be much more tempted, and inclined, to engage in unhealthy behaviours. One might think: Why not? At the very least, their pessimism may sap them of the motivation to stay in shape, to not take drugs, drink, or smoke tobacco, to eat properly, to advance one's knowledge and skills, and so on.

Others have made far bolder claims on the part of these connections, claiming for instance that pessimism can actually reduce one's immune system response, or is in fact a major cause of clinical depression (an interesting notion, in that it re-conceptualizes what is considered a mood disorder—depression—as the product of a cognitive pattern of thought and belief). The truth of such claims is beyond me, and so I won't endorse them, but it does seem straightforward that pessimism is associated with a reduced incentive to persevere, to engage in healthy behaviours, and in general to putting in determined effort across a range of aspects of one's life—personally and professionally. To this extent, *pessimism is a clear and present danger to those attempting to be happy or find happiness in spite of illness.*[430]

In this regard, there are two kinds of question most frequently asked about optimism and pessimism:

1 Isn't optimism in some sense illusory, or even irrational? Isn't pessimism more realistic? (After all, in the end we all die, and so the future can't *literally* always keep getting better.) And isn't pessimism in fact the most natural pattern of thought after being diagnosed with a serious chronic condition?

2 Even if optimism has been associated with a whole range of desirable outcomes (as described above), can this information actually be of value? In particular, *can we truly just "up and become" optimists*, or are our patterns of thought strongly associated with certain personality and character traits that are resistant to change?

Let's deal with the two questions together, turning once more to evolutionary psychology. Many researchers—beginning with Margaret Matlin and David Stang[431]—have offered strong evidence that, in some sense, optimistic patterns of thought are intrinsic to nearly every human being's mode of thinking, and have probably been naturally selected over time. This is to say that, as a species, we've been conditioned by evolution to be optimists of a kind. This is both good and bad. The bad is that, as we'll see, it does lead us toward patterns of thinking that are self-inflating and potentially self-deceiving—and thus could be called illusory or irrational. The good, especially for those with chronic conditions and struggling with pessimism, is realizing that, deep down, you *want* to have happy thought processes, and *your brain is naturally inclined towards optimism*—so it's not going to be the monumental struggle you may fear.

Consider first the claim by psychologist Chris Peterson: "[H]edonic tone of thought is a potent determinant of all sorts of cognitive processes."[432] This is a high-brow way of saying that most people display a bias toward optimism, and a generally happy style of thought and belief. Don't believe it? Here are some of the most relevant (and revealing!) associations that researchers have proven to be true of the vast majority of people, or at least the vast majority of those not suffering from a severe mental illness:[433]

- People seek out more positive stimuli than negative; they report to others that they encounter positive stimuli more frequently than what they actually do.

- People are quick to realize what will be positive and safe stimuli for them, and take longer to recognize a negative or potentially threatening stimulus.

- People report positive stimuli being larger and more intense than what they actually are.

- People believe that good events are more likely to occur in the future than bad events, even when the objective probability of both is the same. (Insurance companies have long known, and have reflected in the pricing structure of their policies, that *people seriously underestimate the likelihood of bad events happening to them personally.* They even refer to this as "optimism bias.")[434]

- People share good news much more frequently than bad news. (E.g., social media has become notorious for people making maximum use of "impression management," trying to put forward the very best version or image of their lives.)

- In most languages, and certainly in English, pleasant words have a higher frequency of use than negative ones. Moreover, in pairs of opposites, as in the development of language, pleasant words usually appear first (often because the negative is a literal negation of the first).

- When asked to list those they know, people always start with their friends and family before eventually getting to mere associates, much less enemies. Indeed, when asked to make lists about *anything*—products, trips they've taken, books they've read, etc.—people will start with what they like.

- People are more accurate when asked to describe in detail a positive life event versus a negative one. (What would Freud say here about repression? More recently, experimenters have discussed the "deletion" of "negative memory files," as the brain itself pursues a calm and settled frame of mind.)[435]

- As time passes, events in one's life are remembered as increasingly pleasant.

- Most people will agree with the proposition that "most of the events in my life have been positive."

- People seem predisposed to judge things—goods, circumstances, people, groups—in initially positive ways, even when there is little or no evidence one way or the other (e.g., most people say they like the taste of distilled water, which researchers point out has absolutely no chemicals to trigger taste buds one way or the other—it's just raw tasteless liquid).[436]

- Perhaps most tellingly, the vast majority of people will report themselves as being "above average" in terms of positive traits. These include: attractiveness, sexual ability, driving ability, sense of humour, intelligence, moral goodness, and even optimism. (As researchers point out, it cannot—literally or mathematically—be the case that the vast majority are above average in any or all of these traits. Indeed, as in a classic bell curve, the vast majority *constitute* the average in the middle, with outliers at the top and the bottom in small number.)[437]

- Relatedly, the vast majority of people report themselves as being "below average" in terms of the risk of suffering a serious (and at least temporarily disabling) injury or illness. (As above, this cannot be true. In North America, the objective risk of suffering an illness or injury that will require you to take sick leave from work, for at least one month, is one in three.)[438]

Peterson concludes: "Suffice it to say that pleasantness predominates in thought." Nettle has a more jaded take, wittily describing such common background beliefs as "part of the endearingly unrealistic psychology with which we address the world."[439]

We might ask why this is, and what exactly it has to do with evolution. The notion here is that, in many ways, these positive modes of thought have been advantageous—both to our ancestors and ourselves. The advantages are considered to be both personal and interpersonal. Personally, the evolutionary advantage of having such a pleasant predisposition is that it ties together happiness and being pleased with life—enough so that one wants to keep on living, and then pass their genetic material on to the next generation, and so on. We've seen above how optimism increases one's perseverance and resilience, which would've been valuable traits indeed for our earliest ancestors, as they struggled to survive in a hostile and uncertain world. Even for us today, researchers argue that such trends of thought have as their major function *the protection of the self*—the creation of a kind of psychological barrier around the ego—which is useful as a buffer and buttress from stress and challenge, leading us to continue on with our lives and the pursuit of our goals.[440] Interpersonally, there are many functions to such optimistic beliefs. First, they incline us toward cooperation, not conflict (at least initially). Second, such optimistic attitudes and resiliency in action have been shown (in a great many opinion surveys and psychological interviews) to be an attractive trait. Those displaying such were more likely to be successful in passing their genes along, and today we are more likely to want to be with people who are optimistic as opposed to pessimistic. And it goes beyond romance: we're much more inclined to want to work with people who are resilient, resourceful, and hopeful about the future. It would, indeed, be difficult to get motivated (e.g., to start a new business venture) with a pessimist as a partner.

Or to thrive under a manager who sees conspiracies and ruin around every corner.

We can see how, over the long stretch of time—both in our lives and in the history of humanity—optimism is actually *not* going to be some form of irrationality or collective delusion; it's going to—and does—have potent social and individual value. That's why experts like Lionel Tiger assert that optimism must have been selected by the natural processes of evolution, even in spite of the funny psychological tendencies mentioned above.[441]

That said, the very same researchers admit that *optimism isn't always good,* and *pessimism isn't always bad.* Some, for example, distinguish between illusion and delusion. An illusion might refer to an overly optimistic background pattern of thought—as in the above tendencies—which nevertheless leads to decent consequences (owing to the added effort put forth in expectation of eventual reward). A delusion, by contrast, refers to a specific belief that is manifestly false and destructive in its consequences—let's say, someone who sincerely believes that they are the reincarnation of Napoleon. That's not "charming optimism," merely skimming over the obstacles in front of a goal; that's a psychotic condition that, in the end, will only lead to pain. More broadly, there's good and bad optimism. Good optimism is precisely about perseverance in the pursuit of worthwhile goals, and a conviction that one might (or shall) reach them. Bad optimism, for example, is like believing that one is going to win the lottery, and over time succumbing to a gambling addiction, convinced they are always just about to win.[442]

Conversely, we might distinguish between good and bad pessimism. Bad pessimism is the kind of pervasive, global cynicism that leads to paralysis in thought and action, where nothing is pursued or accomplished. Clinical depression, or nihilism, might well ensue: indeed, it's difficult to see how it wouldn't. But there can also be good pessimism, especially as a kind of reality check on the enthusiastic extremes of overly exuberant optimists. For example, it's important to know that most new business ventures do indeed fail, if only to hammer home the need for a great idea, good planning, and hard work if one is to have a realistic chance. And it's important to know one's strengths *and* weaknesses, so as to be able to engage in self-improvement and not just dwell in the pleasant but stagnant pastures of complacent self-deception. Further—and importantly—we can see how the same person might be optimistic in connection with one aspect of their life (e.g., career), while being pessimistic in others (e.g., romance). Relatedly, and commonly, people may shift between periods, or phases, of optimism and pessimism over the course of their long and complex lives.[443]

This is all to say, and I think many of the best researchers would agree, that we can—and should—think of both optimism and pessimism *as strategic conceptual tools to make use of in pursuing happiness*, relative to circumstances faced at different periods of life. Thus, it is natural to be more optimistic while young, especially during the teenage and early adult years, when life stands ahead of you, when you're (more likely) in robust physical condition, and filled with ambition. Likewise, it's natural to be more pessimistic after having suffered a sharp setback such as divorce, getting fired, or succumbing to serious injury or illness. And, of course, as one nears the very end of their life, it's not rational to be optimistic about one's personal future—though it may still make perfect sense to be optimistic about the world, or about one's children and grandchildren, and so on.[444]

In general, it's good news that nature has "cued us up" to be inclined toward optimism. Though at times it leads to amusement, and sometimes to mistakes if we're not careful, it's a nice tool to have, especially when one has a chronic condition. Such background optimism—bouncing one's happiness back up after the initial recoil—can be connected with the kind of reverse hedonic adaptation we referred to previously. *This adaptability may well be one of the most potent natural, instinctual tools we have in our anti-illness toolbox.* And it's important not to fight nature: either with regard to our body's natural healing process, or to our tendency for background optimism.

There's one more issue needing comment. Recall from previous chapters how we discussed the degree to which our brains treat negative information with more salience and weight. This is a real challenge to our happiness—especially in terms of state of mind—leading at times to paranoia, dwelling, and worry about our social status and general future. We also commented, at the time (Chapter 6), about how such heightened attention to negative information—especially criticisms from, and conflict with, other people—can be predicted and explained by evolutionary psychology. This theory tells us that, for our earliest ancestors, the need to survive negative challenges was much more important than constantly being pleased with our lives. Thus, evolution inclines us toward paying more attention to the negative than the positive. How are such remarks consistent with our findings thus far in this chapter, with regard to optimism?

Peterson, for one, is not sure whether there is any consistency in this regard, referring to this as a "tension in thought," which may well be a hallmark of the human condition.[445] Perhaps. But I think these two tendencies can be seen as completely consistent with what evolutionary psychology tells us. The key is the difference between short-term and long-term consciousness and attention. In the short term, it makes perfect sense that our evolutionary conditioning inclines us to put greater salience on potentially negative (and especially threatening) information, as this may well constitute an immediate threat to our well-being—and perhaps our survival. So, our immediate attention, and short-term memory, is going to be primed to focus on the negative. This isn't all bad, especially if such threats turn out to be real and evasive action is needed. But, over the long term, evolution wants us to live, and to be pleased enough with our lives that we want to keep on living, have children and care for them, try to improve the world, and so on. And so, it makes perfect sense that, in our background context of thought, there is going to be bias toward the positive, and toward optimism. The two tendencies go together consistently, each playing different—yet equally needed—roles in our processes of thought and cognition. A key for happiness is to be mindful enough, and aware enough of one's thoughts, NOT to confuse the one for the other (i.e., to not allow short-term dispositions toward paranoia and perception of threat—fight or flight—turn into long-term cynicism, sadness, and anger; and to not allow deep tendencies toward optimism to blind one to evidence of clear short-term threats). Our brains have the necessary tools to maintain perspective and help motivate us to make correct decisions. That, according to Aristotle, would be the proper use of reason.

Tools of Thought?

In the above section, I didn't offer "tools for positive thinking" like so many—too many?—works on the subject tend to do. There are two reasons for this. First, one can consult such works directly, like Norman Vincent Peale's perennial bestseller *The Power of Positive Thinking*, or more recently, Martin Seligman's *Learned Optimism*. Second, I feel that doing so would be like "pushing against an open door," given all these natural predispositions toward positive and optimistic thinking. But I suppose I might say something, by way of wrapping this subject up, on *some tools for disabling negative thought patterns that are especially paralyzing,* as this is likely of special concern for the chronically afflicted.

First, *realize the extent to which you are programmed by nature to think positively.* And not just in terms of the "larger, deeper" trends mentioned above. Consider all the zillions of "micro-scale" ways in which you are inclined to have optimistic beliefs and expectations. When you turn on the faucet in the morning, you expect water to pour out; when you turn on the stove or toaster, you believe it will work; when you pull out a chair, you expect it to hold your weight and not collapse; and when you put something into your mouth, you expect that it won't poison you. You are built to have positive expectations—this is what your brain and human evolution want.

Second, *realize that it's also perfectly natural—in the immediate aftermath of accident, injury, or onset of illness—to be both hurt and pessimistic.* Evolution wants that, too, so that you pay careful attention to what's going wrong, and to what you can do to make it better. Thus, spouting mindless cheerleading slogans during this phase of one's experience is probably not going to work, and may even backfire and deepen an already dark mood as the gap between expectation and reality grows.[446]

Third, *note (so to speak) the positive aspects of pessimism.* As previously mentioned, sometimes—at least in the short term —it can actually be motivating and empowering (and to your long-term benefit) to get angry, to swear never to be used again, or to question doctors and others about the information they've given you. Trying to banish all negative thoughts or pessimistic periods is not natural and is doomed to fail. *Think always of the analogy of "different tools in the toolbox."* While the majority of those tools need to be positive, there's nothing wrong with a few strategic negatives as well. Scissors and saws can, in their own ways, be as useful as screwdrivers and measuring tape. Unhappy thoughts and negative beliefs may, from time to time, result in the knowledge and motivation needed to secure the real and complex objective: a flourishing life expressive of human well-being.

Fourth, *consider Seligman's ABCDE model for challenging negative patterns of thought.* This acronym stands for:

- **Adversity**, such as an unwelcome, painful experience (like coming down with a chronic affliction)

- **Beliefs**, which, in the short term, are typically dark and negative

- **Consequences**, which stretch beyond mere pessimistic beliefs to include a sad/sour/angry mood, associated unhelpful (or even unhealthy) actions, and a bad patch of time in life

- **Dispute**, which, crucially, is about gaining perspective and distance from the A-through-C dynamic, and thinking calmly and critically about it

- **Energization**, which one feels after having achieved all this [447]

The crucial step, obviously, is D, and how to dispute and resist the disempowering dynamic at play in steps A through C. Seligman says the vital thing in retaining a positive cast of mind is understanding that the objective causes of the bad beliefs and bad patches in life have to do with the experience of A, and *not* with entrenched, systemic flaws within oneself. Often, the bad beliefs go well beyond what the experience of A actually warrants: research shows, importantly, *that most people have exaggerated initial responses to almost every substantial event in their life*, probably because of the flight-or-fight mechanism. [448] People then typically calm down and come back toward the middle of what their considered responses actually are. We can hasten that process along, Seligman says, by actively questioning and disputing whether the trigger of A is actually proportionate to our responses in B and C. Rigorous research has shown that actively undermining negative beliefs (by putting forth *alternative accounts of cause* and/or *alternative accounts of how best to respond*) is extremely effective at dismantling negative thought patterns. It is, however, an artificial skill, which takes active and repeated practice. Yet, most people find they can indeed strengthen their "cognitive muscles" in this regard, and thereby come to have better beliefs, better emotional responses, and more constructive plans of action for dealing with the adverse event at the heart of everything.[449]

Sonja Lyubomirsky helpfully suggests that, between Seligman's steps D and E, there's a further "sub-step" that we might label "GPA": the Generation of Positive Alternatives. The D step—Dispute—is more about *critically undercutting negative beliefs* by disputing whether things are really so bad, or whether there's a rational/causal disconnection between cause and consequence, between trigger and one's mental state. But it can be yet a further step *to generate creative and helpful ways of thinking about the situation.*[450] My own absolute favourite is Tony Robbins' suggestion that, when you are confronted with a bad situation with negative consequences, force yourself to ask out loud: "WHAT'S GREAT ABOUT THIS?" It's so over-the-top enthusiastic—so joyous and, at the same time, jaded—that it cuts through the clutter of one's stress and confusion, and takes one's mind to a different place. (Robbins himself describes using this technique after a close trusted business partner stole tons of money from him, betraying him brutally.)[451] Try this technique right now, especially if you're saddled with a chronic affliction. *Force yourself to ask: "What's great about my chronic condition?"* And then come up with at least three different, true answers. I think you'll enjoy the exercise and find it energizing. I'll go first. What's great about my brain tumour and epilepsy?

1 Charming (probably helpful) gaps in my memory; plus, extra, unscheduled "naps." Another funny one is the huge variety of things I get to (try to) blame on my tumour. Every time I say or do something really stupid, I can just proclaim: "Hey, that's not me: that's the tumour talking!"

2 Every time I've had a serious, falling-down seizure in public, someone has always come to help me, at times going exceptionally out of their way to do so. Sometimes this is a close friend or loved one; many times, it has been total strangers. This has never failed to move me, and regularly renews my faith in humanity and in our shared social contract.

3 As mentioned, my doctors speculate that I may have been born with my brain tumour, but the epilepsy and seizures didn't kick in until I was thirty—a result of the ageing process and an associated diminished capacity for my brain to "work around" the tumour. My specialists have even suggested that perhaps one reason for my intelligence is that my brain may well have forged greater, and larger, neural connections than normal as it tried to "grow around" and cope with the tumour. If true, then I'm confronted with the truly odd possibility that the very cause of my illness, and so much disruption and suffering in my life, has also been a source of many advantages. Not just that: my very identity, and sense of self, may have been completely different had I not had my brain tumour. Since I like being who I am, at least generally, I may have stronger reasons *to celebrate my tumour* (!) than what one might initially suppose.

Research establishes that, every time the ABCDE procedure is performed, it gets easier and better. In many ways, the ABCDE method is like a sustained process of fully open and clear communication within oneself, about why one feels and thinks the way they do about some event. This can occur completely in private—which may allow for greater honesty—but it can *also be helped along by having such communication openly, with a close other person whom one trusts.* Others can assist in being more objective and less personally invested in maintaining the same old tired patterns of thought responsible for creating pessimism and negativity. Research has shown, repeatedly and perhaps surprisingly, that there's no difference, in terms of long-term success, between getting professional psychological counselling and simply having a great friend with whom one can have the same discussions; however, both, for most people, tend to be more useful than going it alone.[452]

Detailed research has shown that the ABCDE process tends to work. For example, school kids who underwent a three-month program based on learning and mastering the ABCDE process showed substantially reduced rates of sadness and depression compared to a control group—an effect that lasted for two whole years after the initial intervention! Teaching such skills at such a young age is advantageous, but all of us can still profit from them.[453]

Take it from me: don't stand there and be a victim of your injury or disorder. While there is a kind of normal background process for healing, one shouldn't hesitate to try the ABCDE method to hasten their recovery. At the very least, it will: activate your mind; provide valuable reflections as to the causes of your affliction; and lead you to gain as much information about it, formulate constructive plans for how to deal with it, and try to bring it under as great a degree of control as is reasonably possible.

The Role of Others in Positive Thinking

Dialogue provides for us a transition into the important sub-ject of the role of other people in positive thinking processes. As Peterson wisely notes, one of the strangest things about the vast majority of the positive thinking literature is its asocial character: it consists mainly of advice to individuals as to how they should police and tutor their own thoughts, coming to greater self-awareness and self-control. However, according to Peterson, research inquiring into the identities of individuals whose thought processes are typically happier and healthier has discovered that such people also test positively for more active and supportive social networks, describe themselves as having strong social connections, and can specify many more positive social influences in their lives (now, and in their past).[454]

We should realize then that it is an important truth about positive thinking, about optimism over pessimism—and good mental hygiene in general—that *other people play a vital role in this regard,* at least in the following ways:

- Close, trusted others are people with whom to share the ABCDE, or similar process(es) for challenging negative beliefs and brainstorming positive alternative perspectives.

- Others can serve as more objective interlocutors to help interrupt mistaken or biased tendencies of thought, which are unhelpful.

- Others can serve as necessary subjective emotional support that, Peterson says, provides us with a sense of safety, secu-rity, and being loved, thereby enabling the personal strength to grow mentally, to mature and question and challenge, and to gather necessary information.[455]

- Considering things more deeply, it's other people—notably family members, parents, and teachers—who are responsible for one's earliest intellectual development, and have been the source of so much knowledge and information over the years and decades. And not just content: the examples they provide as role models for styles of thought have been proven by research to have deep impact on how people approach information gathering and processing over time (often well past adulthood, when people *could* deliberately change such patterns but often don't).[456]

- Going back even further, the reason for many of the optimistic, positive, long-term tendencies in our thought patterns has to do with our nature as social animals. Witness, for example, the above information about how languages are biased toward the positive terms/concepts within pairs of opposites, and how many of the positive biases in thought have clear roles to play in making us seem more likeable, skilled, and/or attractive to others.

The role of other people in forming good positive thinking habits seems undeniable; it's difficult to overstate its importance. It points toward deep, and perhaps unexpected, connections between this chapter on individual thinking and previous ones on interpersonal relationships and social institutions. That said, research has also shown that other people can, unfortunately, lead us down pathways of thought proven negative for our personal pursuits of happiness. But perhaps the main subject considered in the happiness literature, in this regard, is the myriad ways in which we typically engage in social comparison.

Social Comparison

As Lyubomirsky notes, comparing ourselves to others can be helpful and useful. It can motivate us to improve a weakness as we try to emulate talented others, or it can push us toward an ambitious goal, reasoning that, "if they can do it, so can I!" At the same time, there's much evidence that relentless comparison of self to others is actually one of the clearest causes of mental stress, disappointment, and unhappiness. Particularly debilitating is when we compare ourselves to people who seem "superior" to us in some important respect, such as: wealth, intelligence, attractiveness, fitness, number of good friends, strength of career, social accolades, number and quality of children, niceness of home or car or clothes, and so on.[457] The chronically afflicted are perhaps especially vulnerable to this, with the obvious and perhaps quite large comparison being between themselves (of sub-normal health status) and those unafflicted. As Nettle points out, never have such comparisons been more easily available, and more sharply defined. Thanks to the internet and social media, we can now compare ourselves instantly to anyone in terms of the above categories. In previous eras, our ancestors could only compare and compete against *local* others; now, however, there's a worldwide frame of reference, which is arguably disastrous in terms of the potential for envy and related hits to one's self-esteem.[458] (It is, for example, hard for me to be super happy when I contemplate the life and times of George Clooney or Tom Brady.) We are reminded of the example mentioned in Chapter 4, of the Olympic medallists and their relative happiness. Happiest of all, of course, are the gold medallists at the very top, thrilled with the knowledge that they are the best in the world at their particular sport, in that moment. But next highest in happiness rankings are actually the bronze medallists, who compare themselves to the fourth-place finishers and are thrilled just to have won an Olympic medal at all. Least happy of the three are the silver medallists, who do not think about the bronze medallists at all but, rather, engage only in upward comparison with the gold medallists. Thus, they take a severe hit to happiness, knowing that they have been bested. The most a silver medallist can take away is hope that they are still good enough, four years down the road, to once more go for gold.[459]

Lyubomirsky writes with particular insight on this issue, perhaps due to it being the first happiness subject she investigated. She describes how her initial expectations, in this regard, were exactly as those reported above: those who engage in upward comparison are unhappy, whereas those engaging in downward comparison are happy. But her research actually proved that simple equation wrong. To her surprise, subjects reported that even downward comparison could cause some stress and unhappiness, for instance with some feeling guilty at their good fortune when compared with others who are worse off. Some subjects also noted that they sometimes had to deal with the envy and hostility of those worse off, which proved a drag on their own happiness. Lyubomirsky's initial research found that the happiest people were those who didn't engage in robust social comparison at all, but rather had their own internal standards for success, achievement, pleasure, and happiness. Many of the happiest people had, in her words, "no idea what I was talking about" when she tried to get them to report their happiness status in comparison to others. They just didn't bite.[460]

Further research led Lyubomirsky to the ultimate truth: the very happiest people were those who experienced true personal pleasure at the success of others, and sincere concern when other people failed and suffered pain. The unhappiest people, by contrast, were those who—and note her excellent, exacting wording here—experienced *deflation* upon hearing of the success of others, and were *relieved* at their failure. Such words and experiences surely point to the core issue for such unhappy people: *an insecure sense of self too strongly tied to relative social standing.*[461]

Such an insecure sense of self can result in people getting trapped in processes of thought that Lyubomirsky labels "self-focused rumination." This is an unconstructive thought pattern focused on the problems, experiences, and weaknesses of the self, often in comparison to others and/or in connection with bad memories in one's past (see more below). People prone to such processes of thought have been shown to suffer much higher rates of self-reported stress and sadness, leading to potent and debilitating rounds of self-criticism. They have a very hard time concentrating on other tasks, and their rumination saps them of motivation and initiative, which can result in a lack of helpful action. Ruminative thought processes, it'll come as no surprise, go hand-in-hand with pessimism.[462]

How to overcome such processes? Deploy the tools of optimism as described above, such as the ABCDE process. Second, and I'll put this forcefully: *start caring much less about what others think about you, or how you stand relative to them.* After all, they think about you less than what you think—they've got their own lives to lead—and we all have our own strengths and weaknesses. Truly, no one has it all. (I can confidently say that I have fewer grey hairs than George Clooney, and have published more philosophy books than Tom Brady.) Having a chronic affliction can actually be helpful in this regard, though it might not seem that way, especially at first. Wouldn't you give anything to return to "normal"? I think it's fair to say that, once you've adjusted, your experiences with your affliction can help make you care less about what others think because: a) you've now got more important things to deal with, and b) you know that "the average person" can't possibly understand what it's like to have your affliction, thus you've got a one-up on them in terms of experience. It's like growing older: you become more comfortable in your skin, more self-aware, and gain the maturity and capacity to appreciate what you have. *In this way, sickness can truly liberate your mind.* (Even unafflicted people can glimpse this phenomenon: When bed-ridden with a bad cold or the flu, do you engage in relentless comparison with others, ruminating over what's lacking in your life? No: you just chill out and relax, and ride out the course of the illness. Plus, you seek out nice, small-scale pleasures of food, rest, and leisure, which boost your mood and help aid in your healing.)

Lyubomirsky has further suggestions for breaking out of the cycle of relentless social comparison and excessive self-focused rumination:

- Firmly say, or even yell, "No!" or "Stop!" when you catch yourself ruminating or obsessing enviously. (Perhaps combine this by wearing a sturdy rubber band around your wrist, which you can snap against your skin as an accompanying attention-getter: surprisingly effective.)

- Substantially change whatever it is you're doing. The physical change can trigger a mental change, thereby distracting you from your concerns. (Focus on a reliable source of pleasure, or some demanding kind of physical activity, forcing you to pay attention to it instead of the negative thoughts.)

- Indulge any inclination toward self-focused rumination—but only at a fixed, formally scheduled time. Research has found that, if given thirty minutes a day to focus on ruminating or comparing yourself to others in a negative way, people are often surprised to discover that they are not actually able to use up the full thirty minutes, and find that there is less to complain about, and get concerned over, than what they first thought.

- Talking to a trusted friend (who is not themselves a ruminator) and/or writing down one's worries have also proven helpful, and for the same reason: the friend, and the formal process of writing, force one to take a more objective stance on one's worries, and to think and/or talk about them in a coherent and disciplined way—as opposed to subjective swirls of thought.

- Finally, take a tip from the addicts out there (as discussed in Chapter 3) and take care to notice the existence of any usual "triggers" for such comparisons and ruminations (e.g., smokers, drinkers, and drug addicts usually indulge their habits only alongside particular people, at certain times of day, or in connection with particular activities and/or places.) Avoid all such triggers, making use of the techniques of distraction and changing activities to substantially lessen any impulse to "go there" and suffer the negative consequences.[463]

Thinking About the Past

Many of the just-mentioned strategies also work well when dealing with ruminations that are not merely about oneself, or one's status in comparison with others, but more narrowly about one's past—including sub-optimal, disappointing, and painful moments.

If there are, loosely, three temporal phases to your life—past, present, and future—then this raises the question as to what constitutes happy thoughts in connection with each. Happy thoughts about the future, we've seen, notably include optimism and goal orientation. Goal orientation also helps with peace of mind and other positive thought processes associated with the present (e.g., mindfulness, savouring, and flow). But what of the past, which is no longer subject to or affected by our choices? We all have sub-optimal aspects to our pasts—and these can linger and re-emerge in our consciousness, to drag down our happiness in the present. How do you contemplate your personal history in a constructive way?

- We can use the anti-rumination tools mentioned above to manage bad memories and prevent them from paralyzing us with pain, regret, anger, shame, and/or sadness.

- Using a special variation of the distraction technique, we can leverage our attention toward the other two time periods: being absorbed and mindful about the present, and hopeful and goal-oriented about the future. This is the most effective way of "crowding out" a sub-optimal past and truly overcoming it: embracing the present and being enthusiastic about the future.

- One doesn't always have to "let go" of the past; in many ways, this can be unhealthy denial. In general, the most positive way of thinking about the past is always from a perspective of education and learning. Earlier this chapter, we noted the strong connections between learning and happiness. The learning we do when we're younger doesn't have to, and shouldn't, end. Moreover, one can learn important lessons from both good and bad memories. Thus, it's always healthy to ask: "What can I learn from my past to improve my life today, and moving forward?"

- This naturally raises issues of appreciation of, and gratitude for, the past—especially the good things. These are—alongside learning—the cardinal virtues when it comes to thinking happily about the past. But they are more than just cognitive virtues; they're moral virtues as well, which we'll discuss further in Chapter 10. Suffice it to say, much evidence exists showing how cultivating "an attitude of gratitude" is a powerful happiness booster for most people.[464]

- Finally, in the section ahead on meditation, we'll see how one form of meditation, proven to be just as strong as more traditional, "formal" modes, is to focus mentally on the details and experience of a particularly happy memory. We all have bad memories, yes, but usually some wonderful ones as well. Focusing one's attention on the positive ones can serve as a heart-warming boost of happiness almost anytime. The past isn't always something to overcome: like learning, dwelling on (or savouring) a happy memory shows us how the past can serve as a mighty resource to aid in the pursuit of happiness, both now and in the future.

Religious Belief

Recent research has focused on the degree to which religious belief can influence one's happiness—quite considerably, actually, which is of some concern to an utterly non-religious person like me. Many separate, secular psychological studies have shown that, in general, religious people are happier with their lives and marriages, have lower rates of illness, use narcotics much less, are better at recovering from illness, and just flat-out live longer.[465] Here are three specific examples:

- In a study of individuals who had cardiac surgery, those who defined themselves as religious were three times more likely to be alive six months later than those who defined themselves as non-religious.

- Of those who attended a religious service more than once a week, 47 percent described themselves as "very happy," compared to only 28 percent of those who attended less than once a month or who never attended but still described themselves as religious.

- In a study of individuals hospitalized for cancer treatment currently undergoing chemotherapy, those who defined themselves as religious were described by their nurses are being significantly more happy, serene, active, and social—in short, "better copers"—than those who described themselves as non-religious. (The nurses did not know how the patients described themselves).[466]

Happiness has been associated with religious belief more strongly in women (over men), in black people (over white), with North Americans (versus Europeans), and certainly with older people (over younger—e.g., studies have shown that, for elderly people, the most widely used form of coping with stress *is* "religious coping," including private prayer and participating in religious rituals and activities).[467]

Experts in the field, however, dispute whether the strength of association between religion and happiness is unique to religious belief, or whether it has to do with other factors with which religious belief is packaged. These include:

- a more active social life, and greater degrees of social connection and support (Chapter 6)

- a strong and coherent sense of personal identity and belongingness (Chapter 4)

- a structured, meaningful, and purposeful orientation in life (Chapter 2)

- a more physically fit body (as many religions caution against or restrict smoking, drugs, and alcohol) (Chapter 7)

Secular researchers like to say that we can get all the supposed "happiness benefits of religious belief" without actually being religious: we just need to commit ourselves to having these four things in our lives—but for our own personal happiness, and not for the sake of meeting religious requirements or pleasing God.[468]

Lyubomirsky, however, disagrees. She's of the mind that there is something unique about religious belief that results in it being such a strong booster of people's happiness—that it's not merely "social support and connection" that's fostered by being religious, but *the kind and nature* of the social support that most religions command and create which is key. For instance, it's not just that there are shared ritual practices, such as a formal religious ceremony, group prayer, choir, or coordinated chanting. And it's not merely that being religious augments one's exposure to other people; it's that the other people share your beliefs and values, and about very important things (like the meaning of existence and core moral values). Most religions command their followers to care for others in some non-trivial way, thus being religious offers active mutual support between believers. Most religions place heavy stress on the institution of family, and mutual caring and support within one's family. So, to the extent to which religion increases family connections, and those connections impact one's happiness, it follows that religion is a *further* boost to fulfillment. Most religious organizations also commit to doing shared projects together—building a place of worship, a fundraising drive for charity—and so, again, it's not just enhanced chance of exposure to others; it's emphasis on meaningful shared experiences and purposeful joint projects that deepen both social connections and personal happiness. Finally, Lyubomirsky points out that what secular researchers completely miss is the most basic religious relationship and its many happiness-promoting virtues: that between the religious believer and their conception of God. Lyubomirsky notes that, if you believe in God, this is one of, if not *the*, most important relationship in your life. Moreover, it (unlike every other relationship in one's life) is ever-present. One always feels and appreciates God's presence, and can reach out immediately for support, feeling comforted and secure. One always feels loved, regardless of their relations with other people, and can view every single event in life as being imbued with larger purpose—authored by God. Even if one doesn't understand, or is disappointed, by the event in question, they can still trust that it occurred for a reason. It really doesn't get more meaningful, or purposeful, than that. Lyubomirsky notes how very valuable such an attitude can be for anyone—and is, in fact, for most religious believers—especially when dealing with pain, illness, loss, stress, and trauma.[469]

Much as I cannot relate, these facts may be of particular interest for the chronically afflicted. *Even the sickest people can still pray, after all, and can still enjoy and appreciate an interior relationship with God.* This is especially the case if one has tried many of the other happiness-boosting activities to little effect. I must admit that, in writing about this, I've more recently considered trying to become more religious, or re-connecting with the religion of my childhood. And, looking back, I'm surprised that, during my lowest times, it didn't even occur to me to turn to God or re-engage with religious practice. What can I say? I lost my faith as a teenager—not for any dramatic reason, I mainly just lost interest relative to career-development and such, and eventually it ceased playing a role in my life. And while I have more recently reconsidered my faith, I also doubt whether it's possible to simply "up and believe" for the purely strategic reason of improving my happiness status.[470] (Religious belief, in this regard, is unlike optimism, for which there are strong reasons to believe in evolutionary predisposition. It's much easier to grasp some version of optimism than to "make oneself believe" in God just for the benefits.) In my own case, I don't really know, and my overwhelming inclination is still toward considering these things from a secular perspective.

Religious belief/practice may also, for some people, be a nice way to take one's mind off their sickness, injury, or affliction.

As Lyubomirsky points out, at the core of nearly every religion is a norm of self-transcendence—not merely toward others in a shared social practice but also toward God and larger, deeper questions (about the meaning of life, the scope and profundity of the universe, and existence itself). It is perhaps the ultimate tool of cognitive distraction if one is feeling especially pained or hopeless while confronting/attempting to manage their condition. And self-transcendence is the very opposite of self-focused rumination, which, as we've seen, has strong connections with pessimism, unhappiness, and bitter and unhelpful social comparisons.[471]

One thing I feel obligated to point out (which Lyubomirsky does mention, in spite of her otherwise very positive view of religion as a happiness booster) is that it's possible that, for some people, religion may actually decrease their happiness:

- There are social connections, expectations, and rules regarding conduct—and while some find these things helpful and wonderful, others can experience them as oppressive and confining, and would be happier being free and orienting their lives by their own personal values, whether they overlap or differ. We've seen repeatedly throughout this book that autonomy and personal control are major factors in most people's experience of happiness, and most organized religions are not very big on individual autonomy—the norm is much more social, and about fitting in with the group and its practices and values.

- A number of religions have been associated with two potent sources of unhappiness: guilt with self (feeling unworthy, or when one violates the core values) and anger at God (when one cannot make sense of certain negative events that have happened).

- Thinkers like Freud have further argued that religion, historically: a) can stand and has stood in the way of many sources
  of pleasure (particularly sexual pleasures); b) can, by providing maybe too much meaning and orientation, help close
  people's minds off to different perspectives, thus preventing
  learning and new experiences; and c) can, by providing too
  much identity and defining said identity in contrast to others of different beliefs, provoke disagreement, lack of charity
  toward others, and even open conflict.

- Lastly, recent, proven evidence links certain kinds of religious belief with negative health behaviours. For example,
  research has shown that in cases where individuals sincerely
  believe that God determines their health status, such people
  are more passive and inactive when it comes to maintaining their health, and as a result are generally worse off than
  people lacking such belief. This is especially true for: weight
  management, exercise, following doctor's orders, and completing necessary medical courses of action.[472]

Meditation

Talking of religion, ritual practices, and especially personal
prayer makes for a natural transition into the subject of meditation. One of the firmest, most recent, and most repeated
discoveries in connection with happiness is that *the regular
practice of meditation measurably boosts one's self-reported
happiness level.* Studies have found that those who maintain
a commitment to daily meditation see a measurable increase
in blood flow to their left frontal lobe (which, as we know from
Chapter 2, is associated with happiness), and also a measurable
increase in their immune response. Readers may be especially
interested to know that daily meditation has been shown to
alleviate symptoms of a whole range of specific disorders, both

physical and mental. These range from chronic pain and heart disease to depression and anxiety.[473]

What is meditation? Well, there's a common understanding of what meditation is, but people should also know that the latest research has shown meditation-like results can be had by performing related yet different activities. First, the standard account:

- Always meditate by yourself, in a quiet, secure space where you won't be disturbed.

- Sit properly, back straight. The key to meditation is two-fold: 1) deep, calm, rhythmic breathing; plus 2) a mental state of alert focus and clear awareness that is completely non-judgmental and non-analytical.

- The breathing is straightforward. Don't over-exert yourself, or exaggerate your breathing too much. On paced, natural counts, breathe deeply in, and then out in a controlled way. Hold your breath slightly if so desired, but not for long. It's more about a calm, rhythmic, steady *flow* of breathing. (Indeed, a number of researchers have suggested that the biological reason behind the success of meditation, especially in connection with blood flow and brain activation, is precisely the deeper intake and absorption of oxygen into the blood and brain.)[474]

- As you breathe, try either to empty your mind, or focus intensely on a nearby still object. Stare at it; don't judge it, or be analytical about it, or let it call forth any emotions beyond low-level appreciation.

- Let the oxygen flow, and feel your mind empty as you stare at the object. Some people find it helps if they softly repeat a word or chant ("ohm" or "one") as they breathe.

Only fifteen to twenty minutes of this per day are needed to achieve the desired results. Many do it either as part of their morning ritual, or to de-stress right after work, or at the end of the day/at bedtime. Any amount of meditation helps, even if it's only once a week. All of us, surely, can squeeze in fifteen minutes a week.[475]

Further, as stated above, recent studies have found that similar but different actions can yield nearly the same results as old-school meditation. This can help those who find meditation too much out of "their comfort zone," or cultural familiarity, to practice. Recalling in detail an especially happy memory can accomplish this. So too can paying focused yet non-involved and non-judgmental attention to any piece of art or music. Those who are used to intensive daily exercise can experience the same kind of detached-yet-still-aware experience. The key, though, with all these other options, is that breathing is still required, as is a quiet and secure space.[476]

What's doubly great about meditation or "near-meditation" practices is that they do not require great amounts of effort, space, or even physical well-being. Just as even the very sickest can avail themselves of prayer, so too *the very sickest can avail themselves of meditation, and reap its many happiness-promoting benefits.* There's no reason not to—even the "sitting up straight" part is not crucial. One can lay ill, and still, in bed and either detach mentally or recall a wonderful moment, or stare at a flower at their bedside, breathe more deeply than normal (but still in a soothing way), and keep it up for fifteen minutes. You'll be glad you did.

Your Best Possible Self

There's one final mental exercise to consider, which has been shown to boost happiness over both the short and medium term: "The Best Possible Self," from Laura King, via Sonja Lyubomirsky. For twenty minutes every day, you are to write about your best possible future self, defined as the one wherein you have achieved all your goals and things have gone as well as you could have imagined them. In research studies, people who did this for four days in a row reported significantly higher short-term mood, feelings of control and focus, and enthusiasm and energy for pursuing precisely those goals than those in control groups, who merely wrote down the details of their day. [477] Two things are key:

1. You must write it down, and not merely fantasize about it. Writing gives focus and discipline, and lends plausibility to the whole exercise. Participants in the studies said that it helped them to actually identify and rank their most important goals, and even to see how (or in what order) they might best be achieved.

2. The goals in question, while ambitious and idealistic, are still within the realm of possibility. It's about identifying your deepest goals, and making use of visual and mental imagery to imagine that these goals are actually satisfied. (Still, if you are going to err at all, err on the side of being ambitious.)

Grab some paper, or buy a nice personal journal, and write about the Best Possible You. Let this idea, and vision, of yourself both inspire and transport you toward greater happiness.

CHAPTER 9

Emotional Hygiene

Emotions deal with feelings, or "felt states," and are complex combinations of sensations, states of mind, beliefs and values, physiological responses (like heartbeat and rate of breathing), and patterns of behaviour. When we speak of happiness, we are usually speaking about felt states (or "affective conditions") and, in particular, *a surplus of positive emotion over negative emotion, on a consistent basis.* Thus, this whole book might be said to be about emotional hygiene. Let's reiterate once more how many of these distinctions are purely for reasons of analysis and clear presentation whereas, in reality, there can be (and are) profound interconnections between sensations, emotions, our bodies, and our beliefs.

In Chapter 6, we discussed in great detail perhaps the most positive emotion of all: love, and the deep affection experienced inside a great relationship. Chapter 3 was devoted to pleasure and reliable techniques for enhancing it, which in turn create happier states of mind. Chapter 2 focused directly on emotions as we considered the question, "Why should we pursue happiness?" There it was found that positive emotions, like happiness, bring about a whole range of good consequences (both for self and society), whereas negative emotions—when experienced chronically and with potency—are associated with many serious detriments in life, ranging from morbidity to mortality. Therefore, we are not going to repeat such issues here—though we will return to the function of both kinds of emotion in our broader personality and pursuit of goals. This is integral to what we mean when we speak of "emotional hygiene" (i.e., experiencing emotions in a way that is helpful and healthy over the course of one's life).

This may sound a bit strange at first, as emotions are often thought of as out of control, arising automatically. They may seem as such for many people, but recent research has shown that it's not so simple; factors other than "raw feels" and "brute impulses" are involved in our emotional lives, and emotions can—and ought—to be brought under a certain degree of control and conditioned in such a way so as to serve the final objective: happiness. To paraphrase Aristotle: any fool can (for instance) feel anger at any time—or, indeed, all the time—but only a happy person learns how to feel anger in the right way, for the right reasons, toward the right people, and for the right amount of time.[478] (This is assuming that negative emotions, such as anger, might actually have a positive function, or at least be unavoidably natural and/or still somehow important for proper functioning.) Aristotle's rich insights into emotional experience and affective control are crucial to our overall understanding of putting emotions in service of a happy life.[479]

In addition to this core concern, other subjects we'll investigate this chapter include:

- Paul Eckman's hegemonic account of the six basic, universally recognized emotions and their connection to happiness—particularly for those with chronic afflictions. This ties into evolutionary psychology's understanding of the function of various "emotion programs" in our bodies, minds, and lives.

- The theory of "The Big Five Personality Traits." These are referred to by the acronym OCEAN: 1) Openness to experience, 2) Conscientiousness, 3) Extroversion, 4) Agreeableness, and 5) Neuroticism (defined below). Conscientiousness is mainly a moral trait, so we'll leave that for next chapter. But we need to discuss in detail the other four, especially as two of them get major attention in the happiness literature: 1) the connection between extroversion/introversion and happiness, and 2) the connection between neuroticism/"well-adjusted-ness" and happiness.

- Relating to agreeableness: a sense of humour, gaiety, and laughter, and their roles as positive traits or emotional conditions clearly linked to happiness, and posited as helpful coping skills to cultivate, especially for the chronically afflicted.

- Discussing coping skills in general, both for the chronically afflicted's particular interest in the subject as well as coping with negative emotions and developing and sustaining a kind of resilience in life (especially in the face of challenging or painful circumstances).

- And "emotional intelligence" (EQ). Daniel Goleman's account of EQ has been both high-profile and influential, and provides a decent framework—even a kind of structural summary—of most of the elements we'll consider in this chapter, especially as aided and abetted by Aristotle and the evolutionary psychologists.

Six Universal Emotions

As Chris Peterson points out, and as we all know, emotions are strong drivers of human belief and behaviour. This is illustrated by the very etymology of the word, clearly linking "emotion" and "motion." Emotions drive us, move us to action, and are responsible for some of our greatest, and lowest, moments in life.[480] Recently, research has stressed the complexity of emotions. Though sensations of pleasure and pain cause emotional responses of happiness and suffering, emotions themselves are typically longer lasting than mere sensations. Likewise, brain scans have shown that emotional responses call forth more complex brain activity, across wider and deeper brain regions, than mere sensations. And emotions can't be neatly categorized as mere felt states, either (though they obviously are such things). Emotions involve beliefs, cognitive faculties, even full-blooded rationality— this in spite of the fact that, historically, reason and emotion are often portrayed as separate, even at odds with one another.[481]

Likewise, researchers have argued that, when felt properly, emotions might serve not just rational goals but even act as "shortcuts" that one's brain and central nervous system deploy to arrive at a complex conclusion in a timely, motivating way. Similarly, emotions can also involve value systems and moral beliefs (e.g., often anger is a response to a perceived injustice on the part of another person toward oneself). Finally, as noted above, emotions tend to involve clearly measurable physiological responses: different brain regions light up with activity depending on the emotion involved; various responses exist for heartbeat, rate of breathing, dilation or narrowing of pupils, sweat and/or colouration of the skin, and so forth. The most rudimentary emotions are also associated with distinctive facial expressions.[482]

Eckman, starting in the 1960s, conducted interesting and influential research on emotions, and whether any are universally recognized.[483] It turns out that, across cultures, not only are there six basic emotions that are universally recognized, they each have unique facial patterns, also universally recognized. As Daniel Nettle notes, in a nod to the automotive industry, these six emotions seem like "standard features on your basic model *homo sapiens*."[484] They are, in alphabetical order: anger, disgust, fear, joy, sadness, and surprise. Note, of course, that these do not capture the full range of human emotion and are not meant to be exhaustive, or even thought of as the most important (e.g., love). They are the emotions proven to be: a) universally felt and recognized, and b) tied to characteristic facial expressions and physiological responses. Many other emotions have been left out of this admittedly basic list—powerful ones, too. These include: jealousy, shame, and feeling creative/inspired. Again, this does not mean that such emotions aren't important; it just means that they have not been proven to be part of every human culture we know of, and/or have not been proven associated with distinctive facial expressions and physiological responses.

Eckman's "basic six" have attracted a lot of attention, as well as helpful related research and speculation about the most basic functions of emotions. Thus, it benefits us to consider them, and to focus on those especially relevant to the chronically afflicted, which notably include anger, fear, and sadness. Disgust may come into it, to an extent, but I speculate less so than those three just mentioned. (Yes, certain injuries and afflictions can produce some gross-looking, icky-feeling, foul-smelling consequences, but these don't last as long, and don't threaten one's peace of mind nearly so sharply as chronic fear, sadness, or anger.) And surprise just doesn't seem relevant to our concerns, at least after initial diagnosis. The general goal of it all, of course, is to do what one can to aim toward the joy that forms the focus of this entire book. So, let's consider these issues.

Something of immediate note: of the six basic emotions, four are classified as negative—anger, disgust, fear, and sadness. Only one is positive—joy—and the final one, surprise, is neutral. Thus,

67 percent, or *two thirds of the universal basic emotions are typically experienced in a negative kind of way*: they make us feel uncomfortable and bad, ruin our peace of mind, and make us long for escape. They also trigger a whole host of sub-optimal physiological responses, like flooding the body with cortisol and creating all kinds of stressors within the body that affect heart rate, quality of breathing and sleep, digestion, and so on. These truths are rather depressing, and can quickly lead us to skepticism regarding the possibilities for objective and lasting human happiness. As Nettle remarks: "An excess of the negative emotions . . . is one of the most potent causes of unhappiness."[485]

There's no denying that. But Nettle is also correct in pointing out that some relief can come simply by knowing the functions of these basic emotion systems. That way, one can talk to oneself in "the heat of the moment," so to speak, and come to greater realization as to *why* they are having such an emotion, and thereby (at least start to) gain better control over it. Consider, as Nettle says, that "[t]he function of each emotion program is highly specific and totally different from the others."[486] Each of the four negative emotions signal that something bad has happened, but they differ in: a) the cause of the bad thing, and b) the response called forth.

1 Fear signals that *there is a potential serious harm coming one's way*. The response demanded or triggered, in the first instance, is of the fight-or-flight variety—more commonly flight, as one worries whether they can match and defeat the threat. Associated with flight are: evasion, denial, anxiety, sleeplessness, rapid heartbeat, running and hiding, and so on.[487]

2 Anger signals that *something unexpected has happened, which has strongly disappointed and/or hurt you*. Often, it's that another person has committed an injustice (real or perceived)

against you. Here the response is also typically fight-or-flight, the nature of which depends on both the situation and the person. Many people simply move away from the situation and/or offending person, not because they are scared but because they are angry yet don't wish open conflict. However, others do respond with fight, and so we need to note how the function of anger—over thousands of years of evolution—has prompted our bodies and minds to be prepared for such a situation and associated behaviours (e.g., yelling, threatening gestures, actual violence) and bodily strains (e.g., heart racing, shortness of breath, a flood of adrenaline, intense focus, muscle tension).[488]

3   Disgust, Nettle says, comes from *an awareness of a threat of contamination to oneself.* The function of this emotion program is to get us to do the equivalent of "spitting it out and avoiding it,"[489] whether the disgust has to do with discovering one has accidentally eaten something rotten, or had sex with someone infectious, or had one's time wasted on something completely banal and stupid.

4   The function of sadness is *to notice and express the loss of something valuable to oneself.* Nettle defines this more narrowly in terms of "lost support," but that's perhaps too heavily skewed toward relationships and ignores how one can (and does) feel sadness over the loss, say, of one's healthy body, or a favourite material possession, or the family pet, or even a phase of one's life. What's triggered by such feelings of loss? Nettle suggests: "Save energy, and tread carefully until conditions improve."[490] Related, there's a kind of cathartic function to sadness and grief: for example, in expressing and dispelling the excess of negative emotion via crying until exhausted, which enables a kind of stability that functions as a prelude to recovery.[491]

In other words, thinkers like Nettle draw upon the insights of evolutionary psychology to understand how and why we have come to have the basic emotions we do. The function of the negative emotions is: a) to get us to notice something bad or threatening in our environment, and b) to move us to take action appropriate to the nature of the threat—be it fight, flight, spitting it out, expunging paralyzing states of mind, or hunkering down until we feel good enough to seek out a replacement for whatever valuable thing we've lost. Because negative emotions have their origins as "evolutionary warning systems," *we have been programmed to feel them very intensely and immediately, so as to prompt a swift and efficacious response*. The problem—at least for our personal happiness—is that the intensity of such feelings can often be disproportionate to the situation, and can result in a long, difficult time "coming down" from a flood of negative emotion. We need to know this, and call our own attention to this in moments when we are suffering disproportionately from negative emotions: they have been programmed by nature and evolution to be very strong. Why? Nettle explains: "The negative emotion system is *supposed* to be hyper-active, because suffering ten false alarms is better than getting killed."[492]

This is quite different from positive emotions such as joy. The function of said feeling says to us: a) something positive has happened, and b) we should therefore do nothing. Nettle adds that it's no surprise, given how substantially these two emotion systems differ, that there is much more rapid "hedonic adaptation" (Chapter 1) to positive emotions than negative: negative ones are designed to get and hold our attention, and prompt remedial action, whereas positive emotions call for no action beyond savouring the moment. Thus, they are not as strongly felt, and are readily "gotten used to," bringing us down more quickly from pleasant heights than what negative emotions allow when climbing up from unpleasant lows. Nettle concludes that, in comparison to positive emotions, negative ones can seem to have "an imperialistic quality" about them: feeling so much stronger, getting more of our attention, "bossing us around" and causing us so much more suffering than positive ones.[493]

Yet, as we saw in Chapter 2, theorists such as Barbara Frederickson have argued more recently that positive emotions have been under-appreciated by evolutionary psychology, and that they play a much more important role than what's been perceived. Recall that, for Frederickson, positive emotions such as joy and love signal safety and security, and as such encourage more than mere savouring the moment. Positive emotions allow us to feel confident and try new things; they encourage us to be curious and inspired to improve our lives. Above all, they energize. As Frederickson states, positive emotions have a profound "broaden-and-build" effect (whereas negative ones have more of a "detect-and-dismantle" consequence). As such, the regular experience of positive emotions turns out to have a huge evolutionary advantage: it allows us to grow our knowledge and skill sets enormously, in ways that might turn out to be valuable in the future.[494] We also know, from Chapter 6 on relationships, that the frequent feeling and displaying of positive emotion is attractive to others, and thus plays a vital evolutionary role in terms of attracting partners with whom we might mate and have and raise children, as well as plugging us into social networks that are valuable for knowledge, assistance, and the handling of threats. More recently, and intriguingly, it's been proven that, when negative emotions are followed by positive emotions, the experience of the positive emotions *helps undo the bad physiological effects brought about by the negative emotions.*[495] This is very valuable over the long term (as seen in Chapter 7) with respect to the toll unhappy stressors take on our long-term physical well-being. These are all crucial, huge, and hard-headed advantages that fail to be captured by the traditional, dismissive caricature of positive emotions.

Still . . . tell it to our feelings, right? Even if, intellectually, we can see how positive emotions have been under-appreciated, and how they actually play a vital role in our evolutionary success, there's still no denying the felt reality of how intense, distracting, and just plain crummy negative emotions can make us feel. So, what's a human being to do—especially a chronically afflicted one, who probably suffers on average more negative emotion than a non-afflicted person? Well, as Nettle remarks, the answer is simple and two-fold: *decreasing* the impact of negative emotions, and *increasing* the intensity of positive emotions.[496]

FIG 18 AN EMOTIONAL KEY TO HAPPINESS

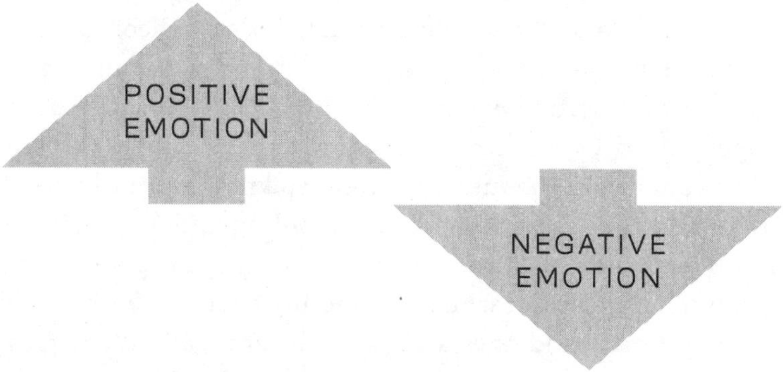

The question, of course, is how?

Diminishing Negative Emotions

How can we decrease negative emotion such that it doesn't ruin our peace of mind, our interpersonal relationships, and the ability to achieve our broader goals in life? There are several proven techniques, ranging from simple to complex:

1) Gather Data, and Purge

Pay close attention, over the course of three weeks, to what things prompt negative emotional reactions in you. Keep an "emotions journal" to ensure greater objectivity. Then, resolve to do fewer of those things, or get involved in those situations less and less (e.g., if there's a particular person who always brings you down, and you can avoid them, do so). Other common causes: excess alcohol, too little sleep, and/or being over-heated almost always diminish emotional control. Don't underestimate the degree to which the causes may be physical and related to fundamental things like sleep, diet, sex, and exercise (or the bad management thereof). See Chapter 7 on the body for more information. Further, it's been known for people to *transfer unhappiness* from one aspect of their lives to another: from work to relationships, or vice-versa. Get clear on what is actually the cause, using data from the journal, and then deal with it. (Recent studies have also confirmed that taking a low-dose daily aspirin—as approved by your doctor—over ten years substantially reduces the risk of depression. Researchers aren't sure why, but speculate that aspirin reduces inflammation, and systemic inflammation throughout the body contributes to pain and bad mood.)[497]

2) Short-term Stoppers

Some of the tools mentioned last chapter, for breaking a stranglehold by ruminative thoughts, can also be employed to stop a swirling cycle of negative emotion. These include: yelling at oneself to "Stop!" or saying "No" in a commanding way (perhaps while including a self-snap on a wrist-worn rubber band);

substantially changing what you're doing when in the grips of said emotion, counting on the *physical* change to trigger an *emotional* change; and learning to employ exercise and physical movement as both a tool of distraction and a means for channelling and taming emotional responses.[498]

3) The (Multi-functional) ABCDE Process

Nettle says that the ABCDE process described last chapter—for challenging disempowering or depressive beliefs—has also been proven an effective technique for mitigating and transforming negative emotions. Experiments have shown that those completing a fifteen-to-twenty-session course in how to use the ABCDE process displayed, at course's end, not merely better emotional coping or higher self-reported levels of happiness but *actual shifts in the very pattern of their brain-wave activity.*[499]

The reason it works, Nettle opines, is that it creates an empowering dialogue—and strengthens the interconnections already there—between the shrill and "siren voices of the negative emotion system" and "our more rational, analytic, and cognitive resources."[500] Before our negative emotions become super-heated, our cognitive resources are (through this process) able to throw cold water on them, so to speak. After all, the two largest and most typical ways in which people make mistakes with their emotional lives are: a) they feel/display emotions that are *not appropriate to the situation* (e.g., the above-mentioned tendency to transfer frustration at work into one's relationships), or b) the emotion felt/displayed is *appropriate but out of proportion* (such as the tendency mentioned in Chapter 6 regarding how relationships-at-risk suffer from arguments featuring rapid leaps from small-scale accusations of particular wrong-doing to sweeping generalizations about the other's character). It's the resources of reason, encouraged and cultivated by the ABCDE process, which are most fit to diagnose such things, put them into perspective, and tame and channel these emotional tendencies.[501]

But *can* the emotions be modulated? Yes, with sufficient practice in these and related techniques (more below). Note how we all have felt the efficacy of this process at some point—for instance, when experiencing an irrational fear later dispelled upon further consideration of evidence (such as seeing a "spooky shape" outside and turning on the light to discover it was merely a tree branch in the moonlight). The emotions *are* amenable to control: we just need to know how to do so, and be aware that we, individually, may find some emotions harder to control than others. Research has shown, for example, how men tend to struggle more with containing anger, whereas women tend to struggle more with managing anxiety. Noting weak spots can add to awareness about where and when mistakes are more likely to be made, and stand in need of correction.[502]

4) A Buddhist Trifecta

Matthieu Ricard elegantly adds helpful tools of emotional self-management taken from Buddhism.[503] The Buddhists have insightful things to share in this regard, being convinced that negative thought patterns and negative emotions are some of the largest causes of unhappiness. (They are convinced, as a first principle, that the world is full of suffering, which makes them especially germane to the chronically afflicted.) Ricard suggests three techniques for controlling negative emotions: antidotes, liberation, and utilization.

4a) Antidotes

Ricard points out that the feeling of some emotions is inconsistent with the feeling of others (e.g., when one extends their hand for a handshake, they cannot at the same time clench that hand into an angry fist). He claims that *the emotional antidote for anger is the attitude of loving kindness, or at least patience.* Either will do. The more one cultivates loving kindness, or patience, toward someone (or something, like an affliction), the less they're able to feel anger toward them (or it). For example, consider how being patient with a child allows one to put up with certain irritating behaviours, and how such patience winds up benefitting all parties. Ricard says: "These antidotes are to the psyche what antibodies are to the body."[504] He continues along these lines, considering the challenge of those who retort that this notion of treating negative emotions with their opposites: 1) goes against the natural appearance and feeling of such emotions; and/or 2) that the complexity of human personality allows for multiple, conflicting emotions to be felt at the same time.

As to the "naturalness" of negative emotions, there's no denying that they can come up seemingly unbidden and are a natural part of human personality in general. But two cautions: first, as Ricard observes, "disease is a natural phenomenon too. We do not resign ourselves to it or welcome it as a desirable ingredient in life. It is just as legitimate to treat afflictive emotions as it is to treat disease."[505] As we've seen previously from evolutionary psychology, negative emotions do indeed have a valuable role to play (e.g., emergency alerts), but they have been programmed to be extra-aggressive, rough-hewn, to overshoot the mark, and to err on the side of false alarms. They are *not* innate truth devices, or anything like that: they are prone to being disproportionate, and that disproportion can cause plenty of suffering. We shouldn't put up with such negative consequences merely on grounds that some kind of negative emotion is unavoidably part of who we are. It's about making such emotions work for us.[506]

The second caution regarding "naturalness" is that many people, including distinguished experts, have for the longest time believed that emotions are like a mechanical force or process within us, and we just have to let them "run their course." If we don't—as Freudians have long argued—we shall artificially repress such emotions until one day they either manifest explosively and inappropriately, or else gradually over time as forms of psychosis (e.g., obsessive-compulsive disorder). More contemporary research has stressed how inaccurate and even bad this can be, especially with anger. There's evidence that failing to nip anger in the bud can lead to a harmful and irrational escalation in one's emotional state, which is just as bad (or actually quite worse) than any repression that might come out at some far-off date.[507] Now, we did mention above how crying during sadness may serve the cathartic function of exhaustion, which leads to rest, and then re-appraisal and rebuilding. So, I'm not denying that there can be a cathartic function to some kinds of emotional expression, we just need to be very careful—particularly with anger. Any catharsis via anger can easily lead to destruction. It's also difficult to see how letting either disgust or fear go on the rampage will result in any positive or empowering "cleansing." Much more common is a downward, "frazzled" spiral in which one becomes increasingly entrapped in the clutches of the negative emotion, with serious anti-happiness consequences for oneself and others. As Ricard notes, this should be the test: *it only counts as a good catharsis if there are genuinely good results from the torrent of emotion felt and expressed.* Usually, this doesn't happen with unrestrained negative emotion, and allowing such emotion to vent and spiral leads to being out of control, miserable, and quite likely to say or do something with negative consequences. Control, integration, and management are better.[508]

What about "the complexity of human emotion" allowing for the feeling and/or expression of contradictory emotions? Again, this is a common view, and may come once more from Freud's influential (yet largely speculative, reductive, and bleak) view of human psychology. There's no denying that we are complex creatures, and that we feel a vast range of positive, negative, and neutral emotions. But Ricard's notion is centrally about *training the negative emotions so that they serve their proper role in our lives*, and not allowing too easily for their unrestrained feeling and expression. Plus, think about it: Can you truly both love and hate someone at the same time? You can love certain *traits*, and dislike or even hate other traits, but overall (if you have such strong feelings for them at all) you either love them or you hate them. Such feelings produce distinctive and incompatible kinds of behaviour. And we commonly (and rightly) view it as hypocrisy when someone swears they love us yet treats us repeatedly in un-loving ways. As Ricard observes: "True love and hatred cannot co-exist, because the former wish is for the other's happiness, and the latter for his unhappiness." He adds: "There definitely are mental states which are completely incompatible: pride and humility, envy and joy, generosity and avarice, calm and agitation."[509] Thus, the residual meaningfulness of the claims that: a) one can go about treating negative emotions with their opposite, positive emotions; and b) one must be deliberate and mindful in the moment about resisting poisonous spirals of negative emotion. And that—in addition to challenging such emotions cognitively (as in the ABCDE process)—one should also *challenge such emotions with other emotions*, namely their specific and positive "antidotes." It's not just about "cultivating positive emotion"; it's about learning how to do so repeatedly, regularly, and on an extended basis, so that one can then *call on specific emotions when one needs them most*, such as to treat a downward spiral of a particular negative emotion. You develop the patience muscle, or the loving-kindness muscle, so that it's strong enough in the moment to push back and handle a surge of anger. It's about true emotional self-mastery: a very difficult task worth pursuing insofar as, like Spock's father says in the 2009 *Star Trek* reboot, "One controls one's emotions, so that they do not control you."[510]

4b) Liberation

This is the most abstract, and perhaps most distinctive, of the three main methods of Buddhist emotional management. It's about seeing how empty and transient the negative emotions are, thereby being freed from their power to cause negative consequences. Consider Ricard's eloquent metaphor:

When you see a great black cloud in a stormy sky, it seems so solid that you could sit on it. But when you approach it, there's nothing to grab on to; it is only wind and vapor. The experience of anger is like having a high fever. It is a temporary condition, and you do not need to identify with it. The more you look at anger in this manner, the more it evaporates under your gaze, like white frost under the sun's rays.[511]

I'm not very taken with Buddhist talk about the emptiness of things, but it's not so much that anger is literally empty; it's that it's temporary and—above all—there's *no need to identify with it*. When you do so identify, it gets a hold of you, and you can suffer powerfully negative consequences as a result, especially if said anger turns out to be a disproportionate false alarm. The trick here is to try to disassociate from your own negative emotion and gaze upon it as if it were an external phenomenon. You're not harmfully repressing it: you allow it to come up, and you feel it *to that extent*. But then you observe it almost as if you were in meditation, or in a scientific lab (or, indeed, watching another person). What an interesting object! Here's what it looks like, what it sounds like, and so on. In this way you gain perspective and control over the negative emotion, and can learn to neutralize it. Particularly powerful here would be if one could, in the moment, view oneself as a completely different person: look at what that person is saying and doing. What a jerk! What a goofball! (Or, maybe: what an impressive human being.) This would be the ultimate form of emotional modulation: *if this emotion, and its consequences, were being felt and displayed by someone else, would you approve or disapprove?* We should all strive to be the kind of person who displays emotions and behaviours that we would approve of as disinterested observers concerned about human well-being. It's a neat, provocative way to try to reorient one's mind and gain distance from, and control over, negative emotional processes.[512]

This may sound difficult, but many have shown that something like this is actually possible, and even desirable. Too many people give in too easily to the flow of their emotions, and seemingly can't help but identify with them—until they've run their course and produced bad consequences. How much better to avoid those bad consequences and, instead, train yourself not to identify with negative emotions until you're fully aware and alert, and can determine whether the emotion is being felt in the right way, at the right time, and is at least understandable if not reasonable. So, *as you feel a negative emotion arise, pay heightened attention to it*: Why am I feeling this negative emotion? Is it appropriate to the situation? I know that such emotions are programmed to be overly strong, and to have many false alarms: Is this one of those misleading situations? Should I "own this emotion" and identify with it? What will be the consequences of doing so? Will I find those results desirable or not?

If this kind of process sounds unusual—and deliberately artificial—it's worth asking why. No doubt it has something to do with how little effort, as a culture, we put into the correct training of our emotions—in contrast to the massive investment we put into training our minds (at school), or even our bodies (with fitness and sports). Yet, as we all know, our emotional lives have as much of an impact on our overall health and well-being, and satisfaction in life, as our bodies and minds. There's no reason to think that people can't benefit from emotional education and training, nor is there reason to suppose that emotions are raw forces of nature that cannot be controlled. Ricard offers wise advice when he says that few people regret the years of effort and hard work it takes to develop an employable skill, or a rewarding career. So "why complain about the perseverance needed to become a well-balanced and truly compassionate human being"?[513] You don't have to buy into Buddhist philosophies of compassion to see the point of and worth in the work, discipline, and effort needed in recognizing your emotions for what they are, and how they need to be controlled and modulated. It's like diet and exercise: you have to subject yourself to the discipline for it to work.

4c) Utilization

Ricard's notion here—and it's not unique to Buddhism—is that you might achieve greater control over a negative emotion by making good strategic use of *other* negative emotions, in proper situations. He notes that, "anger rouses us to action and often allows us to overcome obstacles. It also contains aspects of clarity, focus, and effectiveness that are not harmful in and of themselves."[514] We've spoken in previous chapters about how anger might actually be well used as a compelling "negative motivation" to rouse oneself out of a bad situation, or to overcome fear. But recall that research evidence shows that, over the long term, negative motivation is not as successful as positive motivation (i.e., "wanting to move toward" as opposed to "wanting to avoid") in creating and sustaining happiness over time. This is consistent with what Ricard stresses—that negative emotions might sometimes be used, especially as short-term motivators, but that they cannot be allowed to run out of control or be indulged on a persistent basis over the longer term. According to Ricard:

When we fall into the sea, it is the water itself which buoys us and allows us to swim to shore. But we still need to know how to swim—that is, to have enough skill to exploit the emotions to good effect without drowning in their negative aspects.[515]

Ricard's picture is germane to our previous understanding of "tools in the toolbox," which we elaborated on last chapter in terms of optimism versus pessimism. There, we endorsed the notion that it's too simple to adopt a sweeping "either/or" ideology in terms of positive thinking: specific optimistic thoughts, and specific pessimistic thoughts, may well serve useful roles in the overall job of building a happy and thriving life. As it is with mental hygiene, so to with emotional hygiene: it's about using the wide range of emotional tools we have, whether positive or negative, to serve their proper functions at the right times, to forward the overall, life-long pursuit of a happy and satisfying life.

5) Courage and the Complex Self

Our final large technique or element for bringing negative emotions under control, and lessening their destructive impact on our lives, draws inspiration from previous chapters. Recall, from chapters 2 and 3, that research shows that a more complex self—one with a complex, multifaceted identity and many different interests—is not only a more variegated source of possible pleasure(s) but also a self structured to be buffered against setbacks in any one sphere of life. Selves with only a handful of roles, identities, and interests are more vulnerable to negative emotions and unhappiness, should setbacks happen, such as in one's career or relationship. *Cultivating a wide range of roles and interests* is yet another tool to protect oneself from paralyzing emotions, as a setback in one sphere can be offset by the positive emotions and experiences from another.

The last word here must be on the role of courage, which we spoke of in Chapter 2. Confronting negative emotions is not easy, given how they have been structured over thousands of years—and how, sometimes, they actually *do* point to a truly threatening condition or circumstance. Confronting such circumstances, and trying to tame the powerful tide of negative emotion that may or may not be properly felt, requires cognitive resources (ABCDE process), emotional resources (the Buddhist trifecta), physical resources (of movement and distraction), and a kind of strength of will even in the face of poor odds and/or danger. This is courage, and it's something very much needed in this regard. We'll explore it further next chapter, as it's one of our greatest virtues, whether we are well or ill.

Increasing the Positive Emotions

Step two in Nettle's overall prescription for a happier emotional life is to not merely settle for reducing negative emotional experiences, rather to try and do what one can to *augment* positive emotional experiences. What can we do in this regard? This section can be developed quickly for two reasons: 1) this whole book is about increasing the overall positive emotional experience of happiness; and 2) more narrowly, Chapter 3 on pleasure presented a number of very targeted pieces of advice on how to increase and enhance pleasurable experiences and their attending positive emotions. These ranged from being more open to beauty and excellence to increasing one's interactions with nature; from adopting techniques of mindfulness and savouring to sharing positive emotions with others and writing about and/or lingering on them afterwards. Remember constraints like hedonic adaptation and how it's important to pursue activities resistant to it, and to cultivate many different sources of pleasure and interest, all of which ties into "the complex, richly textured self" concept just reiterated.

Note here that the journal idea can work the other way, too: while keeping track of your negative emotions over three weeks, and discerning cause and effect, try and do the same with positive emotions. Track what gives you greater joy and happiness, and do more of it. For most people, the most reliable sources tend to revolve around: quality time with loved ones; enjoying leisure time with favourite activities; good food and drink; sexual contact and other active, efficacious uses of the body (like sports or dancing); music; pleasant surprises (such as unexpected gifts); and the orientation toward, and successful attainment of, worthwhile goals.

The Two Big Personality Traits

Personality, as we all know, has to do with traits or character-istics of what we are like as people: how we behave, how we think, how we feel, the things we value. To count as a personal-ity trait, the thing in question needs to be: stable over time (as a genuine show of personal identity); relatively stable across most situations (again, as a reveal of identity and as a way to predict what the person is likely to do in different situations); and more generally, these traits need to differ between people, so as to con-struct a resonant sense of individual "personality." Thousands of typologies of human personality have been proposed, but many studies have determined that there are five characteristics that reliably make a meaningful difference to one's personal-ity. These exist under the acronym OCEAN, as mentioned at the start of the chapter: Openness to experience, Conscientiousness, Extroversion, Agreeableness, and Neuroticism.[516] This section, we'll focus on the two dimensions that Daniel Nettle contends are the two most salient, and certainly the most relevant to happiness: extroversion and neuroticism. These are potently connected, respectively, to both positive and negative emotion.[517]

Neuroticism

Neuroticism gets defined precisely as the degree to which one feels, and is adversely affected by, negative emotions (e.g., fear, anger, sadness, shame, guilt, anxiety, and worry). "Adversely affected" in the sense that one: feels these emotions very strongly, feels them very often, has a difficult time functioning normally when experiencing them, and has a hard time "coming down from them." So, there is indeed a tight connection between neuroticism and the negative emotions—so much so that Nettle proposes we could just as soon label neuroticism as "negative emotionality."[518] Research has shown many important things about those who score high on measurements of neuroticism:

- The *higher* the rate of neuroticism, the *lower* the rate of happiness. Both rates as determined by self-reporting (e.g., "How satisfied are you with your life?" "How often do you feel worry?"). This inverse relationship stands to reason, Nettle notes, because the elements of neuroticism are inconsistent with what we mean by happiness, in the straightforward sense of a surplus of positive emotion over negative.[519]

- High rates of neuroticism correlate strongly with: being prone to clinical depression, difficulty maintaining stable and satisfying interpersonal relationships, and a range of poor, long-term health outcomes. (This last is of special interest to us: cause-and-effect relationships aren't clear as to what comes first, suggesting the possibility that the chronically afflicted will have higher neuroticism scores, thus dragging down their happiness.)[520]

- Many people's neuroticism scores at one point in life tend to correlate highly with their scores later in life, suggesting a stable trait (worthy, and important, for discussing people's personalities). Some theorists have proposed a biological or genetic basis for the stability of this trait (a subject canvassed back in Chapter 1).[521]

One important thing to note: more recent research has honed in on how "happiness" is defined and tested in neuroticism experiments, and has found further information. In particular, it has distinguished between "negative happiness" and "positive happiness." Negative happiness is better known as unhappiness, whereas positive happiness, of course, refers to an experience along the range of happiness superior to both unhappiness and a kind of neutral "meh," or middling level of happiness. Importantly, this research has found that high neuroticism is *only* strongly correlated with high rates of unhappiness, and *not* correlated with low rates of positive happiness. Put more clearly, neurotic people can still experience a lot of joy in-between experiencing fear, anger, sadness, worry, etc.[522]

This is an important finding for a variety of reasons. First, it shows that individuals suffering from high neuroticism need to do what they can to control or diminish their negative emotions, which are potent sources of suffering and unhappiness. The five techniques canvassed last section are designed to serve that function. Equally important, however—maybe even more important—is to not neglect the augmentation of positive emotions; research shows that *it's possible to feel lots of both kinds* of emotionality or affectivity. So, let's say that, owing to your personality and/or chronic condition, you find you can't do much to contain your negative emotionality, even with the techniques above. Don't surrender and give in; do what you can to augment the positive experiences that research has shown you are just as capable of enjoying as someone scoring low on neuroticism. *You can train yourself to feel lots of high highs,* thereby: 1) bringing up your aggregate happiness score and status, and 2) giving you joyous moments to cherish and dwell upon while they last.[523]

Further, as Nettle stresses, let's not forget the whole "life of meaning" issue discussed in Chapter 2. Recall how many stand-out contributors to our culture have been figures that, obviously, would've scored very high on the neuroticism scale. He suggests that it's no coincidence, arguing in part that the magnitude of dissatisfaction experienced by some of these figures was, or has been, a driving force behind their artistic or inventive creations, and/or their unrelenting commitment to political and legal reform. Thus, a life high in unhappiness need not be thought of as a life lacking meaning, or indeed one that doesn't go on to have a large, important, and positive impact on the lives of others.[524]

Extroversion

Recent research has also found an interesting, important connection between extroversion and the positive emotions. It is not quite as strong as the connection between high neuroticism and high unhappiness (something Nettle declares "one of the strongest predictors known" in the entire field of happiness research), but it's nevertheless real and, according to Nettle, even serves as a sort of "mirror image" to the findings regarding neuroticism.[525] The definition of extroversion versus introversion is more contested, at least in the technical happiness literature, and, while stable, it doesn't seem as stable a trait over time as neuroticism. (There has been talk more recently, at least in comparative terms, of "ambiversion," capturing this notion that much of the talk surrounding extroversion versus introversion ignores how situational these behavioural responses can be, and that most people can flip back and forth between these phases (e.g., most people will be more extroverted with their friends and more introverted among a crowd of strangers).[526]

All that said, research scientists have proven some stability in this regard. And perhaps the "ambi" part of ambiversion's appeal rests with the different terms researchers have used while testing these traits. Some say that the real difference between extroversion and introversion has to do with one's own internal mental and emotional experience of social events: extroverts enjoy them and are thus energized, whereas introverts find them stressful and draining. There is much to be said for this "internal" definition, particularly as it shows how introverts, contrary to cliché, can actually be completely functional and even very good at social situations—they just don't particularly enjoy them or seek them out, and frequently need to decompress and/or recharge afterwards. Research psychologists focus on the seeking out part, as they prefer to define the difference between extroversion and introversion in purely external, behavioural terms: the degree to which people set out to get involved in social situations. It's important to note that much of the verified research findings are based on this *second* definition of the terms.[527] These are the most relevant findings:

- The *higher* the rate of extroversion, the *higher* the rate of happiness. More precisely, the higher the rate of positive emotionality, or positive happiness, as defined above.

- Extroverts also tend to be more talkative, have more friends, be married, and seek out novel situations and changing circumstances.

- In experiments where introverts were forced to act in a more extroverted manner, they found it difficult to do so—yet almost always reported themselves as feeling happier for having done so.

As a result of findings like these, it's become common to believe that there exists a completely positive, mutually reinforcing relationship between extroversion and happiness, and to view the introverts of the world as suffering major hits to their well-being as a result of this personality trait.[528] It's not so simple, though. Here's where Nettle's "mirror image" comes into play. The more precise research findings are that, while high extroversion is indeed associated with high positive happiness, it is *not* also correlated with low negative happiness. This is to say: gleeful extroverts who thrive on lots of social contact can also experience deep emotional lows, often when lonely. Research has also found that the extroverted tendency toward novelty and change often leads to risk-prone behaviour, putting extroverts at higher risk for things like physical injury and sexually transmitted diseases. While extroverts *are* more likely to get married, they are also more likely to be unfaithful to their partners, and their restlessness leads to much greater long-term instability in their relationships than introverts. Extroverts have also been found to be more prone to addiction and, intriguingly, to have quite the sweet tooth, putting them at higher risk for diabetes over the long term.[529]

Nettle proceeds to suggest that perhaps a better definition of extroversion is that it's not about social situations per se; rather, it's about how a person engages with their external environment in general. Extroverts are much more likely to be unable to resist the allure of any potentially pleasant offering in their environment. As a result, on average they *are* going to experience more pleasant things than introverts, and on aggregate over a lifetime be happier in that sense. But the trait does have its downsides, as sometimes that inability to resist temptation can lead to doing things that cause harm and/or create negative consequences.[530]

I like Nettle's approach, as it's more value-neutral and objective, noting that there are both strengths and weaknesses to each of these important personality traits. *Extroversion is thus not an unalloyed recipe for happiness.* Introverts may be less inclined to sample widely from the buffet of life, but they are also more likely: to be faithful and loyal to their friends; to avoid high-risk behaviours that can sometimes backfire; to avoid serious diseases like STDs and diabetes; and to be able to focus, concentrate on, and stick with, an objective and/or goal, as opposed to extroverts who can prove more easily distracted. Introverts also don't need to be around others to get as internally charged and stimulated, thus they are less prone to deep loneliness and actually get energized by being alone.[531]

It's important to stress that within these two dimensions of personality, the separate pairings don't have to line up: extroverts, while full of positive emotions, may also score highly on negative emotionality (coming down hard from happy social experiences and variegated risk-taking). And introverts, while not scoring as high on positive emotionality, might not score highly on negative emotionality either: indeed, all that time alone, engaged in regular, personal projects, may put them on a more even emotional keel that helps them avoid deep unhappiness. All that said, it remains true that *if* one is both highly introverted AND highly neurotic, their risk of deep and prolonged unhappiness is profound, and ought to be resisted with every single tool presented in this chapter and book—and probably with some added external support.[532]

We've noted previously how *those with chronic conditions are much more likely to suffer from both*, by virtue of the effects of the condition itself: driving them inwards, making them self-focused or affliction-obsessed, which in turn makes it harder to go out for social occasions, and also provoking and deepening the experience of such poisonous negative emotions as anger, fear, sadness, worry, and anxiety. I'd go so far as to assert that, for all of us with chronic conditions, we've likely experienced each and every one of these things, and thus need to take what action we can. To combat high neuroticism, employ techniques to increase positive emotion and decrease negative emotion. To combat high introversion, force yourself to sample more aggressively from the buffet of life—to get out there and have more experiences. (Recall, for inspiration, what country singer and Rhodes Scholar Kris Kristofferson memorably wrote: *"Freedom's just another word for nothing left to lose."*) The research shows that it is possible to will yourself into doing such things, if you wish, and moreover most introverts actually report themselves as being happier for having forced themselves to do so. They do not feel like "fakes" or "phonies" when behaving extrovertedly: they report themselves as sincerely flushed with happiness.[533] And note how, as with Nettle's broader definition of extroversion, there are many things one can do, both for their own sake as well as for the good practice of being in a novel situation (whether social or otherwise). These include: preparing and eating new food, playing a new game, going online to research a new destination, visiting somewhere new, watching a new

TV show or listening to a new genre of music, or taking up a new physical activity or team sport. Finally, don't forget how, if doing these things with people similarly afflicted, there is likely to be more understanding and patience, and perhaps an easier social experience.

Those Two Other Traits: Openness and Agreeableness (Including Sense of Humour)

Of lesser importance to happiness, yet still real, are the two further OCEAN personality traits of "openness to experience" and "agreeableness." In many ways, and especially as we've defined it, there's not much separating openness to experience and extroversion. It's perhaps more helpful to categorize the former under the latter. Research has indeed found that *the more open one is to new experiences, the happier they tend to be.*[534] Presumably for reasons identical to the extroversion described above: in trying more things, you're going to try more pleasant things, and thus your happiness status will be boosted. However, we've noted that there can be a downside to such experimentation, so one still needs to be mindful of risk-management and Aristotelian moderation. We also need to admit just how much of a struggle this can be for some (perhaps most) of the chronically afflicted. Their afflictions can be substantial, sapping both energy and risk-prone *joie de vivre*. (For example, while writing this chapter, I had another substantial up-tick in my seizures, which forced me away from social situations and made me want to seek out the solace of familiarity. Even worse, for the first time in a very long time it made me *anxious* about my epilepsy, constantly worrying that I'd have a seizure while out in the world. I'm coming down from it now, but I've had to take my own advice and research to heart, and deliberately deploy the techniques previously mentioned to come to renewed mental and emotional control over my response to my condition.) One major objective of this book has been to try to show the chronically afflicted the sheer range of new, plausible, pleasurable things for them to try, in order to help them enjoy a more diverse and fulfilling life, whether it's meditation, yoga, a daily stroll in nature, new foods, praying, deep-breathing techniques, rhythmic touching, a new book, TV series or movie, or, above all, more social engagement in any form.

There's more to be said about agreeableness. It stands to reason that, the more agreeable one is, the happier one is likely to be. Here, too, we note the close connection to openness to experience, and thus extroversion, but it's not a personality trait of the same depth and import as, say, neuroticism. Still, agreeableness has been found to be moderately associated with happiness.[535] Only moderately because, while agreeableness presumably helps one get along with others—increasing one's social life, and their happiness—there are limits to such agreeableness, and unhappiness can result from going along with things just for the sake of fitting in, especially when at odds with one's values or what gives them pleasure. Others might even take advantage of a person's agreeableness, which never ends well, for the relationship or one's happiness status. One needs authenticity, and to be free from oppressive social control. Therefore, agreeableness is primarily a tool for augmenting otherwise pleasurable time with one's family, friends, and associates.

The subject I'd like to discuss most under the heading of agreeableness is a sense of humour. We haven't yet spoken of this, but humour clearly suggests a kind of agreeableness. Moreover, it's famously said that laughter is the best medicine, and a sense of humour constantly polls among personality traits found most appealing to others. So what role should humour and laughter play in a happy life, especially for the chronically afflicted?

A landmark book in this field is Norman Cousins' 1979 work, *Anatomy of an Illness*.[536] Cousins was a life-long journalist, author, peace activist, and adjunct professor who, in the late 1960s, came down with a crippling condition of unclear origin and diagnosis. (It's since been agreed that it was some kind of severe, degenerative, crippling arthritis, but of unclear causation. Thus, treatment was never exact or precise.) His doctors told Cousins he would die of the condition, perhaps within one year. This made him miserable, as did the gloomy hospital in which he felt trapped. Partially for the sake of "Why not?" and partially to take his treatment into his own hands, Cousins checked himself out of the hospital and into a luxury hotel room. (It must be said: this *was* with his doctor's blessing, perhaps because they felt there was nothing more to be done.) There, Cousins embarked on an unusual self-made plan for treatment and recovery: a) enormous mega-doses of Vitamin C (via injection, and as inspired by Dr. Linus Pauling[537]), b) savouring pleasant sensations (like tasty room service, being waited on, and not having to clean), and c) marathon sessions of deliberately induced humour and laughter—for instance binge-watching comedy shows such as *Candid Camera*. Cousins claimed that ten minutes of laughter could allow him to sleep pain-free for two hours, which was very welcome relief from the near-constant physical pain his illness imposed upon him. It was "humour therapy."[538] Subsequent studies have indeed shown that humour and laughter:

- break up the tension associated with a chronic condition, measurably reducing inflammation in the body

- indirectly increase one's immune system (by decreasing the immuno-suppressive effects of stress)

- decrease levels of the stress hormone cortisol in the blood stream

- measurably increase pain tolerance (for most people)

- reduce blood pressure

These physiological effects are on top of well-known psychological effects of laughter, such as boosts in short-term mood, enhancement of creativity and idea generation, and an enhanced social orientation (e.g., humour tends to be highly social, prompting one to want to share jokes with others).[539]

I don't have to belabour the claim that a sense of humour is a robust part of a good and happy life, and a useful tool in achieving such. What I do want to do, though, is *stress the role of humour and laughter as a coping tool*, especially for the chronically ill. It's an interesting idea, to mimic Cousins' methodology and try bingeing humour/forced laughter to tantalize one's senses. Now, we all have our own tastes, but in consulting the many lists out there regarding the most popular TV- and movie-based comedies (some based on laughs-per-minute, some on viewer opinion polls, some on expert/media critic ranking), the following fifteen keep coming up. If you haven't watched some of them, check them out:

FIG 19 COMPILED LISTS OF THE MOST POPULAR COMEDIES

TV Shows	Movies
Arrested Development	Airplane
The Big Bang Theory	Anchorman
Cheers	Animal House
Curb Your Enthusiasm	Blazing Saddles
Frasier	Borat
The Fresh Prince of Bel-Air	Bridesmaids
Friends	Caddyshack
I Love Lucy	A Fish Called Wanda
Martin	Life of Brian
Modern Family	Monty Python and the Holy
Saturday Night Live	Grail
Seinfeld	Naked Gun
The Office	Young Frankenstein
The Simpsons	Superbad
30 Rock	The Hangover
	The Jerk

It can also be fun to search online for jokes about one's chronic condition—*it helps to add a sense of control and perspective to one's condition by being able to laugh at it.* A funny contemporary podcast on the subject, called *Sickboy*, is put on by a young man with cystic fibrosis. Here's a handful of some other online sickness jokes:

"I have Auto-Immune Disorder, because the only thing tough enough to kick my ass . . . is me!"

"What do you call an epileptic cow? Beef Jerky!"

Also for epilepsy: "It's not that I'm falling down . . . it's that I'm doing random gravity checks."

Finally: "When I was young, I wanted to date a doctor for money. Now, it would be for the prescriptions."

Here are a couple of amusing illness-themed cartoons:

" Between you and me, I'd rather be *me*. "

It's interesting, when searching online, to see how angry and defensive some of the illness-based "humour" is. It can even be a bit off-putting, and actually call attention to the negative aspects of one's illness. At the very least, it indirectly shows the struggle with negative emotion, which so many afflicted people have. In my view, it's not so much about finding the humour in your illness—though, that's terrific if you can. It's more about what Norman Cousins did: *making deliberate, systematic efforts at increasing the amount of humour and laughter in your life, and surrounding and exposing yourself to lots of funny things in general.* So, watch your favourite comedies, or listen to some hilarious stand-up routines. Combine different kinds of humour, such as physical comedy with situation comedy, word play with satire, and so on. Force out a deliberate belly laugh for ten seconds. Cultivate a funny way of approaching things—including your affliction—by asking, "What would a stand-up comedian say about this?" And enjoy not just a lightened mood and a more fetching personality, but some modest health benefits as well.

Oh, and what happened to Cousins? He survived with his condition for over twenty-five years, published many books, was given many awards (mainly for his peace activism), saw *Anatomy of an Illness* made into a Hollywood movie, and had four children and twenty-six grandchildren. Truly, he had the last laugh.

Coping

Coping refers to how we deal with a significant negative event in our lives, whether it's getting fired, divorced, losing a loved one, or coming down with a chronic condition. Sonja Lyubomirsky reports that half of all US adults will experience at least one severely traumatic event in their lives, which actually seems low (by about half!).[540]

There's a big distinction in the literature between problem-focused coping (PFC) and emotion-focused coping (EFC). With PFC, one focuses on the problem and deals with it; with EFC, one focuses instead on how they think and feel about the problem. Crucially, Lyubomirsky says that both methods are "essential when you cope with a chronic problem," like a challenging injury or illness.[541] Interestingly, there's evidence that these methods are typically deployed by the genders in different ways, with men showing preferences for PFC and women for EFC. This finding has led to important research discovering that, given these background biases, each gender profits most from explicit training in the *other* coping method (i.e., men benefit most from learning about EFC whereas women benefit most from learning PFC).[542]

The essential steps for PFC are:

1 correctly **identify** the problem

2 **gather information and advice** (especially expert advice) about how to deal with the problem

3 **draw up a plan of action**

4 **execute that plan,** putting aside or delaying other activities until the problem has been dealt with to the best of one's ability and resources[543]

With EFC, the essential steps are as we've described both in this chapter and last. (Note that *EFC tends to be best employed when, for whatever reason, PFC can't actually work*: when the problem can't be solved and one must endure it, thus considering how to think and feel about the issue becomes paramount.) They include:

1 correctly **identify** the problem

2 **cognitively re-interpret** the problem and/or its consequences (e.g., by considering what might be good or beneficial about the otherwise bad experience); recall and deploy the ABCDE process

3 **emotionally use all the tools** listed previously to both **decrease** one's negative emotions about the problem and subsequently **increase** their positive emotions as a kind of buffer

4 consider **seeking religious solace**

5 **deploy techniques of distraction** when feeling overwhelmed (humour helps)

6 never underestimate **the value of physical well-being in helping you cope**: good sleep, proper diet, relaxing breathing, and daily physical activity and motion/exercise[544]

Further, *beware and resist the allure of any negative coping strategies*—those that only distract one's attention temporarily, and otherwise undermine their long-term ability either to solve the problem or to develop better thoughts and feelings about it. Such negative coping strategies notably include substance abuse (Chapter 3).

Lyubomirsky points out that, whether one deploys PFC, EFC, or both, the evidence shows that if one can *turn to other people for social support* for any of the above procedures, one ought to do so. This has been proven to be perhaps the most effective overall way of coping with trauma. One feels less alone, gains added perspective and information, experiences kindness and support, is able to share their thoughts and feelings, and is made better by the touch and closeness of others. One impressive statistic in this regard: it's been shown that female cancer survivors who attend weekly support groups end up living, on average, eighteen months longer than those who don't. They also display (possibly related) greater immune system activity than those not participating in social support groups.[545]

Other studies have shown the benefits in particular of achieving step two in the EFC process. Men who'd had a heart attack between the ages of thirty and sixty, and who were able to find benefit in the experience (e.g., a better perspective on life) within seven weeks of the attack, were less likely to have a recurrence of heart problems for the following eight years compared to those who couldn't see any such benefit.[546] Similarly, men with HIV who had lost at least one loved one to HIV/AIDS, and who found some benefit in the experience, showed greater immune function and lived longer in the three-year period following whichever was the more recent trauma (i.e., the death of the other or their own diagnosis).[547] The most common benefits reported from all such traumatic experiences:

- a deeper appreciation of life

- a deeper appreciation of, and commitment to, spending more time with close friends and loved ones

- a "wake-up call" to re-order their priorities in life, particularly in terms of work-life balance and spending less time at work (or on chores) and more time with family and friends

- renewed spirituality

- a greater emphasis on living in the present, and savouring the small-scale "joys of today"[548]

We've spoken multiple times throughout this book about considering how one's chronic condition might actually provide some benefits. This is *not* to deny the associated costs and pains imposed upon you; it is to consider it a goal to force oneself to see *some* benefit coming out of the suffering. As Lyubomirsky says, with eloquence and insight: "There's absolutely nothing good about tragedy and loss, but something of value can come from the struggle in their aftermath."[549] The evidence shows that, if you can force yourself to see these possible benefits, it will indeed improve your life and happiness.

Conclusion: Emotional Intelligence (EQ) and Maturity

This final subject makes for a convenient bird's-eye view summary of this chapter, and has the virtue of re-stressing the substantial interconnections between reason and emotion— between beliefs and feelings. Daniel Goleman's popular 1995 book *Emotional Intelligence* made the argument that emotional intelligence: a) exists, and b) is at least as important (probably more-so) for success in life as more traditional measures of intelligence such as IQ (or Intelligence Quotient, with its heavy emphasis on mathematical reasoning, abstract logic, and critical thinking puzzles, as well as spatio-temporal reasoning). It's important to note that, in many ways, Goleman's intended audience was well-read business people and professionals. The main argument, he explicitly states, has to do with leadership (i.e., that those who rank highly in emotional intelligence (EI) make not just better leaders but *much better* leaders than those with low EI/EQ. At the time, Goleman offered such examples as then-US President Bill Clinton, who has both high EQ and IQ, but with the high EQ accounting for much more of his success and electability.[550] Since then, the theory has come under much scrutiny, especially from research psychologists.

Emotional intelligence is a construct, or a kind of "basket" of psychological and emotional traits used to rate an individual's competence with their emotional life. These traits include:

- Under the heading of *self-awareness*, the traits of emotional self-insight (i.e., not just having an emotion but knowing *why*) and realistic self-confidence (i.e., knowing and appreciating one's strengths but also being aware of their limitations and weaknesses).

- Under the heading of *self-management,* three traits: 1) self-motivation (the ability to motivate oneself to not be passive about what to do in the face of someone else's agenda), 2) resilience (the ability to handle setbacks, whether through PFC or EFC), and 3) the very broadly described notion of "emotional balance," which one exhibits on a regular basis, akin to the Aristotelian ideal of feeling the appropriate emotions, in the proper situations, for the right time and right set of reasons. Emotional balance implies the absence of chronic suffering from out-of-control negative emotions or neuroticism.

- Under the final heading of *relationships with others,* five traits: 1) cognitive empathy (i.e., the ability to understand another person's beliefs, values, and emotions, particularly when they differ from one's own); 2) emotional empathy (i.e., the ability and regular practice of being able to understand—and even share—the emotions of others); 3) being a good listener; 4) being able to communicate clearly with others, especially about one's beliefs, feelings, and values; and 5) being a team player when properly called for (which implies related traits, like the ability to self-regulate, communicate, compromise, listen, and empathize).[551]

All that adds up to ten traits organized under three headings, which Goleman and others believe are expressive of EI, and stress as being helpful to aspiring leaders in particular. Research psychologists, since publication, have criticized the notion as mere "pop psychology," in particular arguing that these lists of traits seem if not arbitrary then at least lacking in systematic organization, skewed toward the self-serving interests of Goleman's intended audience, and, above all, not worth so grandiose a label as a kind of "intelligence." Perhaps most witheringly, there's criticism that the notion of EI adds nothing above and beyond what's implied by discussion and analysis of each of the above ten traits. Thus EI/EQ is merely a catchy marketing label with no higher claim on psychological insight.[552]

That said (and admittedly these are fair criticisms), we might nevertheless maintain that the listed traits *are* clearly skills, even if one hesitates to use the term "intelligence," and we know that such skills are stronger in some people and weaker in others. Moreover, and crucial to our purpose, we know that *skills and traits like these can lead to greater self-reported happiness for most people.*[553] Hence my decision to include them here, though only at the end of this chapter and by way of convenient summary. As revealed in the chapter title, I prefer the term "emotional hygiene" to "emotional intelligence," as I wish to stress the connection to health, and to a healthy versus non-healthy way of living one's emotional life. But whatever the label, it's the set of traits that matters, and being able to strengthen them within oneself. As Nettle says, use the tools within this chapter to achieve the basic, all-important happiness equation of: 1) decreasing the impact and experience of negative emotions, and 2) augmenting the number and intensity of positive emotions.

Erik Erikson has crafted a related list, with perhaps a more distinguished psychological pedigree. He labels it the core ingredients of "emotional maturity," and they hook into, and summarize, much of our findings. Controversially, he attaches these traits to quite specific ages and stages of personal development and growth. His colleagues have tended to be skeptical of this linkage, but few can deny that having the following traits, as described by Erikson, paints a compelling overall picture of what it might mean to be emotionally well-balanced, and to have one's emotions play their proper role in the life-long pursuit of happiness:

- **trust** versus mistrust

- **autonomy** versus self-doubt

- **initiative** versus guilt

- **competence** versus inferiority

- **identity** versus role-confusion

- **intimacy** versus isolation

- **generativity** (or the capacity for constructive change) versus stagnation

- **ego-integrity** versus despair[554]

We note once more, in ending, how such richly textured and complex traits blend elements not merely of belief and feeling, or of reason and emotion, but of courage and willpower. We need to consider this more deeply as a main subject in the next chapter, on the role of values within happiness.

CHAPTER 10

Moral Character

We began, and now end, with inspiration from Aristotle. For him, the pursuit of happiness and the process of moral development were so closely connected as to be inseparable. His definition of human happiness was so complex, robust, and demanding that—as many commentators have noted—it truly offered a picture of the ideal human life (which would of course include moral goodness, if not outright excellence).[555] We ourselves have shied away from soaring ideals of perfection: indeed, the motivation behind this book is about how to pursue an ideal of happiness given sub-optimal, even severe constraints of illness, injury, and affliction. Yet it turns out that there are clear (and perhaps surprising) connections between morality and well-being—between being good and being happy—and they serve as a fitting final subject for our investigations. We have already discussed some aspects of this connection:

- In chapters 1 and 2, we investigated the possibility, and desirability, of happiness being *the* goal in life that one ought to pursue to the best of their ability and resources. As we saw, this only makes sense if the case for genetic determinism is false—and it is. This is perhaps *the* major connection to morality: the vital importance of taking responsibility for one's own happiness, and not being passive and accepting of a sub-optimal status quo, blaming your sick body for everything, or expecting someone else to fulfill your every dream.

- Related, it's vitally important to let others take responsibility for *their* own lives and choices. This follows both from respect for their freedom and autonomy as separate persons (chapters 5 and 6) as well as from a concern for one's *own* freedom and autonomy, and the right to pursue one's own happiness and *not be a prop* in someone else's projects. Human beings, as Kant once declared, are "ends-in-themselves," and not "mere means" toward the serving of other people's, or society's, goals.[556]

- In Chapter 4, we spoke of equal access and fair treatment at work, especially for those suffering from chronic conditions. We also delved into research showing that societies suffering from excess income inequality are much less happy, on average, than those committed to providing for everyone's basic needs, and hopefully—even more so—*containing* the degree of inequality.

- In Chapter 5, we offered a systematic look at the connection between how social institutions are set up in a given country (indeed, globally) and the happiness of the people who live there. This led to the discovery of some powerful correlations, or features, which the very happiest countries reliably share. All together, they add up to a vision not only of human happiness but also social justice. Such features, or correlations, between institutional design and human well-being include: respect for human rights; robust personal freedoms; non-discrimination; democratic governance; low corruption; high social trust; low rates of crime; high rates of literacy, numeracy, and educational attainment; and a "mixed economy" that allows for entrepreneurial freedoms while protecting the most vulnerable from material deprivation. A health care system devoted to prevention, basic medical services, and strong health outcomes—including for the chronically afflicted—was also mentioned.

- In Chapter 6, we were concerned with how best to get along with other people—especially those closest to us—involving, at least partially, moral and ethical behaviour. Equality and shared reciprocity are features of the happiest interpersonal relationships, likewise for decent behaviour, which leads to strong, intimate, and trusting connections. Such basic ethical regard seems a necessary condition for anything resembling a healthy and happy relationship: it's just very hard to care deeply for, and enjoy a close relationship with, a person one believes to be immoral and/or someone who treats you badly and thus cannot be trusted.

- Last chapter (9), on emotional hygiene, we discussed in detail how such negative emotions as anger—and any inability to contain, control, and channel such—can be absolutely ruinous to one's peace of mind and personal happiness. Anger can also lead to poisonous conflict with, and rough treatment of other people, thus raising further issues of morality and ethical behaviour.

We won't repeat such subjects here. But a handful *do* remain for our consideration, and the completion of our picture of happiness in spite of illness. In particular, the happiness literature talks a lot about gratitude, kindness toward others, and forgiveness. We've yet to discuss those things, and need to do so now. What unites them is that, in addition to being happiness boosters, they are all virtues of character. And it just so happens that Aristotle's understanding of morality and ethics focused on personal virtues. Using his framework, we'll explore each of these characteristics and their connection to happiness. We'll finish off by focusing on one final virtue—perhaps that which Aristotle thought most highly of, and which is of manifest importance for the chronically afflicted: courage.

But Really?

I've taught university courses in ethics, morality, and justice for twenty years now, and there's always a substantial subset of young students who express profound skepticism about any so-called connection between being *happy* and being *moral*. They ask: Aren't the dreary duties and onerous obligations of ethics and justice necessarily at odds with the freedom and self-regard needed to pursue one's personal happiness to the very fullest? Isn't it actually one of the coarse-grained truths of the world that "nice guys finish last"? Above all, the pursuit of happiness is supposed to be fun, right? Isn't this in tension with "proper behaviour" and always "doing what you're supposed to do"?

It's probably accurate that being moral is not sufficient to make one happy. Perhaps for some that's the case. But, for most of us to be happy, we do need to be free to think our own thoughts, feel our own feelings, and pursue our own interests—and not be completely subservient to the needs and interests of others. As we've seen, one of the clearest truths of the research shows that robust degrees of autonomy and personal freedom are necessary ingredients for happiness. But, while perhaps not sufficient, there are compelling reasons to agree that some baseline moral behaviour is, in fact, necessary for the life-long and maximal pursuit of happiness.

Perhaps the main reason has to do with the importance of other people in one's pursuit of happiness. We've seen that one of the strongest determinants of personal happiness concerns both the quality and quantity of one's relations with other people. This is especially true of their friends and loved ones, but we've also seen it in connection with coworkers (Chapter 4) and fellow citizens who are complete strangers: one of the hallmarks of an unhappy society, as seen in Chapter 5, is one torn by open conflict and/or corroded from within by widespread lack of social trust and mutual respect.[557]

The key thing is: What is your response when subject to harmful treatment by others? The answer is, overwhelmingly, that you do one of two things: 1) either you move away from that person, ending (or at least distancing) that relationship so they cannot do continued harm; and/or 2) you get payback and revenge on that person, treating them the same way (or worse) than they treated you. In either case, that person's bad behaviour has damaged their relationship with you, thus costing them the benefits from it they used to enjoy. This is the basic, quite worldly truth of "what goes around, comes around": if you behave badly toward others, it's highly likely—based on how they're most likely to respond and retaliate—that you will suffer some loss or price that will reduce your happiness. Maybe not in the immediate short term, and perhaps not always (it's not a perfect world), but over the long term there's a mountain of evidence that bad treatment of others comes back to haunt the doer, reducing their happiness by poisoning the quantity and quality of their relationships.[558]

I used to teach Business Ethics, a course with perhaps the highest percentage of skeptics regarding any connection between morality and happiness, much less morality and business success (the latter of which, of course, they cared deeply about). Yet, by course's end, I was usually able to persuade them that, at the very least, bad behaviour is bad for business. There are just too many cases, ranging from the Ford Pinto scandal in the 1970s to the Volkswagen fake emissions scandal of 2015, and from the Enron scandal to Bernie Madoff's pyramid scheme, which amply illustrate that bad behaviour eventually comes back to haunt and hurt the doer, sometimes enormously.[559] After all, when you treat people badly, they tend not to let it go. Either they cut you off and/or they retaliate—both diminish your happiness, and may even leave you with other serious and costly things with which to contend (e.g., legal problems). It's just easier, nicer, simpler, and more honest to do what you can *to minimize conflict with others* and strive, at the very least, *not to do harm to others*. These are vital ingredients to happiness!

As a result, I think of this issue much like the old cliché that "ignorance is bliss" (Chapter 5). Except it's not; in the end, ignorance is a recipe for misery in a whole range of human endeavours, from work and career to health and safety, from choosing close relationships to having as much freedom and autonomy as possible. Likewise, unethical behaviour is not a ticket to happiness: there aren't too many well-adjusted thieves and killers out there, and we all know what ridiculous, tangled knots liars get involved with and the kinds of payback that get meted out to nasty jerks. The truth is that some kind of basic decency is required for good relationships with others, to say nothing of more abstract yet still real concerns, like self-respect and having a clear and unconfused direction in life.[560]

This may be of relevance to the chronically afflicted, as perhaps your affliction has led some to treat you in rough ways. Unfair and crappy ways, to be sure. I myself, as mentioned in the Introduction, have suffered from such crappiness as medical negligence, and poor treatment from ignorant, self-absorbed others who were unwilling or incapable of helping, or even understanding. I'd wager that many of the chronically afflicted can say, or relate to, similar things. We'll talk more about forgiveness later, but for now it needs to be said that using such things as grounds for retaliation may not ultimately be in your long-term, self-interested pursuit of happiness, and that this needs to be considered prior to acting. Nor should other things typically associated with chronic conditions lead you, perhaps insensibly, to indulge in bad behaviour: just because you're sick doesn't mean you should lie, be rude, commit infidelity, steal, or be cruel. Recall that research finds that many chronic conditions drive people inwards, at least initially, and that that kind of self-absorption might not only make you more introverted, it also might make you less morally sensitive—something to guard against. Recall from Chapter 3 that the chronically afflicted are more likely to succumb to substance abuse, which is associated with poorer treatment of others (as anyone who's seen an angry drunk can attest). Misery may love company, but don't love it in return—and certainly don't let it take root in your heart. You don't want to indulge in unethical, harmful behaviour toward others because you're angry at, or hurt by, your own affliction. Remind yourself that, in the final analysis, being unjust and harmful to others is shameful to one's self-image, elicits painful payback, drives other people away, and is corrosive to any effective, long-term pursuit of happiness. Find more constructive ways to vent, such as exercising (Chapter 7), chasing after flow (Chapter 3), meditating (Chapter 8), getting politically involved (Chapter 5), landing a better job (Chapter 4), or simply resolving to be a great friend, parent, and loved one (Chapter 6).

Virtues (and Vice) in General

A virtue is one kind of character trait, in the sense that it is (or must become over time) an evident, real, reliable, and stable part of one's personality and behaviour. Aristotle said that a virtue is neither natural nor automatic; to the contrary, it can only be developed over time through much conscious and deliberate effort, like exercising a muscle. Though we have the natural potential to become virtuous, and though being virtuous actualizes what is best within us as human beings, Aristotle drolly observed that virtues are "corrective" of many natural

deficiencies typically displayed by humans. Thus, industriousness as a virtue is corrective of our tendency toward laziness.
And honesty is corrective of tendencies we may have to lie.
Aristotle noted that virtues are "traits we praise in others, and
strive to develop in ourselves" (such as patience, intelligence,
or empathy); he argued that a trait doesn't count as a true virtue
unless it benefits *both* the self and others. (This is what makes
it a genuinely moral excellence, or opposed to an excellence
of personal skill, which might only benefit the self.) Finally,
Aristotle's definition of virtues suggested that, usually, they are
seen as occupying "the mean between extremes" of a course of
action or range of behaviour.[561]

Some thinkers have wondered whether this last criterion
can be applied to all the virtues: Bertrand Russell, for example, sarcastically questioned whether honesty was supposed
to occupy the mid-point between lying and being lied to.[562] Yet
the notion of "the mean between extremes" seems to hold for
most of Aristotle's cardinal virtues: courage, justice, moderation, and prudence. Moderation very literally, of course; and (as
we've seen, and will re-discover) courage was thought by him
to be that kind of behaviour that is neither too cowardly nor
too foolhardy, but somewhere in-between. Prudence certainly
does suggest a kind of wise awareness and smart choice-making
capacity, which is neither too dumb and cautious nor too sharp
and risk-prone. Perhaps then the only one of Aristotle's cardinal
virtues that does not clearly reside within a mean between two
extremes would be justice. And this, even on Aristotle's terms,
as he developed a robust account of justice that goes beyond
mere personal behaviour and includes a complex set of social
institutions (Chapter 5). Yet, Aristotle's favourite sweeping and
abstract definition of justice was "giving someone their due."
Justice is about everyone getting what they deserve, which I suppose would literally involve giving someone neither too much
nor too little. And a final reminder of something previously

mentioned (chapters 5 and 7): Aristotle observed that tending to the mean between extremes almost always strengthens, protects, and enhances the life of an animal (human included), thus for him there was a very tight connection between being moral and being happy and well: it's both the *right* thing, and the *good* thing to do.[563]

It's important to note what immoral behaviour would be on this account. In general, the vices have always been defined in ways that portray them as extremes of behaviour, thus violating Aristotelian moderation. For instance, within the famous seven deadly sins are such classic examples of immoderation as gluttony, lust, greed, and sloth. Traits and behaviours that are too self-regarding violate Aristotle's definition of virtue; such deadly sins as pride and envy satisfy that understanding. The final deadly sin—anger—meets Aristotle's conception insofar as it's not a trait we praise in others or strive to develop in ourselves.

But what actually causes unethical behaviour? For Aristotle, it was weakness of will. He believed, quite refreshingly, that almost everyone knows the good or right thing to do in a given situation: the truths of ethics and justice are not complex calculations. Ignorance is not usually the problem (at least not for rational adults). The problem is a failure of willpower in making one's behaviour adhere to what they know is true.[564] How does such a failure happen?

- One might not have had a good enough upbringing, either by parents or society, to condition their behaviour in a positive way. Discipline must be learned and practiced, and one needs to have had a good head start in that regard.

- Relatedly, contemporary research has shown that social pressure in favour of unethical behaviour can be a prime cause, particularly if one is being "egged on" by friends and/or an authority figure. Stanley Milgram's experiments on authority are classic and disturbing illustrations of what many people are willing to do—including the administering of electric shocks to others, to the point of severe harm—when ordered to by an authority figure, and when assured that they will not be held personally accountable.[565]

- Particular stresses or strains in a situation might also lead to ethical failure. Contemporary research has shown that even apparently unrelated things, like temporary hunger or lack of sleep, or even just feeling rushed and over-busy, can make people measurably more unethical than when they are feeling calm, well fed, and well rested.[566] This is where chronic afflictions, and/or their effects, may lead one down the path of insensitive and even wrong behaviour: the illness can sap one's strength of the will to do the right thing, and/or cause one to care less about others in general.

- Another thing of relevance to the chronically afflicted: how when one's negative emotions run so strongly that they cannot be controlled it sometimes leads to ethical mistakes. Aristotle's teacher Plato had a vivid metaphor of emotions being like wild horses to which the chariot of one's overall personality is attached. Unless one gains mastery over them—through reason and willpower—the horses will run wildly, leading to chaos, confusion, and perhaps even hurt, harm, and ruin.[567]

- A fifth factor in unethical behaviour is when one's own interests and pleasures are placed ahead of others'. To an extent, this is inescapable as a matter of the human condition. But what we are most concerned with here is pursuing one's own interests and pleasures in a way that actually harms other people: this is the most objectionable kind of behaviour, and the thing to be most avoided. We saw that Aristotle stipulated that a thing doesn't count as a virtue unless it benefits *both* oneself and others. He claimed the key was this: as human animals, we are hardwired to pursue what we find pleasurable (Chapter 3). There's no changing that. But an equally important truth is that what we find pleasurable is plastic and changeable, and subject to choice, taste, judgment, and decision. In many ways, Aristotle viewed the central real-world problem of ethics as *training oneself over time to get pleasure out of doing excellent, happy, and virtuous things, and to feel pain and shame when behaving in an unethical manner,* especially when it involves unjustified harm to others. Too often, the source of bad behaviour is people merely following their pleasures, taking them as a given and putting no effort at all into considering whether they should be pursuing those things. It's a kind of laziness, really, which leads to weakness of will in the face of the temptations of an ill-conceived pleasure.[568]

- Finally, emerging research has shown that unethical behaviour can be associated with people who otherwise display extreme risk-prone tendencies. They just enjoy breaking the rules and seeing if they can get away with bad behaviour. These people—quite dangerous, actually—would no doubt be seen by Aristotle as either: a) the products of a clearly deficient or even twisted upbringing; and/or b) poster children for the point just made, about giving in to temptations of pleasure while putting no thought into whether one ought to pursue such pleasure; and/or c) not considering the potentially substantial negative consequences to oneself beyond the short-term sensation of power/defiance/sneakiness/self-exemption. It boils down to bad impulse control—perhaps the clearest form of weakness of will. The horses have left the building, so to speak, and are running wild.[569]

In the end, *the ultimate cure for weakness of will originates in, and requires, courage*: courage to stand up to others, to not let fatigue or busyness or illness mar one's moral choices, to try to overcome a bad upbringing, to not give in to temptations, and to take on one's negative emotions and bring them under control. For Aristotle, courage was the be-all and end-all of ethics: the master moral virtue.[570]

Particular Virtues

a) Gratitude

Before returning to the master moral virtue, let's consider some of the lesser ones that have still proven relevant to happiness. Gratitude is one of the most studied virtues in the literature. Repeated studies have shown that feeling and expressing gratitude on a regular basis is productive of happiness, and correlates with other related attributes such as experiencing greater "positive affectivity," more energy, lower materialism, and higher hopefulness.[571] But we should distinguish between at least two different senses of gratitude: 1) *inward* gratitude, wherein one privately ponders what they're grateful for (whether in journal writing, prayer, or simple cognitive appreciation); and 2) *outward* gratitude, which is expressed openly to another person or persons, whether in writing or verbally.

Interestingly, both kinds of gratitude are relevant to our concern in this chapter. This is clearly the case with outward gratitude, because one is being thankful and showing thoughtful appreciation for another person and their efforts. It's just good manners, and is arguably their moral due. But studies have shown that even people who regularly cultivate inward gratitude report themselves (indirectly through other questions) as: having heightened regard for others, having greater degrees of empathy and understanding, and having been more likely to help someone over the past month.[572]

Perhaps the connection is that gratitude, in either form, promotes happiness. And, as we've seen in chapters 2 and 6, happier people are much more likely than unhappy people to have caring regard for others, as unhappy people are more prone to close in on themselves and become more self-absorbed and less other-regarding. Moreover, unhappier people by definition experience more negative emotion, both in terms of quantity and quality. And as we saw last chapter, this carries with it a kind of "detect and dismantle" impulse, as opposed to the "broaden and build" affect of positive emotions. Note further how the detect and dismantle impulse primes one, quite readily, toward not merely unhappiness and self-absorption but also more robustly unethical forms of rough treatment toward others.

How exactly does gratitude boost happiness? According to Sonja Lyubomirsky, the habitual expression and experience of gratitude:

- promotes self-esteem (by calling one's attention to the good things, and people, in one's life) (Chapter 2)

- promotes savouring (through positive recollecting) (Chapter 3)

- helps to resist hedonic adaptation (Chapter 1)

- is a check on envy (appreciating one's own goods and not engaging in negative social comparison) (Chapter 8)

- aids in controlling negative emotions (Chapter 9)

- boosts social connection and enhances relationships of all kinds, whether at work (Chapter 4) or in one's personal life (Chapter 6)[573]

People with chronic conditions will be interested to know that those similarly afflicted, participating in rigorous experiments, almost always report boosts in their happiness after being taught how to cultivate gratitude (in both its forms). And not just long-lasting boosts in happiness—they also report diminished rates of other kinds of illness (i.e., colds and influenzas) compared to control groups. They also claim they get better quality sleep and are able to gain better perspective on, and endurance toward, their affliction. This is to say, as has long been supposed, *gratitude is a potent tool for coping* (especially the emotion-focused kind of coping discussed last chapter).[574]

Lyubomirsky has run experiments trying to determine the optimal strategies for cultivating gratitude. Generally speaking, you can't really overdo outward gratitude, as others simply appreciate it so much and reciprocate—expressing and receiving gratitude never goes out of style. If you've ever written, or received, a detailed letter of gratitude, you know what I mean: they can be very emotional experiences to write, and thrilling to receive. Everyone in the happiness literature strongly urges people to write such letters to those who've had a deep, positive impact on their life.[575] Perhaps a special application for the chronically afflicted might be to write such a letter to someone who's had a deep, positive impact on how one has been able to manage one's affliction, or for their support during the difficult initial diagnosis and transition.

But, apparently, there's only so much inward gratitude you can take. Lyubomirsky's experiments found that, when people were asked to list and describe five things that make them grateful, those who were forced to do so three times a week found it to be too much, and that it made no difference in their happiness level. Conversely, those who did it only once a week reported sustained levels of increased happiness after six weeks. Too much repetition leads to the task becoming a routine chore, as opposed to a genuinely mindful appreciation-booster.[576]

Note both similarities and differences to the important technique mentioned in Chapter 1: the end-of-day routine of listing three things that day that made you happier. The similarity is that the "Three Things" technique *does* ask you to mention things you were grateful for on that day, and/or over time *should* incline one to have a more mindful and appreciative mindset. But the important difference is that this technique really has more to do with small-scale, short-term savouring and pleasure, and things that made you feel nice *that day*. It's quite possible that none of the three things would have the depth and impact to make it, for example, onto a weekly, biweekly, or monthly meditation on the large things in life for which you are truly grateful. This points to another difference: presumably, the large things for which you are most grateful form a rather stable and finite list, whereas the "Three Things" can change day-by-day. Hence, *the latter sports more variety, and doesn't get tired*, whereas frequently repeating a very similar list gets boring quickly. Hence, it's important not to confuse the two: for more happiness in your life, one should do *both* the "Three Things" every day at the end of the day *and then* every week or month, a more considered meditation on the people and things in your life for which you are most grateful, and why.

b) Kindness Toward Others

Apart from being a moral virtue, and great etiquette, being kind toward others makes almost everyone happier. There are several reasons why:

- it makes you feel advantaged and bountiful, and grateful for what you have to offer—and that you have something to offer

- it takes your mind off yourself and, especially if you have a chronic condition, provides a great distraction from the problems of the self

- it expresses and cements your values, especially if one is expressing kindness through volunteering on behalf of a particular cause

- it cements social relationships in all kinds of ways: you get pleasure out of seeing how you've created pleasure for another; the kindness draws you closer together. Additionally, it's reasonable to expect that kindness toward others enhances the likelihood of helpful and perhaps even joyous reciprocity at some point in the future.[577]

A small but moving study of special relevance for us was done on five women with multiple sclerosis (MS).[578] These women volunteered to be "peer supporters" for sixty-five other MS patients. The nature of the peer support had them agreeing to a fifteen-minute phone call to the other patients once a month for three years. At the end of the study, the five volunteers reported numerous happiness-boosting benefits that resulted from their kind acts of voluntarism:

- They reported being happier and more satisfied than they were prior to the study.

- They said the experience gave them much better listening skills, and made them more open to, and tolerant of, other people.

- They reported feeling more in control of their own MS, and less mindful of it. They also said that the conversations with afflicted others gave them more insight into the disease, and various ways of trying to cope with it.

Perhaps most surprising was that, at the same time, the self-reported happiness of the sixty-five other patients was also being tested and recorded. The result? The self-reported life satisfaction of the five volunteers at study's end was *seven times greater* than those who'd received the help! Moreover, and quite the surprise considering hedonic adaptation, the happiness garnered from the volunteering activity *actually increased* the longer the study went on. (Showing once more what was established in Chapter 1: that ongoing commitments to complex and positive experiences with other people are resistant to hedonic adaptation.) Presumably, the reason why is that the volunteers grew into their role, and got better at being good listeners and supporters as time went on. That growing mastery and helpfulness created deeper satisfaction.[579]

Committing to acts of kindness is fun, and beneficial, for all the reasons listed here. The key, according to Lyubomirsky's research, is *to do more than what you are used to doing*: this is what will boost your happiness the most. And vary it up—not just the nature of the act of kindness (be it charitable giving, offering good advice, or just being there for someone) but the people to whom one is kind. Combine anonymous, random acts of kindness with definite, identifiable acts of kindness, and don't forget to display genuine kindness within your closest relationships (Chapter 6)—those people aren't just there for you to vent to and lean on. Lyubomirsky even suggests, as an experiment, picking a particular day of the week for doing one special kind thing that you wouldn't normally do.[580] Finally, especially in light of our concerns here, consider putting thought into how you might be extra kind and helpful to those with the same chronic condition as you, whether it's through charitable giving, offering advice, giving someone a drive, just listening to them vent on the phone, sharing the latest information about possible new treatments, and so on.

c) Forgiveness

The historical influence of Christianity has led many people to believe that forgiveness is a moral virtue, and perhaps even an ethical obligation. I'm not sure I agree on either count; some things should never be forgiven as a matter of justice—severe crimes that result in terrible pain, for instance, or the kind of damage from which it's impossible to recover. Easy talk about "forgiving" the perpetrators of such deeds has always seemed suspect to me.[581]

At the same time, it's clear that you cannot be as happy as you might be if you are holding a grudge about some past wrongdoing on the part of someone else. It's important to get the description right here: what we are talking about is *difficulty dealing with long-term anger* about something in the past. This is what I think is most important about forgiveness for our purposes: it's not telling the perpetrator that you forgive them; it's not declining to press charges; and it's not coming, positively, to wish them well where previously you'd wished them ill. The key thing about forgiveness, in connection with happiness, is letting go of the anger, hatred, and bitterness, but *for one's own sake.*

We've already said plenty about such things in prior chapters, in particular: in Chapter 8, when talking about avoiding rumination and how best to think about the past; and then last chapter, when we spoke of detailed, excellent strategies for trying to minimize and control negative emotions in general—and for dealing constructively with anger in particular. The ABCDE process, stressed so much by cognitive behavioural therapy (CBT), is much commended in this regard, and there is much evidence that it works for a great many people.[582] Thus we need not dwell further on the subject of forgiveness—it only needed mentioning explicitly under this category, as it's a common topic in the happiness literature and I didn't want to ignore it.

Courage, in Conclusion

The upshot of this chapter is that there are two main reasons why being moral is important for being happy:

1 Positively, to do so is expressive of one part of human excellence, and adds to one's pride and self-esteem in trying to go through life as best as one can.

2 Negatively, to fail to do so will involve one in needless, serious conflict with others, resulting in either their retaliation or one's increasing isolation, to say nothing of the raw agitation of the conflict itself.

The basic duties of honesty, fair dealing, doing no harm, reciprocity, not violating rights, gratitude, and simple kindness resonate not merely as rudimentary propositions of ethics but also as vital pieces in the puzzle of what it means to build a just society, rewarding relationships, and a decent, satisfying, contented life.

———

Now, at book's end, we behold the utter *richness* of Aristotle's framework for human well-being: pleasure, the external goods, and the internal goods, too. This conception has stood the test of time and, while not flawless, remains perhaps the single most persuasive picture of happiness yet painted, and it's on offer for our consideration and appreciation. Whether well or ill, we can't help but feel both educated and edified by its structure, seeing how it is both generally proven as well as fortified by the very latest research. We have tried here to apply its many insights in a way both understanding of, and useful to, the lives of those chronically afflicted.

The only thing left to say—of emphatic importance for those with chronic conditions—concerns Aristotle's profound insight, and firm insistence, that the most crucial virtue in life, and perhaps the actual origin and well-spring of human happiness, involves courage. All our vices boil down to a failure of will, to a kind of lazy cowardice in the face of either wrongful pleasure or such negative emotions as anger and fear. A better individual life and happier society require us all to resolve to not back down in the face of such threats, temptations, and mistakes, and to not accept anything less than the best we can do with what we've got.

For those of us with chronic conditions, we realize we're saddled with substantial burdens. Even so, we know that no one has it easy, and that happiness is possible for us, too. With courage in our hearts and the wisdom of happiness research in our minds, we can—and should—resolve never to surrender. *Though wounded and burdened, we still need to be inspired enough, and resolved enough, to complete the mission.* And that mission is to fight against pain, fear, nihilism, fatalism, isolation, and dissolution. It is to keep fighting on in favour of reaching the target: our own best—and happiest—possible selves. Such selves would dearly love to meet us; they beckon with arms outstretched, telling us to fight forward, to come and join them joyously in the sun-lit fields of human happiness.

NOTES

1   Caesar, *The Gallic War*, trans. by C. Hammond (Oxford: OUP, 1996). In Latin, the line is: *"Omni Gallia in tres partes divisa est"* which, in this Hammond edition, gets translated as: "The whole of Gaul is divided into three parts..." (pg. 3).

2   P. Freeman, *Julius Caesar* (New York: Simon and Schuster, 2009).

3   Aristotle, *Nicomachean Ethics*, trans. by M. Ostwalt (New York: Bobbs Merrill, 1962). [Unless otherwise noted, this will be what is meant by any subsequent reference to Aristotle's *Ethics*.] See also C. Reeve, *Action, Contemplation, and Happiness: An Essay on Aristotle* (Cambridge, MA: Harvard University Press, 2012).

4   Aristotle, *Ethics*, Book One. See also: J. Vanier, *Made For Happiness: Discovering the Meaning of Life with Aristotle*, trans. by K. Spink (Toronto: Anansi, 2001).

5   S. Lyubomirsky, *The How of Happiness* (New York: Penguin, 2008).

6   R. Layard, *Happiness: Lessons from a New Science* (London: Penguin, 2006), esp. pp. 172–8. See also M. Anielski, *Economics of Happiness* (London: New Society, 2009).

7   D. Nettle, *Happiness: The Science Behind Your Smile* (Oxford: OUP, 2005), 91–114.

8   Nettle, *Smile*, 91–114.

9   Lyubomirsky, *How*, 285–304, provides a thoughtful overview of different depression therapies, and many helpful resources for further reference.

10 For general information, see J. Engel, *Seizures and Epilepsy* (Oxford: OUP, 2nd ed., 2013).

11 I'm a fan of *Men's Health* magazine. Epileptics may also wish to consult Dr. C. Bazil, *Living Well with Epilepsy and Other Seizure Disorders* (New York: Harper Collins, 2004).

12 T. Ben-Shahar, *Happier: Learn the Secrets to Daily Joy and Lasting Fulfillment* (New York: McGraw Hill, 2007). He thus, pp. 7–8, considers urging us to get rid of the idea of "happiness" (as if it were a closed, fixed, complete idea) and, instead, to rest content with the less ambitious—but more plausible and realizable—notion of becoming happier. Hence, his title.

13 The exact, full quote, with two references to happiness in the second, most quoted, paragraph: "We hold these truths to be self-evident, that all men are created equal, that they are endowed by their Creator with certain unalienable Rights, that among these are Life, Liberty and **the pursuit of Happiness**.—That to secure these rights, Governments are instituted among Men, deriving their just powers from the consent of the governed,—That whenever any Form of Government becomes destructive of these ends, it is the Right of the People to alter or to abolish it, and to institute new Government, laying its foundation on such principles and organizing its powers in such form, as to them shall seem **most likely to effect their Safety and Happiness** [emphases mine]." Full text: http://www.archives.gov/exhibits/charters/declaration_transcript.html

14   On Bhutan, see: A. Braun, "Gross National Happiness in Bhutan" (U of Penn Scholarly Commons): http://repository.upenn.edu/cgi/view content.cgi?article=1003&context=sire. On UAE see: http://www.thenational. ae/uae/government/happiness-is-a-serious-job-uaes-minister-of-happiness-embraces-new-role. On "Happify," see www.happify.com.

15   Apparently, the real quote is: "Anatomy is destiny." See the excellent general study, F. Sulloway, *Freud: Biologist of the Mind* (Cambridge, MA: Harvard UP, 1992).

16   Hawthorne, quoted in Nettle, *Smile*, 184.

17   Nettle, *Smile*, 141–55, with Mill quote at 155.

18   Lyubomirsky, *How*, 285–304.

19   Aristotle, *Ethics*, esp. Books 2 (the mean) and 3 (courage).

20   C. Peterson, *A Primer in Positive Psychology* (Oxford: OUP, 2006).

21   Lyubomirsky, *How*, 205–26.

22   Ben-Shahar, *Happier*, 65–85.

23   Lyubomirsky, *How*, 205–26.

24   Nettle, *Smile*, 82.

25   Nettle, *Smile*, 45–64. See also C. Cunningham, *Genealogy of Nihilism* (London: Routledge, 2002) and consider such recent mega-bestsellers as R. Warren's *The Purpose-Driven Life* (New York: Zondervan, 2002).

26   Lyubomirsky, *How*, 205–26.

27   Lyubomirsky, *How*, 205–26.

28   Ben-Shahar, *Happier*, 65–85.

29   Ben-Shahar, *Happier*, 65–85 and 97–110. See also: Nettle, *Smile*, 65–90; N. Branden, *The Six Pillars of Self-Esteem* (New York: Bantam, 1994); and M. Seligman, *Authentic Happiness* (New York: Free Press, 2002), 165–85.

30   Nettle, *Smile*, 39, 75.

31   R. Easterlin, *Happiness, Growth and the Life Cycle* (Oxford: OUP, 2010).

32   Economists refer to "the law of diminishing marginal utility" in this regard: consuming incrementally more units of the same good brings less quantity and/or quality of pleasure than the first few. See not just Easterlin but also B. Frey and A. Stutzer, *Happiness and Economics* (Princeton, NJ: PUP, 2001).

33   C. Graham, *Happiness around the World* (Oxford: OUP, 2009); Layard, *Lessons, passim*.

34   Lyubomirsky, *How*, 48–52; J. Riis, *et al*, "Ignorance of Hedonic Adaptation to Hemodialysis." *Journal of Experimental Psychology, General* (2005), 3–9.

35   Nettle, *Smile*, 76, 84; Lyubomirsky, *How*, 48–52; Peterson, *Positive*, 54, 73, 97; Layard, *Lessons*, 48–53.

36   Layard, *Lessons*, 48–52; Lyubomirsky, *How*, 48–52. (Indeed, for how much Lyubomirsky stresses adaptation, even with marriage [more below], she goes out of her way to point out, and underline, how her parenting experience with her children resists such a thing.)

37   Lyubomirsky, *How*, 266–70.

38 Nettle, *Smile*, 183–4. See also: C. Taylor, *Sources of the Self* (Cambridge, MA: Harvard UP, 1992); and B. Orend, *Michael Walzer on War and Justice* (Montreal: McGill-Queen's UP, 2000), especially the last chapter which deals with Walzer's plural theory of the self.

39 Nettle, *Smile*, 115–40; Lyubomirsky, *How*, 60–1; RJ. Davidson, "Emotion and affective style: Hemispheric substrates." *Psychological Science* (1992), 39–43.

40 Nettle, *Smile*, 115–40; Lyubomirsky, *How*, 59–60. See also: L. Breuning, *Meet Your Happy Chemicals: Dopamine, Endorphin, Oxytocin and Serotonin* (San Francisco: Inner Mammal Institute, 4th ed., 2014).

41 D. Lykken and A. Tellegren, "Happiness is a stochastic phenomenon." *Psychological Science* (1996), 186–89.

42 Lyubomirsky, *How*, 20 and 39.

43 Lyubomirsky, *How*, 6.

44 Lyubomirsky, *How*, 58.

45 Lyubomirsky, *How*, 58–9; Layard, *Lessons*, 55–60.

46 Stressed by Peterson, at Positive, 97. D. Lykken, *Happiness: The Nature and Nurture of Joy and Contentment* (New York: St. Martins, 2000), with quote at 12.

47 J.C. Crabbe & R.A. Harris, eds. *The Genetic Basis of Alcohol and Drug Actions* (New York: Springer, 1991).

48 G. Reynolds, "How Exercise Changes Our DNA," *New York Times* (Dec. 17, 2014); R. Francis, *Epigenetics: How Environment Shapes Our Genes* (New York: ww Norton, 2012).

49 Lyubomirsky, *How*, 61–8.

50 E. Masoro & S. Austad, eds., *Handbook of the Biology of Aging* (New York: Academic Press, 2010).

51 P. Thagard, *The Brain and the Meaning of Life* (Princeton, NJ: PUP, 2012).

52 I. Kant, *The Groundwork to the Metaphysics of Morals*, edited by Lara Denis (Peterborough: Broadview Press, 2005); B. Orend, *War and International Justice: A Kantian Perspective* (Waterloo: Wilfrid Laurier UP, 2000); B. Orend, ed. of I. Kant, *Perpetual Peace*, trans. by I. Johnston (Peterborough: Broadview Press, 2015).

53 Nettle, *Smile*, 115–40.

54 Peterson, *Positive*, 38–9; Lyubomirsky, *How*, 89–111.

55 Lyubomirsky, *How*, 207–8. See also C.R. Snyder, ed. *Coping* (Oxford: OUP, 1999).

56 The line is from Bram Stoker's *Dracula*. A chronic condition can, like Dracula, conspire to suck the energy, vitality, and motivation out of you.

57 Aristotle, *Ethics*, 15–16.

58 Aristotle, *Eudemian Ethics*, trans. and ed. by J. Barnes and A. Kenny (Princeton, NJ: PUP, 2015), 33.

59 Note how, if happiness is nothing more than the attainment of one's goals, then one could increase one's happiness simply by lowering one's goals. Aristotle, e.g., would have nothing do with such an expectations-lowering approach: we are to aim for the best we can achieve, else what's a human life for?) See Layard, *Lessons*, 73–75.

60 Lyubomirsky, *How*, 216.

61 Lyubomirsky, *How*, 208–10.

62 Ben-Shahar, *Happier*, 74–7.

63 E. Deiner, *et al*, "The relationship between income and subjective well-being: relative or absolute?" *Social Indicators Research* (1993), 195–213.

64 Lyubomirsky, *How*, 210–11; Ben-Shahar, *Happier*, 72–4.

65 See also A. Kleinman, *The Illness Narratives: Suffering, Healing and the Human Condition* (New York: Basic, 1989).

66 Lyubomirsky, *How*, 211–12.

67 Nettle, *Smile*, 91–114.

68 H. Petri & J. Govern, *Motivation* (New York: Wadsworth, 6th ed, 2012). Tony Robbins has spoken of his own constructive use of negative motivation, e.g., in his *Awaken the Giant Within* (New York: Free Press, 1992) and, though he's a popular motivational speaker, he has attracted endorsements from such experts as Tal Ben-Shahar, in *Happier*.

69 Lyubomirsky, *How*, 212.

70 Lyubomirsky, *How*, 213–4.

71 Nettle, *Smile*, 91–114.

72 Lyubomirsky, *How*, 212–13.

73 Aristotle, *Ethics*, 18–24.

74 Lyubomirsky, *How*, 222–25.

75 Lyubomirsky, *How*, 222–25.

76 Consider Chris Kyle's story in *American Sniper* (New York: William Morris, 2012), also made into a Hollywood film of the same name.

77 B. Aldrin & K. Graham, *Magnificent Desolation: The Long Journey Home from the Moon* (New York: Random House, 2009).

78 Ben-Shahar, *Happier*, 3–7.

79 Lyubomirsky, *How*, 14; Graham, *Happiness around the World*, 20–6.

80 Aristotle, *Ethics*, 14–22.

81 Lyubomirsky, *How*, 24–7; S. Lyubomirsky *et al*, "The Benefits of Frequent Positive Affect: Does Happiness Lead to Success?" *Psychological Bulletin* (2005), 803–55.

82 Nettle, *Smile*, 91–114.

83 Lyubomirsky, *How*, 24–7.

84 Nettle, *Smile*, 7–45; Peterson, *Primer*, 94–6; B. Frederickson, "The Value of Positive Emotion," *American Scientist* (2003), 330–35.

85 Peterson, *Primer*, 56–65.

86 E. Diener, *et al*, "Dispositional Affect and Job Outcomes," *Social Indicators Research* (2002), 229–59.

87 Lyubomirsky, *How*, 24–7; Peterson, *Primer*, 75–6.

88 Lyubomirsky, *How*, 285–304.

89 Nettle, *Smile*, 115–40. See also Breuning, *Meet Your Happy Chemicals*.

90 D. Lisle, *Pleasure Trap: Mastering the Hidden Force Which Undermines Health and Happiness* (New York: Book Publishing, 2006).

91 M. Ricard, *Happiness: A Guide to Developing Life's Most Important Skill* (New York: Little Brown, 2008).

92 Peterson, *Primer*, 75–77.

93 Nettle, Smile, 173–4; E. Kanterian, *Wittgenstein* (London: Reaktion, 2007).

94 S. Naifeh & G. Smith, *Van Gogh: The Life* (New York: Random House, 2012).

95 P. Leithart, *Fyodor Dostoyevsky* (London: Nelson, 2011).

96 N. Mandela, *Long Walk to Freedom* (London: BackBay Books, 1995).

97 V. Frankl, *Man's Search For Meaning* (New York, Beacon, 2006).

98 M. McGee, *Self-Help, INC: Make-Over Culture in American Life* (Oxford: OUP, 2007); W. Davies, *The Happiness Industry* (London: Verso, 2015); R. Putnam, *Bowling Alone* (New York: Simon & Schuster, 2001).; S. Binkley, *Happiness as Enterprise* (Albany: SUNY Press, 2015).

99 B. Ehrenreich, *Bright-Sided: How the Relentless Promotion of Positive Thinking Has Undermined America* (New York: Picador, 2010).

100 S. Kierkegaard, *Either/Or*, trans by A. Hannay (London: Penguin, 1992).

101 Ben-Shahar, *Happier*, 71.

102 Nettle, *Smile*, 67–8.

103 Aristotle, *Ethics*, 285.

104 There is a rare condition called "anhedonia": i.e., the inability to feel pleasure. Neurologists and philosophers are fascinated by such cases. I myself am not; and don't believe they shed meaningful light on the general nature of human happiness. [As they say in legal circles: "Hard cases make for bad law."] And my understanding is that such cases are, within psychology and psychiatry circles, controversial as to whether they are actually physiological, or merely psychological, disorders. Thus, best not to dwell on such, looking for insight which may not be there. For more, see: M.S. Ritsner, ed. *Anhedonia: A Comprehensive Handbook*, Vols 1 and 2 (New York: Springer, 2014).

105 Nettle, *Smile*, 12–15.

106 Peterson, *Primer*, 48–50; D. Farhi, *The Breathing Book* (New York: Holt, 1996).

107 P. Rozin, "Pre-adaptation, and the properties and puzzles of pleasure" in D. Kahneman, *et al*, eds. *Well-being: The Foundations of Hedonic Psychology* (New York: Sage, 1999), 109–33; D. Ackerman, *A Natural History of the Senses* (New York: Vintage, 1991).

108 Aristotle, *Ethics*, 279–82. Aristotle also talks, more cryptically, of pleasure "completing or perfecting" the use of a power or faculty.

109 Seligman, *Authentic*, 102–4.

110 D. Buss, *Evolutionary Psychology* (Toronto: Pearson, 5th ed., 2014); Aristotle, *Eudemian Ethics*, 30–42.

111 Vanier, *Discovering, passim*.

112 C. Graham, *Happiness around the World*, 213–31; Nettle, *Smile*, 14–24.

113 Nettle, *Smile*, 45–63.

114 Peterson, *Primer*, 53.

115 Nettle, *Smile*, 45–63.

116 Nettle, *Smile*, 83.

117 Buss, *Evolutionary*; Peterson, *Positive*, 48–9.

118　D. Kahneman, *et al*, eds. *Well-being: The Foundations of Hedonic Psychology* (New York: Sage, 1999); Lyubomirsky, *How*, 193–204.

119　Peterson, *Positive*, 53; D. Kahneman, *et al*, "The endowment effect, loss aversion, and status quo bias" in *The Journal of Economic Perspectives* (1991), 193–206. (Note the similarity between this "endowment effect" and "the mere exposure effect," already discussed. Kahneman, in the article (and as the title shows), suggests that for many people this sort of thing shows a *contentment with the status quo*, combined with a quite *strong risk-averse tendency about losing what one already has*. These things may all combine in the important phenomenon mentioned, namely, that most people tend to report that they are pretty satisfied with what they have in life.)

120　Lyubomirsky, *How*, 266–70.

121　Peterson, *Positive*, 52–4; D. Kahneman, *et al*, "When more pain is preferred to less: Adding a better end" in *Psychological Science* (1993), 401–5.

122　Lyubomirsky, *How*, 202–3.

123　Lyubomirsky, *How*, 197–8; R. Scruton, *Beauty: A Very Short Introduction* (Oxford: OUP, 2011); E. Selhub & A. Logan, *Your Brain on Nature* (Toronto: Collins Canada, 2014).

124　Lyubomirsky, *How*, 195–6; S. Gawain, *Creative Visualization* (+ *Workbook*) (New York: New World, 2002). Readers may also be interested in G. Epstein, *Healing Visualizations: Creating Health Through Imagery* (New York: Bantam, 1989).

125　Lyubomirsky, *How*, 200.

126　Lyubomirsky, *How*, 202–3; Seligman, *Authentic*, 62–82.

127　Lyubomirsky, *How*, 197.

128　Lyubomirsky, *How*, 193–9.

129　M. Williams & D. Pennan, *Mindfulness* (New York: Rodale, 2012). Pennan is someone who, following severe injury, has had to deal with chronic pain. It may thus interest readers to try as well: V. Bruch & D. Pennan, *You are NOT your pain* (New York: Flatiron Books, 2015).

130　Lyubomirsky, *How*, 193–4 & 198–9; Peterson, *Positive*, 69–72.

131　Lyubomirsky, *How*, 194–5; Peterson, *Positive*, 69–72.

132　Lyubomirsky, *How*, 200–1.

133　Lyubomirsky, *How*, 203.

134　Seligman, *Authentic*, 107–11.

135　C. Spence & B. Piqueras-Fiszman, *The Perfect Meal* (London: Wiley-Blackwell, 2014); K. Page, *The Flavor Bible* (New York: Little Brown, 2008); J. McQuaid, *Tasty: The Art and Science of What We Eat* (New York: Scribner, 2015).

136　K. Geiger, *Terrariums Reimagined* (London: Ulysses Press, 2013); M. & M. Hargrove, *Freshwater Aquariums for Dummies* (New York: For Dummies, 1996).

137　E. Selhub & A. Logan, *Brain on Nature*; Reader's Digest, *Joy of Nature: How to Observe and Appreciate the Great Outdoors* (New York: Random House, 1977).

138 G. Khalsa & Y. Bhajan, *Breathwalk* (London: Harmony, 2000) plus Dr. Andrew Weil's audio CD, *Breathing: The Master Key to Healing*. See also D. Farhi, *The Breathing Book* (New York: Holt, 1996).

139 C. Stauth, *Meditation as Medicine* (New York: Atria, 2002); S. Salzberg, *Real Happiness: The Power of Meditation* (New York: Workman, 2010).

140 K. Weber, *Complete Self-Massage Workbook* (New York: Collins Brown, 2015); S. Hess, *Touch: The Power of Human Connection* (New York: Fulcrum, 2015); D.J. Linden, *Touch* (New York: Viking, 2015) and more generally his bestselling *Compass of Pleasure* (New York: Penguin, 2012).

141 C. Van Doren, *The Joy of Reading* (New York: Sourcebooks, 2008); C.J. Ross, *The Pleasure of Reading* (Washington, DC: Libraries Unlimited, 2014).

142 L. Epstein, *The Harvard Medical School Guide to a Good Sleep* (New York: McGraw Hill, 2006).

143 K. Berg, *Prescriptive Stretching* (New York: Human Kinetics, 2011); B. Walker, *The Anatomy of Stretching* (New York: North Atlantic, 2nd ed., 2011); C. Brown, *The Yoga Bible* (London: Walking Stick, 2003).

144 M.L. Gaynor, *The Healing Power of Sound* (San Francisco: Shambala, 2002), and Andrew Weil's audio CD, *Self-Healing Through Sound and Music*.

145 Lyubomirsky, *How*, 277–80; Aristotle, *Ethics*, 33–5; C. Duhigg, *The Power of Habit* (Toronto: Anchor Canada, 2014); G. Rubin, *Better than Before: Mastering the Habits of our Everyday Lives* (New York: Doubleday, 2015), and her bestselling *The Happiness Project* (New York: HarperCollins, 2012).

146 Peterson, *Positive*, 49–50.

147 P. Foot, *Virtues and Vices* (Oxford: OUP, 2nd ed., 2003); K. Timpe & C. Boyd, eds. *Virtues and Their Vices* (Oxford: OUP, 2014).

148 Epicurus, *The Art of Happiness* (New York: Penguin Classics, 2012); Epictetus, *The Art of Living* (New York: HarperOne Classics, 2007).

149 Epicurus, "Selections" in F. Baird & W. Kaufman, eds. *Philosophical Classics: Ancient Philosophy* (New Jersey: Prentice Hall, 2007), pp. 452–75, with quotes at 470. See also: J. Fish & K. Sanders, eds. *Epicurus and The Epicurean Tradition* (Cambridge: CUP, 2015).

150 F. Feldman, *Pleasure and the Good Life* (Oxford: Clarendon, 2004). See also the hilarious *Hedonism Handbook* by M. Flocker (Cambridge, MA: DaCapo, 2004).

151 Epicurus, "Selections," 471.

152 For inspiration, see also D. Klein, *Travels with Epicurus* (New York: Penguin, 2012).

153 Lyubomirsky, *How*, 258–61.

154 Epictetus, *Enchiridion*, in F. Baird & W. Kaufman, eds. *Philosophical Classics: Ancient Philosophy* (New Jersey: Prentice Hall, 2007), pp. 489–502, with quote at 490.

155 Epictetus, *Enchiridion*, 498.

156 Epictetus, *Enchiridion*, 502.

157 Epictetus, *Enchiridion*, 491.

158 E. Sifton, *Serenity Prayer* (New York: ww Norton, 2003).

159 Epictetus, *Enchiridion*, 489–90.

160 W.B. Irvine, *A Guide to the Good Life: The Ancient Art of Stoic Joy* (Oxford: OUP, 2009).

161 Ben-Shahar, *Happier*, 13–30.

162 Ben-Shahar, *Happier*, 13–30.

163 Ben-Shahar, *Happier*, 13–30.

164 Ben-Shahar, *Happier*, 13–30; Lyubomirsky, *How*, 285–304.

165 Marcus Aurelius, *The Meditations*, trans. by G. Grube (Indianapolis: Hackett Classics, 1983).

166 F. McLynn, *Marcus Aurelius: A Life* (Cambridge, MA: DaCapo Press, 2010).

167 Irvine, *Stoic Joy, passim*.

168 J. Stockdale & S. Stockdale, *In Love and War* (Annapolis, MD: Naval Press Institute, 2nd ed., 1990); J. Stockdale, *Courage Under Fire: Testing Epictetus' Doctrines in a Lab of Human Behaviour* (Stanford, CA: Hoover Institute, 1993).

169 J. Hubbard & P. Martin, eds. *Substance Abuse in the Mentally and Physically Disabled* (New York: Informa Health Care, 2001).

170 Note though how 9% of the US population (of 326 million people) equals 29 million people, which for instance is greater than the population of the entire state of Texas.

171 The "co-occurring" rate, or co-morbidity, of substance abuse with mental health problems is much more widely and deeply, and thus better, studied.

172 See the National Institute on Drug Abuse, at www.drugabuse.gov, for excellent statistics and further studies on causation.

173 Nettle, *Smile*, 115–40; C.F. Levinthal, *Drugs, Behavior and Modern Society* (New York: Allwyn & Bacon, 6th ed, 2009); M. Henrie & W. Skinner, *Substance Abuse in Canada* (Oxford: OUP, 2009); G. Mate, *In the Realm of Hungry Ghosts: Close Encounters with Addiction* (Toronto: Vintage, 2009).

174 Nettle, *Smile*, at 120–5.

175 M. Earleywine, *Understanding Marijuana* (Oxford: OUP, 2002); J. Holland, ed., *The Pot Book* (London: Park Street Press, 2010); B. Kilmer, *et al*, eds. *Marijuana Legalization* (Oxford: OUP, 2012).

176 http://www.camh.ca/en/hospital/health_information/a_z_mental_health_and_addiction_information/alcohol/Pages/low_risk_drinking_guidelines.aspx; http://www.patient.co.uk/health/Recommended-Safe-Limits-of-Alcohol.htm

177 http://www.helpguide.org/articles/addiction/drug-abuse-and-addiction.htm

178 M. Csikszentmihalyi, *Flow: The Psychology of Optimal Experience* (New York: Harper and Row, 1999); Lyubomirsky, *How*, 181.

179 Csikszentmihalyi, *Flow, passim;* Seligman, *Authentic*, 111–16; Peterson, *Positive*, 65–70; Lyubomirsky, *How*, 180–84.

180 Lyubomirsky, *How*, 182–83.

181 Csikszentmihalyi, *Flow, passim;* Seligman, *Authentic,* 111–16; Peterson, *Positive*, 65–70.

182 Lyubomirsky, *How*, 184–85.

183 Lyubomirsky, *How*, 184–85.

184 Lyubomirsky, *How*, 185–86.

185 Ben-Shahar, *Happier*, with Lincoln quote at p. 141.

186 Nettle, *Smile, passim*.

187 Nettle, *Smile*, 65.

188 Ben-Shahar, *Happier*, 98. The more recent studies include Monster. ca's 2013 survey of 8,000 workers across 7 countries: http://www.cbc. ca/news/business/canadians-top-job-satisfaction-survey-1.2430864

189 *Men's Health*, "Found! The Secret to True Happiness," *Men's Health* (May 2016), 22. The humour study cited is from *The Journal of Labour Economics*. The productivity study cited in the December 2015 edition of *Men's Health*, pg. 112.

190 *Men's Health*, "Found!," 22.

191 V. Shannon, "Keys to Happiness," *New York Times* (April 01, 2016).

192 *Men's Health*, "Found!," 22; M. Kelly, *Off-Balance* (New York: Avery, 2011).

193 A. Wrzesniewski, *et al*, "Jobs, Careers and Callings: People's Relations to Their Work," *Journal of Research in Personality* (1997), 21–33.

194 This prominent study is also referred to, and discussed, in Peterson, *Positive*, esp. pp. 196–219.

195 Seligman, *Authentic*, 165–84.

196 A. Wrzesniewski & J. Dutton, "Crafting a Job: Revisioning Employees as Active Crafters of Their Work," *Academy of Management Journal* (2001), 179–201.

197 Wrzesniewski & Dutton, "Crafting," 179–201; Seligman, *Authentic*, 165–84.

198 S. Rao, *Happiness at Work* (New York: McGraw Hill, 2010); S. Achor, *The Happiness Advantage* (New York: Crown, 2010).

199 Lyubomirsky, *How*, 181–90.

200 Layard, *Lessons*, 63–5; J. Helliwell, *Globalization and Well-Being* (Vancouver: UBC Press, 2003).

201 Layard, *Lessons*, 62–75, with first quote at pg. 172 and second quote at pg. 68.

202 For the U.S. in general: D. England, *The Essential Guide to Handling Workplace Harassment and Discrimination* (San Francisco: NOLO, 3rd ed., 2015). For Canada: D. Harris, *Avoiding Workplace Discrimination: A Guide For Employers and Employees* (Toronto: Self-Counsel Press, 2014).

203 https://alis.alberta.ca/ep/eps/tips/tips.html?EK=165

204 The inventor's name is Emma Mogus: http://www.cbc.ca/news/ technology/tongue-controlled-computer-mouse-1.3677813

205 P. Loisel & J. Anema, eds., *Handbook of Workplace Disability* (New York: Springer, 2014); L. Piechowski, *Evaluation of Workplace Disability* (Oxford: OUP, 2011).

206 https://alis.alberta.ca/ep/eps/tips/tips.html?EK=165. See also this, from the Ontario Disabled Employee's Network: http://odenetwork.com/tag/hiring/.

207 Consider examples from this website: http://www.washington.edu/doit/strategies-working-people-who-have-disabilities

208 Seligman, *Authentic*, 134–64; Ben-Shahar, *Happier*, 97–110.

209 Ben-Shahar, *Happier*, 97–110; Kahneman, *et al*, eds. *Well-being, passim*.

210 Seligman, *Authentic*, 134–64.

211 C. Natali, *Aristotle: His Life and School* (Princeton, NJ: PUP, 2013).

212 D. Ross, *Aristotle* (London: Routledge, 6th ed., 2004).

213 J. L. Ackrill, *Aristotle the Philosopher* (Oxford: Clarendon, 1994); Aristotle, *Ethics*. Most relevant for this subject are Books 6 (pp. 146–74) and 10 (pp. 286–302).

214 D. Kagan, *Pericles of Athens and the Birth of Democracy* (New York: Touchstone, 1991).

215 Aristotle, *Ethics*. Most relevant for this subject are Books 6 (pp. 146–74) and 10 (pp. 286–302). See also J. Barnes, ed. *The Cambridge Companion to Aristotle* (Cambridge: CUP, 1995).

216 R. Easterlin, *Happiness, Growth and the Life Cycle* (Oxford: OUP, 2010).

217 Lyubomirsky, *How*, 138–49.

218 Ben-Shahar, *Happier*, 51–64.

219 C. Graham, *World*, 43–62.

220 Aristotle, *Nicomachean*, 3–32.

221 Layard, *Lessons*, 62–75 & Graham, *World*, 24–87.

222 Nettle, *Smile*, 65–90; Lyubomirsky, *How*, 13–27.

223 B. Orend, *Introduction to International Studies* (Oxford: OUP, 2nd ed., 2018), 307–32; UN Human Development Program Annual Reports http://hdr.undp.org/en; A. Sen, *Development as Freedom* (New York: Anchor, 2nd ed., 2000).

224 Layard, *Lessons*, 62–6.

225 Layard, *Lessons*, 170–9. There is thought, additionally, to be a potentially complex but very real interaction between economic recession, personal financial struggles (such as either unemployment and/or enormous debt problems) and addictions, for instance either to gambling (on the debt side) or else to drugs and alcohol (which can impact one's income on the employment side). See the discussion on addiction in Chapter 3 for more.

226 C. Dickens, *David Copperfield* (London: Dover, 2005). For more on happiness and money/spending, see: E. Dunn & M. Norton, *Happy Money: The Science of Happier Spending* (New York: Simon and Schuster, 2013); and J. Roberts, *Shiny Objects: Why We Spend Money We Don't Have in Search of Happiness We Can't Buy* (New York: HarperOne, 2011).

227 E. Dunn & M. Norton, *Happy Money*; M. McCue, "Turn Your Tax Refund Into This," *Men's Health* (May 2015), 87–9.

228 Unfortunately, I didn't catch the name of the planner, who was being interviewed on TV years ago. But see in general Dunn and Norton, *Happy Money*.

229 Lyubomirsky, *How*, 42–5, 136–7.
230 Lyubomirsky, *How*, 42–5, 136–7; Layard, *Lessons*, 62–72; & E. Diener and R. Biswas-Diener, *Happiness: Unlocking the Mysteries of Psychological Wealth* (London: Wiley-Blackwell, 2008).
231 Layard, *Lessons*, 150–6; Lyubomirsky, *How*, 112–24.
232 Ben-Shahar, *Happier*, 51–64.
233 A. Lewis, *The Cambridge Handbook of Psychology and Economic Behaviour* (Cambridge: CUP, 2008).
234 http://www.techtimes.com/articles/3973/20140303/bill-gates-is-again-the-worlds-richest-person-despite-massive-donations-to-worthy-causes.htm
235 Orend, *International*, 277–306; www.gatesfoundation.org
236 S. Manes and P. Andrews, *Gates* (San Francisco: Cadwallader and Stern, 2013); M. Becroft, *Bill Gates: A Biography* (New York: Greenwood, 2014).
237 Lyubomirsky, *How*, 125–49; J. Santi and D. Chopra, *The Giving Way to Happiness* (New York: Tarcher, 2015).
238 Layard, *Lessons*, 44–5.
239 Layard, *Lessons*, 41–7.
240 D. Redelmaier & S.M. Singh, "Survival in Academy Award-winning actors and actresses," *Annals of Internal Medicine* (2001), 955–62.
241 R. G. Wilkinson, "Health, hierarchy, and social anxiety," *Annals of the New York Academy of Science* (1999), 48–63; R.M. Sapolsky, "The influence of social hierarchy on primate health," *Science* (2005), 648–52.
242 Nettle, *Smile*, 65–90; M. Marmot & R. Wilkinson, eds. *The Social Determinants of Health* (Oxford: OUP, 2nd ed, 2005); Orend, *International*, 277–306.
243 Nettle, *Smile*, 65–90 (especially 71–74 for the numbers).
244 Nettle, *Smile*, with quotes at 74–75.
245 Nettle, *Smile*, 65–90.
246 Layard, *Lessons*, 51–3.
247 T. Piketty, *Capital in the Twenty-First Century*, trans., by A. Goldhammer (Cambridge, MA: Harvard UP, 2014); J. Stiglitz, *The Price of Inequality* (New York: WW Norton, 2012).
248 Lyubomirsky, *How*, 25. The first quote is attributed to various people, from Kathy Lette to Coco Chanel to Bo Derek. Most impute it to the fashion maven Chanel.
249 D. Defoe, *Robinson Crusoe* (London: Dover Classics, 1998; originally published in 1719).
250 Aristotle, *The Politics*, passim; Aristotle, *Ethics*. Most relevant for this subject are Books 1 (pp. 3–33) and 5 (pp. 111–45).
251 Peterson, *Positive*, 249–75.
252 Aristotle, *Politics*, 12–31; B. Yack, The *Problems of a Political Animal: Community, Justice and Conflict in Aristotelian Thought* (Berkeley, CA: University of California P, 1993); H. R. Clinton, *It Takes a Village* (New York: Simon and Schuster, 2nd ed., 2006).
253 D. Ross, *Aristotle* (London: Routledge, 6th ed., 2004).

254 Ross, *Aristotle, passim*; J. Annas, *The Morality of Happiness* (Oxford: OUP, 2nd ed., 1995); J. Annas, *Intelligent Virtue* (Oxford: OUP, 2011).

255 Marmot & Wilkinson, eds., *Social, passim*; A. Davidson, *Social Determinants of Health: A Comparative Approach* (Oxford: OUP, 2014).

256 F. D. Miller, *Nature, Justice and Rights in Aristotle's Politics* (Oxford: OUP, 1995); L. Baradat, *Political Ideologies* (London: Routledge, 11th ed., 2011).

257 J. Rawls, *A Theory of Justice* (Cambridge, MA: Harvard UP, 1971); J. Rawls, "The Basic Structure as Subject," *American Philosophical Quarterly* (1977), 159–65; T. Pogge, *Realizing Rawls* (Ithaca, NY: Cornell UP, 1989).

258 While drawing heavily on Rawls and Pogge, this is an embellishment and extension. Rawls, e.g., was criticized—especially by feminists—for not realizing or giving full credit to the magnitude of impact of the family on people's lives. Yet it obviously deserves to be there, whether for good or bad. See R. Abbey, ed. *Feminist Interpretations of John Rawls* (Philadelphia: Penn State UP, 2013). Culture is also a new inclusion, especially in light of the impact of the internet and social media. For more, see Orend, *International*.

259 For the full rationale, methodology and data, see the United Nations' *Human Development Report*: http://hdr.undp.org/en

260 Gallup: http://www.gallup.com/poll/182009/mood-world-upbeat-international-happiness-day.aspx

261 Gallup: http://www.gallup.com/poll/182009/mood-world-upbeat-international-happiness-day.aspx

262 Gallup: http://www.gallup.com/poll/182009/mood-world-upbeat-international-happiness-day.aspx. GDP data come from the World Bank: http://data.worldbank.org/indicator/NY.GDP.PCAP.CD.

263 Gallup: http://www.gallup.com/poll/182009/mood-world-upbeat-international-happiness-day.aspx. We spoke, in Chap. 1, about the so-called "framing effect" and how potent it can be regarding people's reported levels of happiness. This involved, e.g., the experiment of finding a surprise dime, and rating not just one's day but *one's whole life* more positively as a result. If a dime will have such an impact, we can then infer that substantial real-life improvements (in terms of relative peace, and growth in wealth, compared to the recent past) are going to make those reported levels of happiness go way up. Conversely, some have said that the reverse phenomenon can explain some of the low-levels of happiness reported especially in Eastern Europe, during its long, difficult transition post-1989 from communism.

264 J. King, ed. *The Cambridge Companion to Modern Latin American Culture* (Cambridge: CUP, 2004); S. Castro-Klaren, *A Companion to Latin American Literature and Culture* (London: Blackwell, 2013).

265 Orend, *International,* Chapters 9 and 10.

266 UN's "World Happiness Report": http://worldhappiness.report/. See also: OECD Better Life Index: http://www.oecdbetterlifeindex.org/#/11111111111

267 Social Progress Index: http://www.socialprogressimperative.org/data/spi

268 Most generally, free-market capitalism is a kind of economic system which:
a) allows for the *private property ownership* (i.e., the non-governmental ownership) of the means of economic production (such as natural resources and one's own labour power);
b) allows business people the freedom to set up their own businesses, and to keep some of *the profits* they earn for themselves and for their own private enjoyment;
c) encourages *trading* between buyer and seller as the means of distributing goods and services in the economy. (This is the "free-market" part; as opposed to, say, the government dictating who gets what);
d) uses *money as the means of exchange*, to facilitate the trading of goods and services (i.e., the buyer and seller in a transaction agree upon a *price* which is mutually acceptable); and
e) features a court system of public laws for the peaceful handling, and non-violent resolution, of economic disputes.
(Free-market capitalism is in contrast to other economic systems, such as communism, wherein the state owns and controls everything, and/or where the private profit motive is not so central, usually because the state taxes back all the gains for its own public purposes. Capitalism is also in contrast to earlier, more primitive economic systems of barter exchange [i.e., good-for-good, or favour-for-favour, *non-money* exchanges] or forced exchange [i.e., *the use of violent coercion* to conquer and control the means of economic production, notably including territory and resources.]) From Orend, *International*, 20.

269 A welfare state, in general, means having a government with a positive, robust, and intervening role to play within an otherwise capitalist economy, especially with regard to constructing "a social safety net" for the worst-off. This is done (at least ideally) through the taxation system: taxing the wealthy and using their surplus resources to provide welfare payments to the very poor and unemployed, alongside publicly-funded infrastructure-, education-, and health care systems. From Orend, *International*, 71–5.

270 B. Orend, *Human Rights: Concept and Context* (Peterborough, ON: Broadview Press, 2002); C. Pierson, *et al*, eds. *The Welfare State Reader* (London: Polity, 3rd ed., 2013).

271 For the libertarian view, see e.g.: R. Nozick, *Anarchy, State and Utopia* (Cambridge, MA: Harvard UP, 1974).

272 F. Fukuyama, *Trust: Human Nature and the Reconstruction of Social Order* (New York: Simon Schuster, 1996); K. Hawley, *Trust: A Very Short Introduction* (Oxford: OUP, 2012).

273 Contrast the political moderation, e.g., called for by Rawls' *Theory of Justice* (or his later *Political Liberalism* (New York: Columbia UP, expanded edition, 2011)) with, say, the description in D. McAdam and K. Kloos, *Deeply Divided: Racial Politics and Social Movements in Post-War America* (Oxford: OUP, 2014). See also: P. Mishra, *Age of Anger* (New York: Farrar, Strauss, Giroux, 2017) and B. Moffitt, *The Global Rise of Populism* (Palo Alto, CA: Stanford UP, 2016).

274 T. Bingham, *The Rule of Law* (London: Penguin, 2011).

275 Orend, *Human Rights*, 101–28.

276 O. Richmond, *Peace: A Very Short Introduction* (Oxford: OUP, 2014); Orend, *Human Rights*, 101–29.

277 On literacy statistics, see UNESCO: http://www.uis.unesco.org/literacy/ Pages/data-release-map-2013.aspx. On developing basic capabilities, especially amongst women: M. Nussbaum, *Creating Capabilities: The Human Development Approach* (Cambridge, MA: Belknap Press, 2013). See also Orend, *International*, 268–72.

278 R. Ritchart, *et al*, *Making Thinking Visible* (London: Josey-Bass, 2011); M. Pearse, *et al*, *Teaching Numeracy* (London: Corwin, 2011).

279 For education statistics, see UNESCO: http://www.unesco.org/new/en/ education/themes/leading-the-international-agenda/education-for-all/ resources/statistics/ And the World Bank: http://data.worldbank.org/ topic/education

280 Nussbaum, *Creating, passim*.

281 Nussbaum, *Creating, passim*.

282 J. Lewis, ed. *Children, Changing Families and Welfare States* (London: Edgar Elgar, 2007).

283 P. Norris, *Digital Divide?* (Cambridge: CUP, 2001); J. Donner, *After Access: Inclusion, Development and a More Mobile Internet* (Cambridge, MA: MIT Press, 2015).

284 J. Helliwell, *Globalization and Well-Being* (Vancouver: UBC Press, 2003).

285 R.D. Putnam, *Bowling Alone: The Collapse and Revival of American Community* (New York: Simon and Schuster, 2001); R. D. Putnam, *et al*, *Better Together: Restoring the American Community* (New York: Simon and Schuster, 2004).

286 Orend, *Human Rights, passim*.

287 Not that social institutions can't, or shouldn't, try other things. But realizing human rights are the most important. Richard Layard, e.g., draws interesting conclusions about how public policy might change in light of what we know regarding sources of pleasure and pain. One source of pain which is very hard to get used to is loud and intermittent noise. Layard then goes on to say that such a fact should be of prime concern to those who call for vast expansion of air travel and airports, saying that the added convenience and slight reduction in cost of flights probably won't offset the substantial reduction in quality of life to those living near airports, and thus should be rejected. (See Layard, *Lessons*, 48–50.) In general, I'm in favour of any deliberate measures which authorities have evidence to believe will produce greater happiness, of course, but stand with firm conviction that, before any such decisions get made, there must first be assurance that everyone has their human rights satisfied, as these are so keyed in to the most basic components of well-being. As Layard himself goes on to say (pg. 231), it is perhaps *easier for public policy to aim at a reduction in misery as opposed to the maximization of pleasure*, and so the institutional focus is probably better set at the most obvious and rudimentary things, such as what I call The Foundational Five objects of our human rights claims.

288 Orend, *Human Rights* (pp. 15–36).

289 Seligman, *Authentic*, 185–207; E. Deiner & M. Seligman, "Very happy people," *Psychological Science* (2002), 80–3.

290 H. Reis & S. Gable, "Towards a Positive Psychology of Relationships" in C. Keyes & J. Haidt, eds. *Flourishing: Positive Psychology and the Life Well-Lived* (Washington, DC: American Psychological Association, 2003), 129–59.

291 Peterson, *Primer*, 261. (Incidentally, one interesting finding in the happiness research is that, when it comes to the issue of children, the very happiest people are those who have either zero, or one, child. Subjective surveys suggest that having multiple children does not lead to maximum happiness for most people. They may be genuine blessings, and certainly do bring their own unique and wonderful kinds of happiness with them, but children also take a ton of time, resources, and can test one's patience, ingenuity, energy, and resolve. Having more than one, of course, compounds the challenge.)

292 Reis & Gable, "Towards," 129–59.

293 David B, *Epileptic*, trans. by K. Thompson (New York: Pantheon, 2005).

294 B. T. McWhirter, "Loneliness," *Journal of Counselling and Development* (1990), 417–22; Peterson, *Primer*, 255–58; http://time.com/5248016/tracey-crouch-uk-loneliness-minister/.

295 Ben-Shahar, *Happier*, 74–7; 111–22; Peterson, *Primer*, 255–58.

296 Peterson, *Primer*, 255–58.

297 E. Hatfield, "Passionate and companionate love," in R. Sternberg & M. Barnes, eds. *The Psychology of Love* (New Haven, CT: Yale UP, 1988), 191–217.

298 Peterson, *Primer*, 255–8.

299 Peterson, *Primer*, 255–8.

300 Peterson, *Primer*, 255–8.

301 Peterson, *Primer*, 255–8.

302 Peterson, *Primer*, 258–63.

303 H. Harlow, *Learning to Love* (New York: Aronson, 1974).

304 Peterson, *Primer*, 253–55.

305 J. Bowlby, *Maternal Care and Mental Health* (Geneva: World Health Organization, 1951); J. Bowlby, *Attachment and Loss* (New York: Basic Books, Vols 1 [1969], 2 [1973], and 3 [1980]).

306 Peterson, *Primer*, 249–52.

307 Peterson, *Primer*, 250.

308 Nettle, *Smile*, 65–90.

309 J. Dupuy, *Integral Recovery* (Albany: SUNY Press, 2013).

310 G. Chapman, *The Five Love Languages* (New York: Northfield, 1995). Thanks to Dr. Jennifer McWhirter, of the University of Guelph, for the original reference.

311 A. Sood, *The Mayo Clinic Guide to Stress-Free Living* (San Francisco: Da Capo Books, 2013). See also A. Sood, *The Mayo Clinic Guide to Happiness* (San Francisco: Da Capo, 2015).

312 D. J. Linden, *Touch: The Science of Hand, Heart and Mind* (New York: Viking, 2015); A. Comfort, *The Joy of Sex* (San Francisco: Harmony, 2009); G. Inkeles, *The Art of Sensual Massage* (San Francisco: Arcata, 2011).

313 Lyubomirsky, *How*, 138–50.
314 Such as Robert Nozick or Ayn Rand. See Nozick's *Anarchy, passim*, or A. Rand, *The Virtue of Selfishness* (New York: Signet, 1964). Note in the latter the articles by Nathaniel Branden, who went on himself to write a good book on relationships: *The Psychology of Romantic Love* (New York: Signet, 1980).
315 Aristotle, *Ethics*, Books 8 (pp. 214–44) and 9 (pp. 245–72). There is also one chapter (Book 7), of lesser depth, on friendship written by Aristotle in his *Eudemian Ethics*, e.g. as translated by noted Aristotle expert A. Kenny (Oxford: OUP, 2011).
316 Aristotle, *Ethics*, 214–27. See also: L.S. Pangle, *Aristotle and the Philosophy of Friendship* (Cambridge: CUP, 2008).
317 Aristotle, *Ethics*, 214–72.
318 Aristotle, *Ethics*, 252–55.
319 Aristotle, *Ethics*, 214–72.
320 At *Ethics*, Book 9, section 4. Or pg. 252 in the Ostwalt edition I've been using.
321 Economists refer to this as "the tragedy of the commons" argument in favour of private property ownership. See: P. Dasgupta, *Economics: A Very Short Introduction* (Oxford: OUP, 2007); A. Sen, *Development as Freedom* (New York: Anchor, 2000).
322 Aristotle, *Ethics*, 214–72.
323 Peterson, *Primer*, 265–7.
324 V. Held, *The Ethics of Care: Personal, Political and Global* (Oxford: OUP, 2005); C. Koggel & J. Orme, eds. *Care Ethics* (London: Routledge, 2013).
325 J. Gottman & N. Silver, *The Seven Principles for Making Marriage Work* (New York: Three Rivers, 1999); J. Gottman, *What Predicts Divorce* (Hillsdale, NJ: Erlbaum, 1994).
326 D. Myers, "The Funds, Family and Faith of Happy People," *American Psychologist* (2000), 56–67.
327 Peterson, *Primer*, 268–71.
328 Gottman, *Divorce, passim*.
329 Gottman, *Divorce, passim*.
330 There is interesting contemporary evidence that simply talking about one's relationship, on a regular basis, with one's partner is as effective over the long-term as a couple attending, and paying for, formal marriage counselling. See A. Booth *et al*, *Couples in Conflict* (London: Routledge, 2001).
331 There's lots of evidence which shows that, the happier the marriage between the parents, the happier and better developed the children grow up to be. See also L. R. Stains, "25 Ways to Save Your Marriage," *Men's Health* (Sept. 2015), 103–9.
332 Gottman & Silver, *Principles, passim*; Lyubomirsky, *How*, 141–50.
333 Nettle, *Smile*, 65–90.
334 Gottman & Silver, *Principles, passim*; Lyubomirsky, *How*, 141–50; Peterson, *Primer*, 268–71.

335 H. Hendrix, *Getting the Love You Want* (New York: St. Martin's Griffin, 2007); H. Hendrix and H. LaKelly Hunt, *Getting the Love You Want Workbook* (New York: Atria, 2003).

336 L. R. Stains, "25 Ways to Save Your Marriage," *Men's Health* (Sept. 2015), 103–9.

337 H. Lerner, *Marriage Rules* (New York: Gotham, 2012).

338 Gottman & Silver, *Principles, passim*; Lyubomirsky, *How*, 141–50; Peterson, *Primer*, 268–71.

339 D. Richo, *How to be an Adult in Relationships: The Five Keys to Mindful Loving* (San Francisco, 2002) and the terrific classic E. Fromm, *The Art of Loving* (New York: Harper, 2006).

340 Gottman & Silver, *Principles, passim*; Lyubomirsky, *How*, 141–50; Peterson, *Primer*, 268 71.

341 Though, the psychologists correctly note that there's a chicken-and-egg problem regarding causation here between happiness and being married. We know that happier people are more likely to get married, and their happiness probably makes it easier for them to attract partners who are going to make them yet happier. And we also know that unhappier people tend to be more introverted, amongst other things, which may make it more likely that they'll stay single. So, to what extent is there a cause-and-effect relationship *from* marriage *to* happiness? It's unclear and can't firmly be teased out. Probably, as most commentators note, *the causation goes both ways*: if happy, they are more likely to be married; and, if married, the companionship boosts pre-marriage levels of happiness. See Nettle, *Smile*, 65–90.

342 Seligman, *Authentic*, 185–207.

343 I'm grateful to Andrew Wilmot for pressing this critique.

344 D. Schnarch, *Passionate Marriage* (New York: ww Norton, 2009). This is an excellent account for keeping love and intimacy alive throughout a marriage. Note his interesting theory of "normal marital sadism" and how it's vital to understand and overcome tendencies towards being thoughtless and even mean on a daily basis towards your partner.

345 Quoted in *Men's Health*, Sept. 2015, pg. 105.

346 Gottman & Silver, *Principles, passim*; Lyubomirsky, *How*, 141–50.

347 This notion comes first from Seligman (*Authentic*, 125–64) and then is further developed by Ben-Shahar, in his *Happier*, 111–25.

348 Ben-Shahar, *Happier*, 111–25.

349 Hence the wisdom of the famous pop-rock song of the '70s (by Crosby, Stills, and Nash) wherein it is sung: "If you can't be with the one you love, honey—love the one you're with!"

350 N. Shubin, *Your Inner Fish: A Journey into the 3.5 Billion Year History of the Human Body* (New York: Vintage, 2009); B. McMillan, *Human Body: A Visual Guide* (New York: Firefly, 2006).

351 In general, see the excellent B. Van der Kalk, *The Body Keeps the Score: Brain, Mind and Body in the Healing of Trauma* (New York: Viking, 2014).

352 M. Bartley, *et al*, eds. *The Sociology of Health Inequalities* (London: Wiley-Blackwell, 2000); J. Csatari, *Your Best Body at 40+: A Men's Health Guide* (New York: Rodale, 2010), 229–71. In a survey, 27% of UK males reported deliberately avoiding a doctor because of fear of hearing the doctor confirm their own suspicions of cancer. *Men's Health*, Nov. 2015, pg. 76, quoting an unnamed article from *The Journal of Health Psychology*.

353 R. Dobelli, *The Art of Thinking Clearly* (New York: Harper, 2014).

354 A. Weil, *Healthy Aging* (New York: Anchor, 2007), 44–6.

355 M. Roizen and M. Oz, *You: Staying Young* (New York: Free Press, 2007), 90–1.

356 J. Morone & L. Jacobs, *Healthy, Wealthy and Fair: Health Care and the Good Society* (Oxford: OUP, 2009); H.P. Krahn, *Damaged Care: A Surgeon Dissects the Vaunted Canadian and U.S. Health Care Systems* (Altona, MB: Friesens, 2013). See also the chapter on "Global Public Health," pp. 277–306 in Orend, *International*.

357 To give three examples: for epilepsy, see C.W. Bazil, *Living Well with Epilepsy and Other Seizure Disorders* (New York: William Morrow, 2004); for diabetes, see G. Arsham & E. Low, *Diabetes: A Guide to Living Well* (Washington, DC: American Diabetes Association, 2004); and for heart disease, see M. Sandmaier, *Your Guide to Living Well with Heart Disease* (Washington, DC: U.S. Health and Human Services, 2012).

358 Nettle, *Smile*, 67.

359 Lyubomirsky, *How*, 244–5.

360 Nettle, *Smile*, 83.

361 Lyubomirsky, *How*, 48–52.

362 Nettle, *Smile*, 85.

363 Seligman, *Authentic*, 58.

364 D. Buettner, *The Blue Zones: Lessons for Living Longer from the People Who've Lived the Longest* (Washington, DC: National Geographic, 2010).

365 D. Buettner, *Thrive: Finding Happiness the Blue Zones Way* (Washington, DC: National Geographic, 2011).

366 J. Hastings, "Live (Almost) Forever," *Men's Health* (Sept. 2011), 90–3.

367 Buettner, *Thrive, passim*.

368 Buettner, *Blue, passim*; Buettner, *Thrive, passim*.

369 Hastings, "Forever," 90–3; Buettner, *Blue, passim*.

370 D. Buettner, *The Blue Zones Solution: Eating and Living Like the World's Healthiest People* (Washington, DC: National Geographic, 2015).

371 Buettner, *Solution, passim*; Hastings, "Forever," 90–3; D. Kochila, *Ikaria: Lessons on Food, Life and Longevity* (New York: Rodale, 2014).

372 Lyubomirsky, *How*, 250–4.

373 Lyubomirsky, *How*, 251.

374 Lyubomirsky, *How*, 252–3.

375 Peterson, *Primer*, 75–106.

376 Lyubomirsky, *How*, 254. Some have credited these insights to some proto-behaviorist remarks by William James and by no less a scientific authority than Charles Darwin. See Lyubomirsky, *How*, 250–4.

377 M. Golden, *Sport and Society in Ancient Greece* (Cambridge: CUP, 1998); S.G. Miller & P. Christesen, *Arête: Greek Sports from Ancient Sources* (Berkeley, CA: University of California P, 4th ed., 2012).

378 V. Hanson, *The Western Way of War* (Oxford: OUP, 1990).

379 W.B. Irvine, *A Guide to the Good Life: The Ancient Art of Stoic Joy* (Oxford: OUP, 2009).

380 Aristotle, *Ethics*, 14–21.

381 Aristotle, *Ethics*, 21.

382 Aristotle, *Ethics*, 33–51.

383 Aristotle, *Ethics*, 21.

384 Lyubomirsky, *How*, 45–7; E. Diener, *et al*, "Physical attractiveness and subjective well-being," *Journal of Personality and Social Psychology* (1995), 120–9.

385 Lyubomirsky, *How*, 45–7; B. Meyer, *et al*, "Happiness and despair on the catwalk: Need satisfaction, well-being and personality adjustment among fashion models," *Journal of Positive Psychology* (2007), 2–17.

386 M. Argyll, *The Psychology of Happiness* (London: Routledge, 2001), 34–5; Peterson, *Primer*, 92.

387 Lyubomirsky, *How*, 47.

388 Peterson, *Primer*, 256–67; Lyubomirsky, *How*, 45–7, 197–9.

389 M. Oz and M. Roizen, *You: The Owner's Manual* (New York: Free Press, 2nd edition, 2014).

390 Oz and Roizen, *Owner's*, 12–6; J. Metzl, *The Exercise Cure* (New York: Rodale, 2013).

391 C. Brown, *The Yoga Bible* (London: Walking Stick, 2003); C. Meyers, *Walking: A Complete Guide to the Complete Exercise* (New York: Ballantyne, 2007).

392 M. Lauren and J. Clark, *You Are Your Own Gym* (New York: Ballantine, 2011); B.J. Gaddour, *Your Body is Your Barbell* (New York: Rodale, 2014).

393 M. Murphy, *Ultimate Dumbbell Guide* (New York: Rodale, 2007); L. Schuler & M. Mejia, *The Home Workout Bible* (New York: Rodale, 2002). A. Campbell, *The Men's Health Big Book of Exercises* (New York: Rodale, 2009), and the companion A. Campbell, *The Women's Health Big Book of Exercises* (New York: Rodale, 2009).

394 J. Laurita, *Anatomy of Cycling* (New York: Firefly, 2013).

395 M. Young, *The Complete Guide to Simple Swimming* (New York: Educate & Learn, 2013).

396 J. Flood, *The Complete Guide to Indoor Rowing* (New York: AC Black, 2012); J. Burren, *Shadow Boxing Secrets* (Amazon Digital, 2015).

397 J. Villepigue, *The Body-Sculpting Bible for Men* (London: Hatherleigh, 3rd ed., 2011); and the companion J. Villepigue, *The Body-Sculpting Bible for Women* (London: Hatherleigh, 3rd ed., 2011). For the final claim: G. Reynolds, "Which type of exercise is best for the brain?" *New York Times* (Feb. 26, 2016).

398 J. Csatari, *Your Best Body at 40+* (New York: Rodale, 2010), 103–44; G. B. Grossman, *Restorative Yoga for Life* (New York: Yoga Journal, 2014); D. Lacerda, *2,100 Asanas: The Complete Yoga Poses* (San Francisco: Black Dog, 2015).

399 Oz and Roizen, *Young*, 268–92.

400 Lyubomirsky, *How*, 244–50.

401 Lyubomirsky, *How*, 245.

402 Lyubomirsky, *How*, 244–50.

403 Lyubomirsky, *How*, 244–50; Oz and Roizen, *Young*, 268–92; Csatari, *Best Body*, 1–32.

404 L. R. Stains, "What's Killing White Middle-Aged Men?" *Men's Health* (March 2016), 85–9.

405 G. Keillor, "Life is good," *Men's Health* (April 2016), 124.

406 Stains, "Killing," 85–9; P. Staats & M. Wallace, *Pain Medicine and Management* (New York: McGraw Hill, 2nd ed., 2015).

407 T. Graham & D. Ramsey, *The Happiness Diet* (New York: Rodale, 2011), 1–4.

408 Oz and Roizen, *Young*, 151–74.

409 Graham & Ramsey, *Diet*, 4–5.

410 Graham & Ramsey, *Diet*, 4–14, with quote at 14.

411 G. Sharp, *The Ultimate Guide to Hydration* (New York: RC Media, 2015).

412 *Men's Health* (July/August 2014), 29, citing M. P. Gardner's research published in the *Journal of Consumer Psychology*.

413 *Men's Health* (Sept. 2011), pg. 18 and *Men's Health* (Sept. 2012), pg. 30, citing research published in the journal *Public Health Nutrition*.

414 *Men's Health* (Jan./Feb., 2013), 36.

415 A. Weil, *Eating Well for Optimum Health* (New York: Knopf, 2001).

416 M. Roussell, *The Six Pillars of Nutrition* (New York: Rodale, 2012).

417 J. Stewart, "Do the New Milks Deliver?" *Men's Health* (Oct. 2015), 45–8.

418 Csatari, *Best Body*, 15–84.

419 T. Reinhard, *Superfoods* (New York: Firefly, 2nd ed., 2014); J. Sygo, *Unmasking Superfoods* (New York: Harper Collins, 2014).

420 http://www.cnpp.usda.gov/DietaryGuidelines; http://healthycanadians. gc.ca/eating-nutrition/healthy-eating-saine-alimentation/food-guide-aliment/index-eng.php

421 Aristotle, *Ethics*, 174–202.

422 See the works of Paul Thagard in general, such as his *The Brain and the Meaning of Life* (Princeton, NJ: PUP, 2010).

423 Aristotle, *Ethics*, 176–200.

424 Nettle, *Smile*, 12–5.

425 Lyubomirsky, *How*, 101–3.

426 Lyubomirsky, *How*, 101–3.

427 Peterson, *Primer*, 108–9.

428 Peterson, *Primer*, 108–27; Lyubomirsky, *How*, 101–3.

429 Peterson, *Primer*, 109–10.

430 Peterson, *Primer*, 120–3.

431 M. Matlin & D. Stang, *The Pollyanna Principle* (Cambridge, MA: Schenkman, 1978).

432 Peterson, *Primer*, 111.

433 For an excellent chart on a closely-related list, see Peterson, *Primer*, 112, who credits Matlin and Stang, *Pollyanna*.

434 T. Sharot, *The Optimism Bias* (Toronto: Viking Canada, 2012).

435 R. Penrose, *The Emperor's New Mind* (Oxford: OUP, 2nd ed., 2016).

436 Peterson, *Primer*, 111–3.

437 Peterson, *Primer*, 112–4.

438 B. S. Levy, et al, *Occupational and Environmental Health* (Oxford: OUP, 2011); Ontario Ministry of Labour: www.labour.gov.on.ca

439 Peterson, *Primer*, 112; Nettle, *Smile*, 54.

440 L. Tiger, *Optimism: The Biology of Hope* (New York: Simon and Schuster, 1979).

441 Tiger, *Biology*, passim.

442 Peterson, *Primer*, 123–5.

443 Peterson, *Primer*, 123–5.

444 Seligman, *Authentic*, passim; M. Seligman, *Learned Optimism* (New York: Simon and Schuster, 2010); Peterson, *Primer*, 123–6.

445 Peterson, *Primer*, 112–13.

446 Ehrenreich, *Bright-Sided*, passim.

447 Seligman, *Authentic*, 93–101.

448 Nettle, *Smile*, 12–5.

449 Seligman, *Authentic*, 93–101; Seligman, *Learned*, passim.

450 Lyubomirsky, *How*, 109–11.

451 T. Robbins, *Awaken the Giant Within* (New York: Free Press, 1992).

452 Seligman, *Authentic*, 93–101; Seligman, *Learned*, passim.

453 Lyubomirsky, *How*, 109–11; Seligman, *Learned*, passim.

454 Peterson, *Primer*, 126.

455 Peterson, *Primer*, 125–7.

456 Peterson, *Primer*, 125–7; S.J. Robbins, et al, *The Psychology of Learning and Behaviour* (New York: Norton, 5th ed., 2001).

457 Lyubomirsky, *How*, 116.

458 Nettle, *Smile*, 87–8.

459 Nettle, *Smile*, 38.

460 Lyubomirsky, *How*, 117.

461 Lyubomirsky, *How*, 116–19.

462 Lyubomirsky, *How*, 116–19, with the term quoted from 116.

463 Lyubomirsky, *How*, 119–24.

464 Lyubomirsky, *How*, 89–101.

465 Lyubomirsky, *How*, 229–39.

466 Lyubomirsky, *How*, 228–29.

467 Lyubomirsky, *How*, 233–4.

468 M. Ricard, *Happiness* (New York: Little Brown, 2007); Lyubomirsky, *How*, 228–39.

469 Lyubomirsky, *How*, 228–39.

470 Though "Pascal's Wager" and William James' "Will to Believe" have long been cited as purely strategic arguments in favour of believing in God.

471 Lyubomirsky, *How*, 228–34.

472 Lyubomirsky, *How*, 234–39.

473 S. Salzburg, *Real Happiness: The Power of Meditation* (San Francisco: Workman, 2010); Lyubomirsky, *How*, 240–44.

474 Salzburg, *Real*, 43–8.
475 M. Ricard, *Why Meditate? Working with Thought and Emotion* (San Francisco: Hay House, 2010); Lyubomirsky, *How*, 240–44.
476 Lyubomirsky, *How*, 240–44.
477 Lyubomirsky, *How*, 103–8; L. King, "The health benefits of writing about life goals," *Personality and Social Psychology Bulletin* (2001), 798–807.
478 Aristotle, *Ethics*, 100–01.
479 K. Kristjansson, *Aristotle, Emotions and Education* (London: Routledge, 2007).
480 Peterson, *Primer*, 56–7.
481 R. C. Solomon, *What Is an Emotion?* (Oxford: OUP, 2009); Peterson, *Primer*, 56–8.
482 M. Lewis, *et al, Handbook of Emotions* (London: The Guiliford Press, 3rd ed., 2010).
483 P. Eckman, "An Argument for Basic Emotions," *Cognition and Emotion* 6 (1992), 169–200; D. Evans, *Emotion* (Oxford: OUP, 2001).
484 Nettle, *Smile*, 12.
485 Nettle, *Smile*, 145.
486 Nettle, *Smile*, 31.
487 Nettle, *Smile*, 30–2; J. Plamper & B. Lazin, *Fear: Across the Disciplines* (Pittsburgh: University of Pittsburgh P, 2012).
488 Nettle, *Smile*, 30–2; J.P. Wetty, *et al, Psychology of Anger* (New York: Nova Science, 2011).
489 Nettle, *Smile*, 30–2; W. Menninghaus, *Disgust* (Albany, NY: SUNY Press, 2003).
490 Nettle, *Smile*, 30–2, with quote at 31. See also: D. A. Karp, *Speaking of Sadness: Depression, Disconnection, and the Meanings of Illness* (Oxford: OUP, 2009).
491 E.J. Langley, *et al, Psychology of Sadness* (New York: Nova Science, 2012).
492 Nettle, *Smile*, 30–2, with quote at 154.
493 Nettle, *Smile*, 30–2, with quote at 145.
494 Nettle, *Smile*, 7–45; Peterson, *Primer*, 94–6; B. Frederickson, "The Value of Positive Emotion," *American Scientist* (2003), 330–35.
495 Peterson, *Primer*, 58.
496 Nettle, *Smile*, 145.
497 Lyubomirsky, *How*, 258–9. On aspirin, see: K. Souter, *An Aspirin a Day* (London: Michael Meara, 2012).
498 Lyubomirsky, *How*, 285–305.
499 Nettle, *Smile*, 145–50.
500 Nettle, *Smile*, 149.
501 K. Oatley, *Emotions: A Brief History* (Oxford: Blackwell, 2004); R.C. Solomon, *True to Our Feelings* (Oxford: OUP, 2006).
502 J. Gross, ed., *Handbook of Emotional Regulation* (London: The Guiliford Pres, 2nd ed., 2015); K. Vohs & R. Baumeister, eds., *Handbook of Self-Regulation* (London: The Guiliford Press, 2013). For the specific two emotions, see: G. Chapman, *Anger: Taming a Powerful Emotion* (New York: Moody, 2015); and E. Bourne, *The Anxiety and Phobia Workbook* (New York: New Harbinger, 6th ed., 2015).

503 M. Ricard, *Happiness: A Guide to Developing Life's Most Important Skill* (New York: Little Brown, 2008).

504 Ricard, *Happiness,* 124.

505 Ricard, *Happiness,* 120–1.

506 Gross, ed., *Emotion Regulation, passim.* For another eloquent Buddhist perspective on a different emotion, see B. Shoshanna, *Fearless: The 7 Principles of Peace of Mind* (New York: Stirling, 2010).

507 Chapman, *Anger, passim;* P. Goldie, ed. *The Oxford Handbook of Philosophy of Emotion* (Oxford: oup, 2013).

508 Richard, *Happiness,* 115–22; Vohs & Baumeister, *Self-Regulation, passim.*

509 Ricard, *Happiness,* 126.

510 See especially: Gross, ed., *Emotion Regulation, passim;* Vohs & Baumeister, eds., *Self-Regulation, passim.*

511 Ricard, *Happiness,* 126–7.

512 Ricard, *Happiness,* 126–36. The method of the disinterested observer suggests John Rawls, referred to in Chapter 5.

513 Ricard, *Happiness,* 136.

514 Ricard, *Happiness,* 128.

515 Ricard, *Happiness,* 129.

516 S. Barondes, *Making Sense of People: The Science of Personality Difference* (London: Pearson Educational, 2nd ed., 2015); H. Friedman & M. Schustack, *Personality: Classic Theories and Modern Research* (London: Pearson Educational, 5th ed., 2010).

517 Nettle, *Smile,* 94–9; D. Nettle, *Personality* (Oxford: oup, 2007).

518 Nettle, *Smile,* 94–5.

519 Nettle, *Smile,* 99–100.

520 Nettle, *Smile,* 94–102.

521 Nettle, *Smile,* 94–102.

522 Nettle, *Smile,* 94–102; Peterson, *Primer,* 62–5.

523 Nettle, *Smile,* 94–102; Peterson, *Primer,* 62–5.

524 Nettle, *Smile,* 161–84.

525 "Strongest predictor," pg. 99; "Mirror image," pg. 102. Both in Nettle, *Smile.*

526 Peterson, *Primer,* 62–3; 92–3; D. White, *Jung's Personality Theory Quantified* (New York: Springer, 2011).

527 Peterson, *Primer,* 62–5; Nettle, *Smile,* 91–115.

528 Peterson, *Primer,* 62–5; Nettle, *Smile,* 91–115.

529 Nettle, *Smile,* 91–115; Nettle, *Personality, passim.*

530 Nettle, *Smile,* 91–115; Nettle, *Personality, passim.*

531 Nettle, *Smile,* 91–115; Nettle, *Personality, passim.* See also the best-seller, S. Cain, *Quiet: The Power of Introverts in a World that Can't Stop Talking* (New York: Broadway, 2013).

532 Nettle, *Smile,* 91–115.

533 B. Brown, *The Gifts of Imperfection* (New York: Hazelden, 2010).

534 Nettle, *Smile,* 91–15.

535 Peterson, *Primer,* 62–5; Nettle, *Smile,* 91–115.

536 N. Cousins, *Anatomy of an Illness* (New York: ww Norton, 1979).

537 L. Pauling, *How to Live Longer and Better* (Corvallis, OR: Oregon State UP, 2006).

538 Cousins, *Anatomy, passim*.

539 Cousins, *Anatomy, passim*. See the multi-part study on the relationship between health and humour online at the U.S. National Institutes of Health: M. P. Bennett & C. Lenegacher, "Humour and Laughter May Influence Health": http://www.ncbi.nlm.nih.gov/pmc/articles/PMC2686627/

540 Lyubomirsky, *How*, 151. See also C.R. Snyder, ed. *Coping* (Oxford: OUP, 1999).

541 Lyubomirsky, *How*, 154.

542 Lyubomirsky, *How*, 151–2.

543 Lyubomirsky, *How*, 151–4; Snyder, *Coping, passim*.

544 Lyubomirsky, *How*, 151–4; Snyder, *Coping, passim*.

545 Lyubomirsky, *How*, 154–60.

546 Lyubomirsky, *How*, 156.

547 Lyubomirsky, *How*, 163.

548 Lyubomirsky, *How*, 151–69.

549 Lyubomirsky, *How*, 160.

550 D. Goleman, *Emotional Intelligence* (New York: Bantam, 10th edition, 2005).

551 Goleman, *Emotional, passim*; S.J. Stein, *Emotional Intelligence for Dummies* (New York: For Dummies Press, 2009).

552 P. Harms & M. Crede, "Remaining Issues in Emotional Intelligence Research," *Industrial and Organizational Psychology* (2010), 154–8.

553 Peterson, *Primer, passim*.

554 Peterson, *Primer*, 242–7; E. Erickson, *The Life Cycle Completed* (New York: ww Norton, 1982).

555 Aristotle, *Ethics, passim*; Aristotle, *The Politics, passim*; & A. O. Rorty, ed., *Essays on Aristotle's Ethics* (Berkeley, CA: University of California P, 1980).

556 I. Kant, *Perpetual Peace*, ed. by B. Orend and trans by I. Johnston (Peterborough, ON: Broadview Press, 2015), p. 11–44.

557 K. Hawley, *Trust* (Oxford: OUP, 2012).

558 D. Gauthier, *Morals by Agreement* (Oxford: Clarendon, 1986).

559 D. Birsch & J. Fielder, eds., *The Ford Pinto Case* (Albany, NY: SUNY, 1994); D. Henriques, *The Wizard of Lies: Bernie Madoff and the Death of Trust* (New York: St. Martin's Griffin, 2012); & B. McLean, *The Smartest Guys in the Room: The Amazing Rise and Scandalous Fall of Enron* (New York: Portfolio, 2013), which was also made into an excellent documentary of the same title.

560 L. McIntyre, *Respecting Truth: Willful Ignorance in the Internet Age* (London: Routledge, 2015); S. Blackburn, *Ethics* (Oxford: OUP, 2003)

561 Aristotle, *Ethics*, 33–51; H. Cruzer, *Aristotle and the Virtues* (Oxford: OUP, 2015); H. Battaly, *Virtue* (London: Polity, 2015).

562 B. Russell, *Wisdom of the West* (London: Rathbone, 1970), 24–5.

563 Aristotle, *Ethics*, 111–45; A. MacIntyre, *After Virtue* (South Bend, IN: University of Notre Dame P, 1981).

564 Aristotle, *Ethics*, 174–213; J. Gosling, *The Weakness of the Will* (London: Routledge, 2014).

565 S. Milgram, *Obedience to Authority* (New York: Harper Perennial Classics, 2009).

566 R. Milo, *Immorality* (Princeton, NJ: PUP, 2014).

567 T. Hoffman, ed., *Weakness of Will from Plato to the Present* (Washington, DC: Catholic University of America P, 2008).

568 Aristotle, *Ethics*, 174–213.

569 Milo, *Immorality*, *passim*, who notes that, in spite of my characterization above as a form of weakness-of-will, Aristotle seems vaguely to say that this one might actually be a distinct cause of immorality: flat-out "wickedness."

570 Aristotle, *Ethics*, 68–79.

571 Lyubomirsky, *How*, 90.

572 Lyubomirsky, *How*, 89–91.

573 Lyubomirsky, *How*, 92–5.

574 Lyubomirsky, *How*, 90–1.

575 Lyubomirsky, *How*, 97–100; Seligman, *Authentic*, 69–75.

576 Lyubomirsky, *How*, 88–101.

577 Lyubomirsky, *How*, 129–30.

578 C. Schwarz & M. Sendor, "Helping Others Helps Oneself: Response Shift Effects in Peer Support," *Social Science and Medicine* (1999), 1562–75.

579 Lyubomirsky, *How*, 131.

580 Lyubomirsky, *How*, 125–38.

581 S.B. Simon & S. Simon, *Forgiveness* (New York: Grand Central, 1991); J. Murphy & J. Hampton, *Forgiveness and Mercy* (Cambridge: CUP, 1990); & M. Nussbaum, *Anger and Forgiveness* (Oxford: OUP, 2016).

582 Nettle, *Smile*, 145–55.

ACKNOWLEDGEMENTS

Thanks above all to Kelsey Attard at Freehand, and to everyone at Freehand and Broadview, for believing in this book and its potential. I owe Leslie Dema a special debt for recommending the m.s. to Kelsey in the first place.

Both Kelsey and Andrew Wilmot improved the book vastly with editing, and I enjoyed our many exchanges in this regard (normal, anyone? ☺). Thanks as well to Natalie Olsen for her creative and excellent design work throughout, including the cover. And most recently to Anna Boyar, for finalizing everything, and for her enthusiasm and expertise in bringing this book into being.

I'm very grateful to Darrin McMahon, Roko Belic, Ronald Anderson, Michael Frisch, Alex Michalos, and Sonja Lyubomirsky, for all best wishes and good advice.

This book has been a long time coming, and I'm delighted to see it finally in print. Thanks to everyone who has spoken to me about happiness over the years!

Brian Orend is a Professor of Philosophy at the University of Waterloo in Canada. He is the author of six books, including *The Morality of War,* one of the most widely-used books on the ethics of war and peace. He is best-known for his work on human rights and post-war justice. His Ph.D. is from Columbia University in New York City, and he has been Distinguished Visiting Professor of Human Rights at Lund University in Sweden. He has lectured around the world and around the web, and has epilepsy owing to a brain tumour, which has motivated his researches into happiness in spite of illness.